D0560085

TOPOLOGY AND MATRICES in the Solution of NETWORKS

F. E. ROGERS
A.M.I.E.E., A.M.I.E.R.E.
Senior Lecturer, Department of Electronics and Telecommunications
The Northern Polytechnic, London

LONDON ILIFFE BOOKS LTD

First published in 1965 by Iliffe Books Ltd
Dorset House, Stamford Street, London, S.E.1

Printed and bound in England by
Butler & Tanner Ltd
Frome, Somerset

BKS 5043

CONTENTS

PREFACE

This book is intended for students following University or comparable Diploma and Professional courses in Electrical and Electronic or Communication Engineering, and also for practising engineers or post-graduate students in these fields.

Electrical networks are intrinsic in electrical systems, and a good knowledge of basic network theory is as essential to the practice of electrical engineering as, for example, biology is to the practice of medical science.

The solution or analysis of any network for its currents and voltages in response to given excitations is basically synonymous with the solution of a family of Kirchhoff-law equations. This is manifest in power engineering, in which by nature the network problems are often adaptable to Kirchhoff's laws in their most direct forms. It is somewhat less apparent in communication engineering, and especially in line communication; for this division of electrical engineering has been dominated by the *image parameter* approach, which, though consistent with Kirchhoff's laws, conceals the basic operative equations in various indirect or secondary concepts originating in the theory of the uniform transmission line.

The most significant feature of modern network theory is, perhaps, the more universal directness with which its approaches are related to Kirchhoff's laws. This is exemplified by the procedures of network synthesis, which are now mostly based on volt-ampere relations, in the forms of driving-point and transfer immittances that may be explicitly expressed as functions of the Kirchhoff-law equations for the network to be synthesised. This modern trend towards more fundamental and general approaches is a simplification, in the sense that it rightly exploits the universality of basic principles; but it is, nevertheless, more demanding in understanding of basic techniques for the systematic solution of networks.

The purpose of this book is to explain, with liberal numerical illustration, the principles of systematic methods for solving linear networks, based on the fact that the pattern of the Kirchhoff-law equations for a linear network is governed solely by its geometrical pattern, in the sense conveyed by a topological graph. The book is not to be regarded as a text particularly on the mathematics of topology and matrices, but rather as one that seeks to show, simply and clearly, how these have a natural place in orderly, economical approaches to the solution of networks, and how to apply such approaches in practice. While further mathematical study is recommended, the essential principles are nevertheless contained in the text, where they are evolved smoothly in a practical perspective in order to crystallise their practical significance.

Throughout, neither the transient nor the steady-state is particularly implied; and while Laplace transformed excitations and responses are introduced and generally assumed, limitations in the reader's knowledge of the transform method need not detract from a full understanding of the text. The opportunity has also been taken to exploit duality, which is moreover extended to quantitatively related networks, in Chapter 3.

The Illustrative Examples and the Problems include some from University and Professional examinations; most, however, have been designed specifically to clarify practical interpretation and procedures. The transistor is prominent, and rigorous solutions for some relatively complex problems are demonstrated in various contexts. Sometimes, alternative approaches to the same problem are shown in order to enhance the reader's insight. It should be noted that complex impedances, which greatly increase arithmetical complexity, do not contribute to an understanding of basic matrix procedures: they have therefore been avoided where they serve no illustrative purpose.

The exposition, especially in the first chapter, has originated from a contribution by the author to a conference on the teaching of electrical engineering, held in the Midlands in 1961. The book as a whole has evolved from the experience of subsequent lectures, notably for a course on The Principles of Modern Network Theory with an Introduction to Synthesis, established at The Northern Polytechnic, and also from lectures to students for a Diploma in Electronics and Telecommunications in the same institution.

The author wishes to express his appreciation to his wife, for her help in many ways, including the typing of the manuscript; to Mr. B. Hulmes, of The Northern Polytechnic, for preparing most of the drawings; to Mr. M. Martinho B.Sc., of Elliott Bros. (London) Ltd., for his practical help and constant encouragement in this work; and to Mr. S. Ghosh B.Sc. (Eng.) Hons., of Standard Telephones and Cables Ltd., for his reading of the page-proofs. Acknowledgement is also due to the following organisations for their kindness in permitting the inclusion of problems from their examination papers: The Senate of the University of London; The Institution of Electrical Engineers; and the Institution of Electronic and Radio Engineers (formerly The British Institution of Radio Engineers). The author alone is responsible for all solutions.

Hildenborough, Kent, 1965 F. E. Rogers

1

THE RUDIMENTS OF TOPOLOGY FOR ELECTRICAL NETWORKS

1. INTRODUCTION

This chapter is concerned with the pattern of the equilibrium equations and with a systematic approach to their solution. By *pattern* is meant the number of simultaneous equations and the number and arrangement of terms within them. This pattern is governed solely by the manner in which the paths in the circuit are connected together: it is independent of the nature of the circuit-elements themselves and of the kind of excitation, except to the extent that these govern the precise mathematical form of each term in specific cases. Thus, the number of equations and the arrangement of terms within each is the same for a given configuration of network branches and sources, whether these branches comprise resistors only, with excitation from batteries, or whether they include inductors and capacitors, with excitation from time-varying sources such as sinusoidal a.c. supplies. Recognition of this fact effects an economy in study, by relegating to a compact phase those features of circuit theory that are common to the whole of it.

The solution of a given network, which must satisfy Kirchhoff's voltage and current laws, may be attempted by writing down as many relationships as can be observed by inspection, in the hope that out of them can be formulated an adequate set of simultaneous equations; or it can be approached systematically, through a relatively simple study of some general principles relating to its arrangement in a geometrical sense. The geometry is of a special kind, however, for it is concerned only with the interconnection of points with lines, and involves neither the shape of such lines, nor the angles between them. For this reason, it is better and commonly called *topology*.

In practice, electrical systems can often be broken down into parts that may be quite simple and subjected, individually, to fairly obvious processes of analysis. In such cases, a formal approach through topology may not seem justified. It is nevertheless important to formulate the general theory on a universal and systematic basis, which is available for application in a formal way when required, and which sets the origins and applications of subsidiary techniques and theorems in proper perspective. For example, in topology, a rectangular table of symbols or numbers, or *matrix*, is an obvious and natural artifice for correlation purposes; but as topology is fundamental to an electrical network, the concept of a matrix has also a natural place in the process of network solution.

2. THE GRAPH OF A NETWORK

For illustrating the principles clearly, it is expedient to consider first a relatively simple network such as that shown in Fig. 1-1(a). In practice, the numbered branches would contain resistors, inductors and capacitors, separately or combined. In the alternative arrangement shown in Fig. 1-1(b), superfluous terminals are omitted, and the branches are marked or *oriented* with currents whose directions are arbitrary except for that in branch 1, which is in the positive sense of the e.m.f. in that branch.

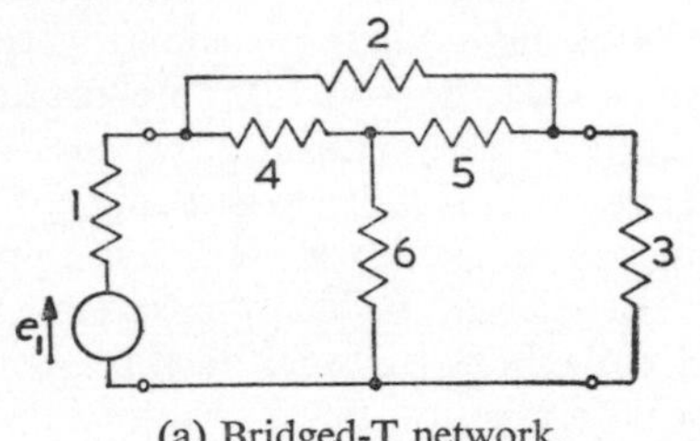

(a) Bridged-T network.

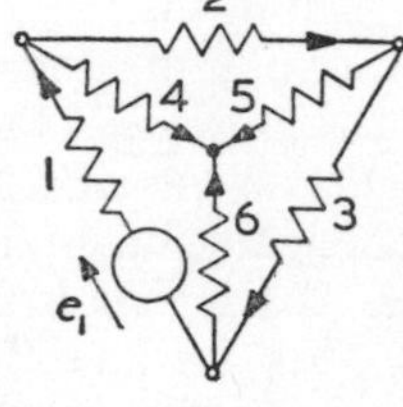

(b) Alternative arrangement with arbitrary branch currents.

Fig. 1-1.

The diagram of the network may be simplified further by representing the branches, including the source, merely by lines, as in Fig. 1-2. Such a diagram, which defines the basic arrangement of conducting paths and junction-points, or its *topology*, is called a *graph*. It may be noted that a branch comprising a capacitor only is included as a conducting path, since it carries current by charge-displacement under time-varying conditions ($i = dq/dt = C\, dv/dt$).

The term *graph*, in this geometrical context, is applied to a form of diagram that indicates the interconnection of a series of points by lines. It forms the basis of a special branch of mathematics[1] concerned broadly

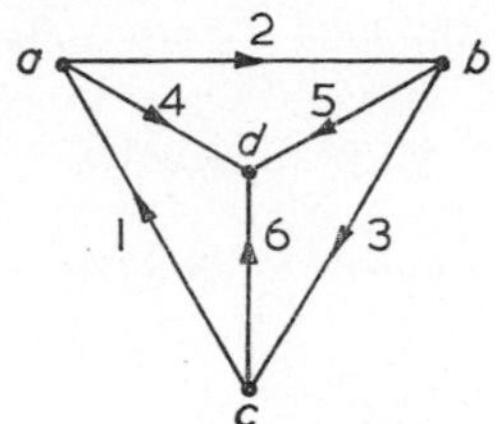

Fig. 1-2. Graph for the network of Fig. 1-1.

with correlating the graphical portrayal of a problem, in which it is possible to represent the entities involved by points and the connections or relations between them by lines, with the algebraic equations governing the problem.

In the case of a physically realisable network, including a non-electrical analogue such as a road or railway system, or a water distribution system etc., the graph is identifiable with the physical arrangement of flow-paths and junction points. In some applications, however, the graph may be in the nature of an analogue, in which no actual physical identity exists. This applies, for example, when a graph is used as an aid to reasoning a problem in logic, or for the solution of algebraic equations as in the application of *signal-flow graphs* for this purpose.[1]

Formally, a graph consists of a finite set of *line segments* or *edges*, terminating in *vertices*. The line-segments and the graph are *oriented* when a sense of action is attributed to the flow or relationship portrayed by the line-segment. Fig. 1-2 is a *linear oriented graph*, in which *a*, *b*, *c* and *d* are vertices, connected by line segments 1–6. The orientation is provided by the arrowheads, which in this case indicate assumed directions of current-flow. It is a convention to regard the orientation as positive when the arrowhead is directed away from a vertex, and negative when it is directed towards it. The term *linear* implies that the graph pertains to a *linear system*, in this case a linear electrical network; that is, one composed of elements which conform strictly to Ohm's law and exhibit a linear relationship between voltage and current.[2]

A graph displays a *pattern of connections or relationships*; a matrix displays the *pattern of the coefficients or variables* associated with an ordered set of simultaneous equations. It is therefore consonant that the algebraic correlation for a problem displayed in the form of a graph should be in the form of a matrix: the theory of oriented graphs is very closely and naturally bound to that of matrices.

The general theory of linear graphs involves special terminology, and an extensive list of definitions and theorems. In this book, however, only the simpler features are involved, in relation to the systematisation of network equations, and in order to introduce the matrix representation in a natural and simple way. It is therefore preferred to use commonplace electrical synonyms where possible. Thus, *branch*, and *junction-point* or *node*, will be used usually in place of *line segment* or *edge*, and *vertex*, respectively.

Two other practical networks having the same graph as Fig. 1-1 are shown in Fig. 1-3.

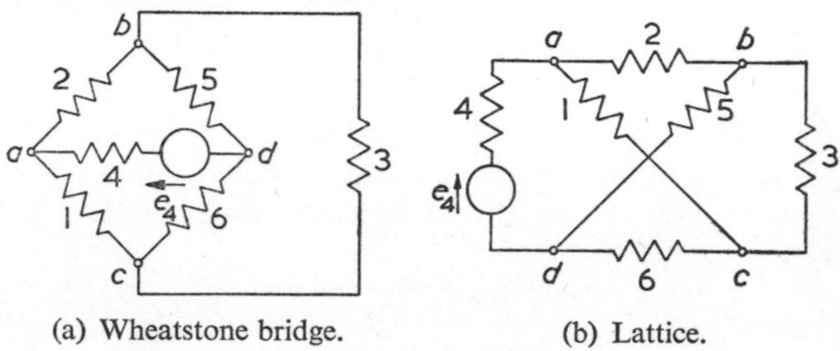

(a) Wheatstone bridge. (b) Lattice.

Fig. 1-3. Other networks having the graph of Fig. 1-2.

The lattice network is identical to the Wheatstone bridge, which is a *planar* or *flat* version of it (having no crossed branches). That the graph is the same for the three networks implies a common algebraic form for their general solution: Figs. 1-1 and 1-3 differ only in respect of the e.m.f. location.

A graph is *connected* if it is in one piece, or more precisely if there exists a path between any two vertices (nodes). The graphs of electrical networks are generally connected, except when mutual inductance is involved with no connection common to the primary and secondary coils. However, in practice it is likely that the graph may be rendered connected by introducing such a connection, without disturbance to the equilibrium equations. In the case of a network having an unconnected graph, the number of separate parts is known as its *connectivity*. Mutual inductance and unconnected graphs are considered in some detail in reference 3.

2.1 THE NUMBER OF KIRCHHOFF-LAW EQUATIONS

The network may be excited from either e.m.f. or current sources,* or both. However, a study of the equations is simplified by excluding the sources from the graph. An e.m.f. source in series with a branch is readily excluded by specifying the branch voltage-drop as the net value between node-pairs as indicated in Figs. 1-4(a) and (b), while a current

* A current-source in practice is likely to be the constant-current equivalent of an e.m.f. source, obtained with Norton's theorem—see Chapter 2, sect. 5.1.

sourcc in parallel with a branch is correspondingly excluded by specifying the current traversing the node-pair as the net value, in accordance with Figs. 1-4(c) and (d).

If a given orientation represents the direction for *fall* in potential *across an impedance*, then the *same* orientation represents the direction for *rise* in potential *across an e.m.f. source*. This is clarified by the polarities marked on Fig. 1-4(a). Thus, to the branch voltage-drop j_kZ_k oriented in the direction of j_k, the e.m.f. e_k, though oriented also in this direction, is negative; and therefore the net branch voltage-drop v_k, oriented in the direction common to j_kZ_k and j_k, is $-e_k + j_kZ_k$ as shown on Fig. 1-4(b). Figs. 1-4(c) and (d) are subject to parallel reasoning.

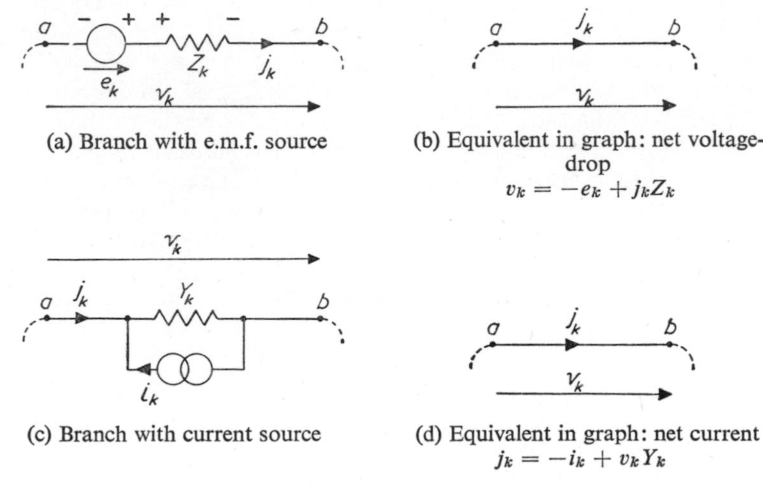

(a) Branch with e.m.f. source

(b) Equivalent in graph: net voltage-drop $v_k = -e_k + j_kZ_k$

(c) Branch with current source

(d) Equivalent in graph: net current $j_k = -i_k + v_kY_k$

Fig. 1-4. Pertaining to exclusion of sources from graph.

In terms of the net currents and voltages, the Kirchhoff current and voltage-law equations are of the forms

$$\sum_{k=1}^{n} j_k = 0 \tag{1.1}$$

and

$$\sum_{k=1}^{n} v_k = 0 \tag{1.2}$$

where n is the number of currents meeting at any node in eqn. (1.1), and the number of branches forming any closed circuit or *loop* in eqn. (1.2). Formally, a loop of a network is defined as a connected *sub-network* having two branches incident with each node. Examples follow.

The graph is important because it reveals:

(a) The number of nodes, and therefore the total number of current-law equations.

(b) The loops, and therefore the total number of voltage-law equations.

While the current-law equations are obvious from the graph, there is a variety of alternative loops that might be traversed in forming the voltage-law equations. In Fig. 1-2 there are 4 nodes *a*, *b*, *c*, *d*, and thus 4 current-law equations; and 7 loops (146; 254; 365; 1256; 2463; 3145; and 123), and therefore 7 possible voltage-law equations. But as there are only 6 branch currents or voltages to be determined, 6 independent equations should suffice.

2.2 DISSECTION OF THE GRAPH, AND REDUCTION OF THE EQUATIONS

The graph of Fig. 1-2 is reproduced in Fig. 1-5(a). All closed loops are just opened when a minimum of three branches are removed. For example, removing branches 245, 165 and 123 gives the structures of Figs. 1-5(b), (c) and (d). These are called *trees*, by virtue of their open-branch appearance; the branches removed are *chords* or *links*; and the group of links removed form a *co-tree*. In this case there are sixteen[3] possible trees, with a co-tree for each. The three co-trees for Figs. 1-5(b), (c) and (d) are shown in Figs. 1-5 (e), (f) and (g), respectively.

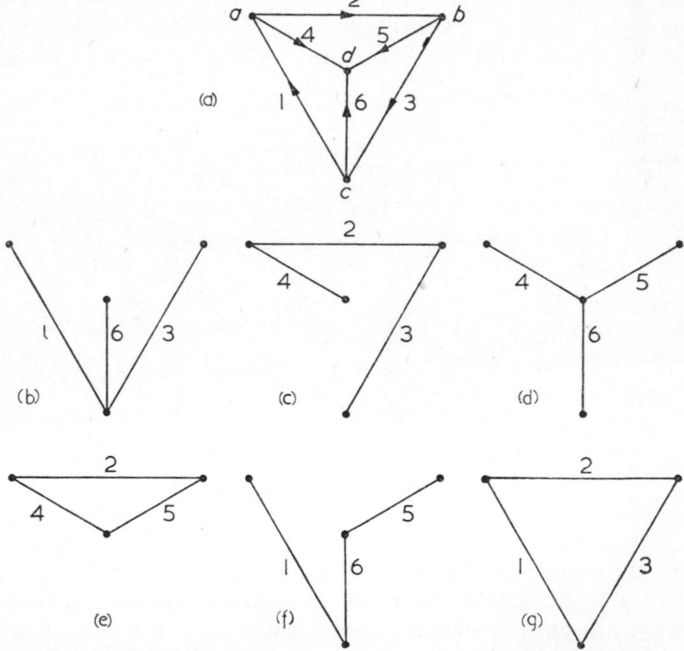

Fig. 1-5. (a)–Graph; (b), (c), (d)–Trees; (e), (f), (g)–Co-trees.

2.2.1 *Determination of branch currents*

Superimposing any co-tree on its corresponding tree restores the full structure of the graph. Therefore, a minimum set of loops that contains all branch currents and voltages is any set formed from the separate loops created by restoring to a given tree one link at a time, out of the set of links forming the corresponding co-tree. The separate structures thus formed are called *tie-sets*. Their formation is illustrated in Fig. 1-6, for the case of tree (b) and the corresponding co-tree (e) in Fig. 1-5.

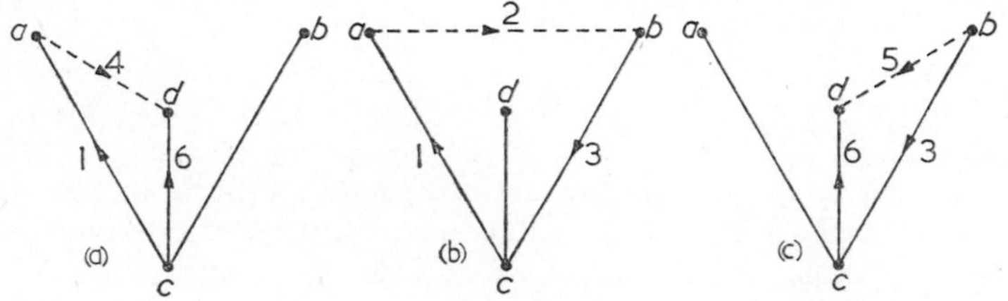

Fig. 1-6. Tie-sets formed by restoring, separately, links 4, 2 and 5 to the tree of Fig. 1-5(b).

The branches in each tie-set are oriented with the currents assumed in the complete graph (Fig. 1-5(a)), and taking the branch voltage-drops in the same senses, Figs. 1-6 give immediately the following equations:

$$\begin{aligned} v_1 + v_4 - v_6 &= 0 \\ v_1 + v_2 + v_3 &= 0 \\ v_3 + v_6 - v_5 &= 0 \end{aligned} \tag{1.3}$$

The voltages in eqns. (1.3) are expressed in terms of the six branch impedances (and the source e.m.f.) which are known, and the six branch currents. But they are insoluble until the independent current-variables are reduced to three.

Inspection of the nodes on the graph of Fig. 1-5(a) gives the current-law equations

$$\begin{aligned} j_2 + j_4 - j_1 &= 0 \\ j_3 + j_5 - j_2 &= 0 \\ j_1 + j_6 - j_3 &= 0 \\ -j_4 - j_5 - j_6 &= 0 \end{aligned} \tag{1.4}$$

It is logical to choose the link-currents as the three independent variables, for the existence of the tree-branch currents depends on closure of the loops by the links. Moreover, while the tree-branch currents are quite easily eliminated from eqns. (1.4), they are explicitly given in terms of the link currents merely by inspection of nodes *a*, *d* and *b*. These are shown segregated from the other nodes by dotted circles in Fig. 1-7.

The branches linking the selected nodes to the others, comprising in each case one tree-branch and two links (heavy lines), are cut by the circles and form *cut-sets*.

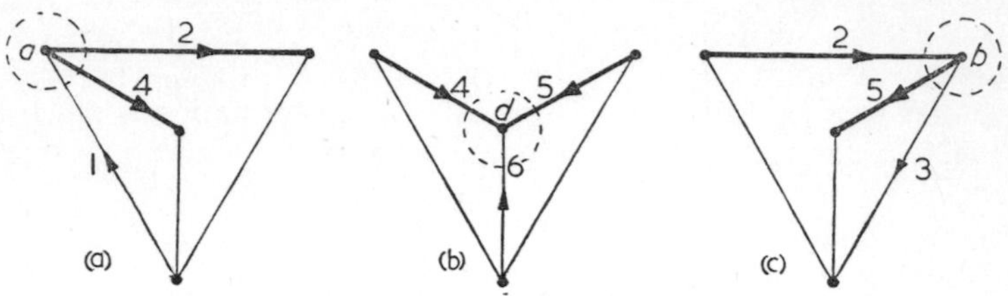

Fig. 1-7. Cut-sets for Fig. 1-5(a).

A *cut-set* may be formally defined as a set of branches whose removal from the graph increases its connectivity by one. In the case of a connected graph, this implies division into two parts. Figs. 1-7 are particular cut-sets, in which the branches cut are all incident at one node in each case. Their function at this point is to elucidate each incidence of a tree-branch current with the link-currents. From Figs. 1-7,

$$\begin{aligned} j_1 &= j_2 + j_4 \\ j_6 &= -j_4 - j_5 \\ j_3 &= j_2 - j_5 \end{aligned} \tag{1.5}$$

In the original network, Fig. 1-1(a), there is an e.m.f. e_1 in branch 1, and by reference to Figs. 1-4(a) and (b), $v_1 = -e_1 + j_1 Z_1$. Then, substituting first for the branch voltages in eqns. (1.3) in terms of all the branch currents and impedances, and then for j_1, j_6 and j_3 from eqns. (1.5),

$$\begin{aligned} Z_1 j_2 + (Z_1 + Z_4 + Z_6) j_4 \qquad\qquad &+ Z_6\, j_5 = e_1 \\ (Z_1 + Z_2 + Z_3) j_2 \qquad\qquad + Z_1\, j_4 \qquad\qquad &- Z_3\, j_5 = e_1 \\ Z_3 j_2 \qquad\qquad - Z_6\, j_4 - (Z_3 + Z_5 + Z_6) j_5 &= 0 \end{aligned} \tag{1.6}$$

Eqns. (1.6) are readily solved for j_2, j_4 and j_5, and then j_1, j_6 and j_3 are given from eqns. (1.5).

2.2.2. *Determination of branch voltages*

All methods of solution rest on the Kirchhoff-law equations, (1.1) and (1.2). The procedure discussed in sect. 2.2.1, leading to determination of the branch currents by solution of eqns. (1.6), is based on substitution from eqn. (1.1) into eqn. (1.2). The alternative substitution, from eqn. (1.2) into eqn. (1.1), will obviously lead instead to the branch voltages, for eqns. (1.1) and (1.2) are of parallel form.

The cut-sets of Fig. 1-7 give immediately one set of junction-law equations,

$$\begin{aligned} -j_1 + j_2 + j_4 &= 0 \\ -j_4 - j_5 - j_6 &= 0 \\ -j_2 + j_5 + j_3 &= 0 \end{aligned} \tag{1.7}$$

in which the currents may be expressed in terms of the branch voltages and admittances. Now, however, it is the tree-branches that conveniently furnish an independent set of variables, for by reference to Fig. 1-6, the link voltages v_4, v_2 and v_5, which are also the potential differences between the pairs of nodes *a-d*, *a-b* and *b-d*, are equal to the sums of the tree-branch voltages in the respective tie-sets. Thus, explicitly,

$$\begin{aligned} v_4 &= v_6 - v_1 \\ v_2 &= -v_1 - v_3 \\ v_5 &= v_3 + v_6 \end{aligned} \tag{1.8}$$

To make the calculation parallel with that in sect. 2.2.1, let the original network (Fig. 1-1) now be driven instead from a current source i_1 in parallel with branch 1 as in Fig. 1-4(c). Then from Fig. 1-4(d), $j_1 = -i_1 + v_1 Y_1$, while any other branch current $j_k = v_k Y_k$. Substituting for the currents in eqns. (1.7) in terms of eqns. (1.8) then gives

$$\begin{aligned} -(Y_1 + Y_2 + Y_4)v_1 \quad & - Y_2 v_3 & + Y_4 v_6 &= -i_1 \\ Y_4 v_1 \quad & - Y_5 v_3 - (Y_4 + Y_5 + Y_6)v_6 &&= 0 \\ Y_2 v_1 + (Y_2 + Y_3 + Y_5)v_3 & & + Y_5 v_6 &= 0 \end{aligned} \tag{1.9}$$

from which v_1 v_3 and v_6 may be found and then v_2, v_4 and v_5 from eqns. (1.8).

2.3 AN INTRODUCTORY NOTE ON DUALITY

Reference has been made to the parallel forms of the two Kirchhoff-law equations, and it is also evident that eqns. (1.6), in terms of currents and impedances, and eqns. (1.9), in terms of voltages and admittances, are also of parallel (though not identical) form.

Two relationships of parallel mathematical form, in which the one is changed into the other by a systematic interchange of coefficients and variables are said to be *dual*; and so also are the quantities involved. Consider, for example,

$$\begin{aligned} v &= Ri, & i &= Gv \\ v &= L\frac{di}{dt}, & i &= C\frac{dv}{dt} \\ v &= \frac{1}{C}\int i\,dt, & i &= \frac{1}{L}\int v\,dt \end{aligned} \tag{1.10}$$

These are dual relations, and establish duality between voltage and current, resistance and conductance (or more generally impedance and admittance), and inductance and capacitance.

There are other examples of dual relationships in which the parameters are physically different. For example, $L\,di/dt$ and $m\,du/dt$, where m is the mass of a body moving with velocity u. In this case, inductance (L) and mass (m), or current (i) and velocity (u) would be described as *analogous* rather than dual. Duality between the fundamental relations for electrical and dynamical systems is such as to permit the analysis of mechanical systems in terms of analogous electrical ones, or the analysis of electro-mechanical systems (motors, generators, galvanometers, servo or control systems etc.) with unified defining equations.

An important implication of duality is the inference of defining equations or the solution for a given system, when these are known for another system that is its dual. Consider, for example, a circuit comprising conductance G in parallel with capacitance C, to which is suddenly applied at an instant $t = 0$ a constant current I (a step-function current, better symbolised by $H(t)\cdot I$, where $H(t) = 0$, $t < 0$ and $H(t) = 1$, $t > 0$). The Kirchhoff current-law equation is

$$Gv + C\frac{dv}{dt} = I \qquad (t > 0) \tag{1.11}$$

But by reference to the dual relations in eqns. (1.10), this has its dual in the better-known problem of inductance L in series with resistance R to which is applied a step-function e.m.f. $H(t)\cdot E$, and for which the Kirchhoff voltage-law equation is

$$Ri + L\frac{di}{dt} = E \qquad (t > 0) \tag{1.12}$$

The solution to this is likely to be well known, and is

$$i = \frac{E}{R}[1 - e^{-Rt/L}] \tag{1.13}$$

Hence, on interchanging symbols, v for i, C for L, G for R and I for E, or *by duality*, the solution of eqn. (1.11) must be

$$v = \frac{I}{G}[1 - e^{-Gt/C}] \tag{1.14}$$

The notion of duality extends to the topology of a network; for the Kirchhoff-law equations (1.1) and (1.2) are dual, and an equation for currents in a cut-set incident at a node has its dual in an equation for voltages round the loop of a tie-set. Moreover, the independent variables for substitution are tree-branch voltages into the current-law equations, and link currents into the dual voltage-law equations. Thus is one justified in regarding a node as the dual of a loop, a cut-set as the dual of a tie-set, and a tree-branch as the dual of a link.

2.4 INTRODUCTION TO THE MATRIX CONCEPT: THE INCIDENCE MATRIX

The branches meeting at a node are said to be incident with the node. The incidence of nodes with branch currents may be coordinated in a table, in which the coordinates of an entry +1 or −1 are a node and a branch current incident with it, having an orientation that is positive or negative, respectively. Following the convention of general linear graph theory, in which the orientation of a line segment (branch) is positive when it is away from a vertex (node), the following table is constructed for the graph of Fig. 1-2 or Fig. 1-5(a):

Node	Branch current, *j*					
	1	2	3	4	5	6
a	−1	+1	0	+1	0	0
b	0	−1	+1	0	+1	0
c	+1	0	−1	0	0	+1
d	0	0	0	−1	−1	−1

Table 1-1. Incidence of branches and nodes for Fig. 1-2.

Each row in Table 1-1 designates the currents incident at a particular node, together with their orientations. Thus, each row defines a current-law equation:

$$\begin{aligned} &\text{Node } a \quad -j_1 + j_2 + j_4 = 0 \\ &\text{Node } b \quad -j_2 + j_3 + j_5 = 0 \\ &\text{Node } c \quad j_1 - j_3 + j_6 = 0 \\ &\text{Node } d \quad -j_4 - j_5 - j_6 = 0 \end{aligned} \qquad (1.15)$$

Now consider, by way of illustration, the family of equations

$$\begin{aligned} a_{11}x_1 + a_{12}x_2 + \cdots + a_{1n}x_n &= y_1 \\ a_{21}x_1 + a_{22}x_2 + \cdots + a_{2n}x_n &= y_2 \\ \cdots\cdots\cdots\cdots\cdots\cdots\cdots\cdots\cdots& \\ a_{n1}x_1 + a_{n2}x_2 + \cdots + a_{nn}x_n &= y_n \end{aligned} \qquad (1.16)$$

A contraction results if the coefficients $a_{11} \dots a_{nn}$ are separated from the dependent variables $x_1 \dots x_n$ and the equations are re-written in a form such as

$$\begin{bmatrix} a_{11} & a_{12} & \dots & a_{1n} \\ a_{21} & a_{22} & \dots & a_{2n} \\ \cdot & \cdot & \dots & \cdot \\ a_{n1} & a_{n2} & \dots & a_{nn} \end{bmatrix} \cdot \begin{bmatrix} x_1 \\ x_2 \\ \vdots \\ x_n \end{bmatrix} = \begin{bmatrix} y_1 \\ y_2 \\ \vdots \\ y_n \end{bmatrix} \tag{1.17}$$

in which it is understood that the original equations are restored by operating on the column of x-variables in a suitable way, and removing the brackets. This way of writing the equations has reduced the number of x-symbols from n^2 to n. A further logical contraction, of great value symbolically, is to replace the arrays in eqn. (1.17) by single symbols,

$$[A]\cdot[X] = [Y] \tag{1.18}$$

The arrays represented by $[A]$, $[X]$ and $[Y]$ are called *matrices*. A matrix may be defined as a scheme of detached coefficients a_{ij} set out in m rows and n columns. It is then said to be of order $m \times n$. In eqn. (1.17) the matrix of a-coefficients is square, and $m = n$. While this is characteristic of the coefficient matrix for a family of soluble simultaneous equations of which there will be n for n unknowns, rectangular matrices having $m \neq n$ are common: $[X]$ and $[Y]$ in eqn. (1.18), for example, are single columns.

A distinctive algebra of matrices, of a non-commutative operational kind, has been founded on the concept of detachment exemplified by eqns. (1.17) and (1.18). Its processes are inherently of a systematic routine nature, and it is of great practical value for the systematic formulation of general solutions to complex problems. Especially it is appropriate to the analysis of systems involving interconnected groups, such as *four-terminal networks* (*2-ports*, or 2 *terminal-pair networks*) connected together in various ways, and to a piecemeal attack on a complex system which can be dissected into manageable parts. This is the sense in which it is embodied in the tensor analysis of networks due to Gabriel Kron.[4,5,6]

The restoration of eqn. (1.17) to the original set, eqns. (1.16), suggests an operation of matrix multiplication:

$$\overset{\rightarrow}{\begin{bmatrix} a_{11} & a_{12} \dots a_{1n} \\ a_{21} & a_{22} \dots a_{2n} \\ \dots\dots & \dots\dots \\ a_{n1} & a_{n2} \dots a_{nn} \end{bmatrix}} \cdot \begin{bmatrix} x_1 \\ x_2 \\ \vdots \\ x_n \end{bmatrix}\downarrow = \begin{bmatrix} a_{11}x_1 + a_{12}x_2 + \dots + a_{1n}x_n \\ a_{21}x_1 + a_{22}x_2 + \dots + a_{2n}x_n \\ \dots\dots\dots\dots \\ a_{n1}x_1 + a_{n2}x_2 + \dots + a_{nn}x_n \end{bmatrix} \tag{1.19}$$

Now consider Table 1-1 and eqns. (1.15). The entries in the table are the coefficients of the currents (j) in eqns. (1.15), and by comparison with eqns. (1.19),

$$\begin{bmatrix} -1 & 1 & 0 & 1 & 0 & 0 \\ 0 & -1 & 1 & 0 & 1 & 0 \\ 1 & 0 & -1 & 0 & 0 & 1 \\ 0 & 0 & 0 & -1 & -1 & -1 \end{bmatrix} \cdot \begin{bmatrix} j_1 \\ j_2 \\ j_3 \\ j_4 \\ j_5 \\ j_6 \end{bmatrix} = \begin{bmatrix} -j_1 + j_2 + j_4 \\ -j_2 + j_3 + j_5 \\ j_1 - j_3 + j_6 \\ -j_4 - j_5 - j_6 \end{bmatrix} \tag{1.20}$$

Thus eqns. (1.15) may be written in the compact matrix form*

$$[A]_m \cdot [J] = 0 \tag{1.21}$$

where

$$[A]_m = \begin{bmatrix} -1 & 1 & 0 & 1 & 0 & 0 \\ 1 & -1 & 1 & 0 & 1 & 0 \\ 1 & 0 & -1 & 0 & 0 & 1 \\ 0 & 0 & 0 & -1 & -1 & -1 \end{bmatrix} \tag{1.22}$$

denotes an *incidence matrix* having m rows. The close connection between the matrix concept and the graph will now be evident, for the matrix $[A]_m$ has been directly conceived from the graph.

It has been shown in sect. 2.2 that 3 independent current-law equations are sufficient in the present illustration, and in general the number required is equal to the number of voltage-law equations. The tree-branch currents to be eliminated (163, Fig. 1-5(b)) are incident at node c; but this node is redundant, for these currents are included in the incidences at other nodes, a, d, and b. Thus, the matrix of coefficients for the three independent link currents is given immediately by deleting the row containing node c from the table, giving the *reduced incidence matrix*

$$[A]_{m-1} = \begin{bmatrix} -1 & 1 & 0 & 1 & 0 & 0 \\ 0 & -1 & 1 & 0 & 1 & 0 \\ 0 & 0 & 0 & -1 & -1 & -1 \end{bmatrix} \tag{1.23}$$

and the matrix equation

$$[A]_{m-1} \cdot [J] = 0 \qquad \text{or} \qquad \begin{bmatrix} -j_1 + j_2 + j_4 \\ -j_2 + j_3 + j_5 \\ -j_4 - j_5 - j_6 \end{bmatrix} = 0 \tag{1.24}$$

whence, removing the brackets,

$$\begin{aligned} -j_1 + j_2 + j_4 &= 0 \\ -j_2 + j_3 + j_5 &= 0 \\ -j_4 - j_5 - j_6 &= 0 \end{aligned} \tag{1.25}$$

which may be compared with eqns. (1.7).

* When it is necessary to indicate the order, or some other distinction for a matrix, this will usually be done with subscripts outside the bracket to avoid confusion with symbols used for the matrix parameters themselves.

3. LOOP-CURRENT AND NODAL-VOLTAGE ANALYSIS

The two procedures discussed in sect. 2.2 might be called link-current and tree-branch voltage analysis: in the first, the voltage-law equations are reduced to the number of links, and the current variables are reduced to the link-currents; and in the second, the current-law equations equal the number of tree-branches, while the voltage variables are the tree-branch voltages. Loop-current and nodal-voltage analysis are essentially aids to the execution of these procedures in practice.

3.1 LOOP-CURRENT ANALYSIS

In this method, a single circulating current is introduced into each tie-set loop. It differs from what has been called link-current analysis only in respect of the way in which the tree-branch currents are eliminated: the final equations are the same, for each circulating or loop-current is identified with the link-current in its tie-set.

The procedure is illustrated by reference to Fig. 1-8. One link at a time (heavy line) is added to the chosen tree (Fig. 1-5(b)), forming three separate tie-sets or closed loops, and a single current circulating in each loop is identified with each link-current. The remaining branches in the tie-sets are oriented with the assumed tree-branch currents.

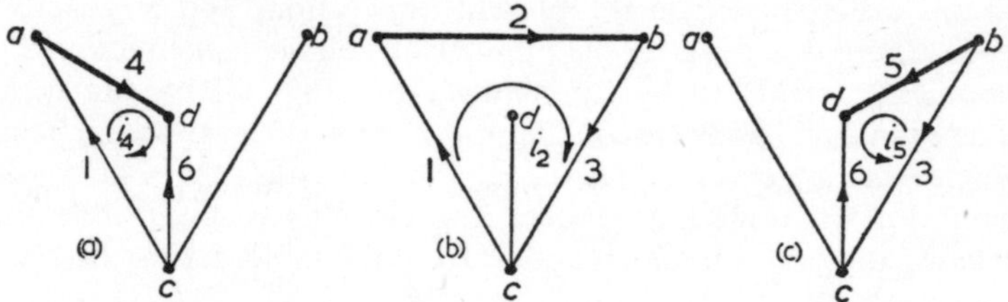

Fig. 1-8. Tie-sets with loop-currents for tree of Fig. 1-5(b).

Denoting the sense of the branch currents in each tie-set relative to the loop-currents by ± 1, the loop and branch currents are correlated in a tie-set schedule, Table 1-2.

Loop-current i	Branch-current, j					
	1	2	3	4	5	6
2	+1	+1	+1	0	0	0
4	+1	0	0	+1	0	−1
5	0	0	−1	0	+1	−1

Table 1-2. Tie-set schedule for Fig. 1-8.

The tie-set schedule reveals both the voltage-law equations and the correlation between branch and loop currents. From the rows, taking the voltages in the same senses as the branch currents,

$$\begin{aligned} v_1 + v_2 + v_3 &= 0 \\ v_1 + v_4 - v_6 &= 0 \\ -v_3 + v_5 - v_6 &= 0 \end{aligned} \tag{1.26}$$

and from the columns,

$$\begin{aligned} j_1 &= i_2 + i_4 \qquad & j_4 &= i_4 \\ j_2 &= i_2 & j_5 &= i_5 \\ j_3 &= i_2 - i_5 & j_6 &= -i_4 - i_5 \end{aligned} \tag{1.27}$$

By means of eqns. (1.27), eqns. (1.26) are now written in terms of the branch impedances and the loop-currents, giving

$$\begin{aligned} (Z_1+Z_2+Z_3)i_2 \quad &+ Z_1 i_4 & &- Z_3 i_5 = e_1 \\ Z_1 i_2 + (Z_1+Z_4+Z_6)i_4 & & &+ Z_6 i_5 = e_1 \\ -Z_3 i_2 \quad &+ Z_6 i_4 + (Z_3+Z_5+Z_6)i_5 = 0 & & \end{aligned} \tag{1.28}$$

The advantage of this loop-current artifice is that the minimum set of voltage-law equations and the correct independent set of current variables are both given by the one tie-set schedule. Eqns. (1.28), however, are algebraically the same as eqns. (1.6), since $i_2 = j_2$, $i_4 = j_4$ and $i_5 = j_5$.

3.1.1 *The tie-set or loop-current matrix*

Like the incidence schedule discussed in sect. 2.4, the tie-set schedule, Table 1-2, may be regarded as a matrix

$$[M] = \begin{bmatrix} 1 & 1 & 1 & 0 & 0 & 0 \\ 1 & 0 & 0 & 1 & 0 & -1 \\ 0 & 0 & -1 & 0 & 1 & -1 \end{bmatrix} \tag{1.29}$$

Then the voltage-law equations in matrix form are

$$\begin{bmatrix} 1 & 1 & 1 & 0 & 0 & 0 \\ 1 & 0 & 0 & 1 & 0 & -1 \\ 0 & 0 & -1 & 0 & 1 & -1 \end{bmatrix} \cdot \begin{bmatrix} v_1 \\ v_2 \\ v_3 \\ v_4 \\ v_5 \\ v_6 \end{bmatrix} = \begin{bmatrix} v_1 + v_2 + v_3 \\ v_1 + v_4 - v_6 \\ -v_3 + v_5 - v_6 \end{bmatrix} = \begin{bmatrix} 0 \\ 0 \\ 0 \end{bmatrix} \tag{1.30}$$

or compactly,

$$[M]\cdot[V] = 0 \tag{1.31}$$

where 0 represents what is more formally a *null matrix*, having all elements zero.

The matrix of branch currents is given in terms of the tie-set matrix and the matrix of loop-currents by interchanging the rows and columns of $[M]$. This is consistent with the fact that the branch currents are given by the schedule on adding the entries in each column. The transposed matrix is

$$[M]^t = \begin{bmatrix} 1 & 1 & 0 \\ 1 & 0 & 0 \\ 1 & 0 & -1 \\ 0 & 1 & 0 \\ 0 & 0 & 1 \\ 0 & -1 & -1 \end{bmatrix} \tag{1.32}$$

$$\begin{bmatrix} 1 & 1 & 0 \\ 1 & 0 & 0 \\ 1 & 0 & -1 \\ 0 & 1 & 0 \\ 0 & 0 & 1 \\ 0 & -1 & -1 \end{bmatrix} \cdot \begin{bmatrix} i_2 \\ i_4 \\ i_5 \end{bmatrix} = \begin{bmatrix} i_2 + i_4 \\ i_2 \\ i_2 - i_5 \\ i_4 \\ i_5 \\ -i_4 - i_5 \end{bmatrix} = \begin{bmatrix} j_1 \\ j_2 \\ j_3 \\ j_4 \\ j_5 \\ j_6 \end{bmatrix} \tag{1.33}$$

or compactly,

$$[M]^t \cdot [I_L] = [J_b] \tag{1.34}$$

3.2 NODAL-VOLTAGE ANALYSIS

As loop-current analysis is based on identifying a single circulating current with a link-current, so nodal-voltage analysis, which is its dual, is based on identifying a single node-pair voltage with a tree-branch voltage.

The procedure is best illustrated. Referring to Fig. 1-9, in (a) is shown the tree with its assumed branch voltages, and in (b) the condition when only one tree-branch voltage is considered at a time (the dual of one link current at a time). The equipotential groups of nodes in the ringed pair *a*, and *b*, *c*, *d*, differ in potential by the node-pair voltage v_{n1} (the dual of a loop-current), that is identified with the tree-branch voltage v_1. The remaining link-voltages v_2 and v_4 (duals of tree-branch currents) that also bridge the node-sets linked by the energised branch (duals of tree-branch currents that complete a tie-set with a link current), are then introduced, forming the first cut-set of Fig. 1-9(c). The other two cut-sets are formed similarly.

The correlation of branch voltages with node-pair voltages is shown by the entries ± 1 in the cut-set schedule of Table 1-3, from the rows of which is inferred the current-law equations and from the columns the branch voltages in terms of the node-pair voltages.

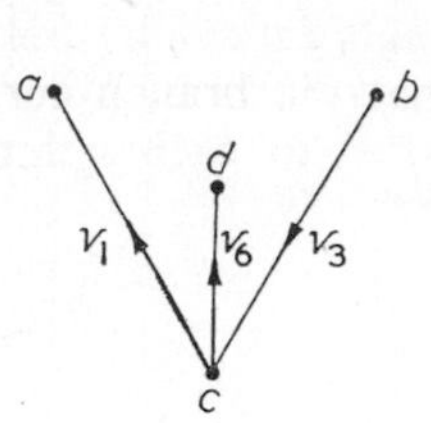

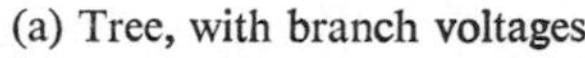
(a) Tree, with branch voltages

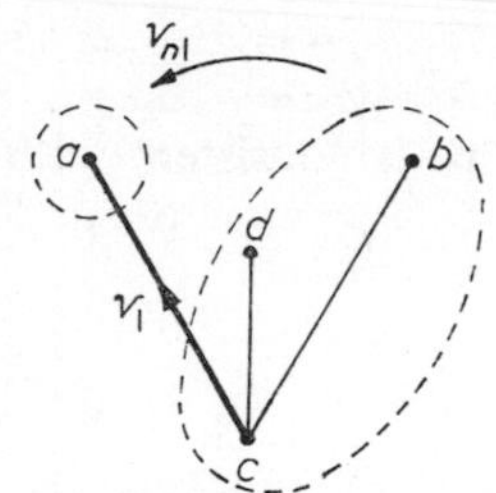

(b) Branch 1 only energised: node p.d. v_{n1} corresponds to tree-branch voltage v_1

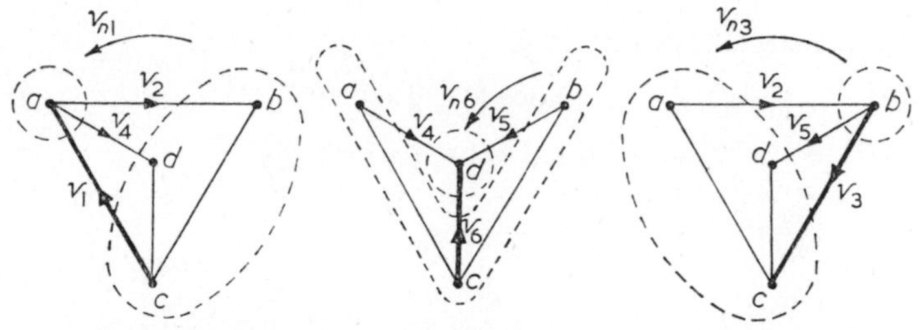

(c) Cut-sets formed by energising one branch at a time

Fig. 1-9. Illustrating the procedure of nodal-voltage analysis.

Node-pair voltage v_n	Branch voltage v					
	1	2	3	4	5	6
1	+1	−1	0	−1	0	0
6	0	0	0	+1	+1	+1
3	0	−1	+1	0	+1	0

Table 1-3. Cut-set schedule for Fig. 1-9.

The cut-set matrix corresponding to Table 1-3 is

$$[Q] = \begin{bmatrix} 1 & -1 & 0 & -1 & 0 & 0 \\ 0 & 0 & 0 & 1 & 1 & 1 \\ 0 & -1 & 1 & 0 & 1 & 0 \end{bmatrix} \qquad (1.35)$$

The current-law matrix equation is

$$[Q] \cdot [J] = 0 \qquad (1.36)$$

or

$$\begin{bmatrix} 1 & -1 & 0 & -1 & 0 & 0 \\ 0 & 0 & 0 & 1 & 1 & 1 \\ 0 & -1 & 1 & 0 & 1 & 0 \end{bmatrix} \cdot \begin{bmatrix} j_1 \\ j_2 \\ j_3 \\ j_4 \\ j_5 \\ j_6 \end{bmatrix} = \begin{bmatrix} j_1 - j_2 - j_4 \\ j_4 + j_5 + j_6 \\ -j_2 + j_3 + j_5 \end{bmatrix} = \begin{bmatrix} 0 \\ 0 \\ 0 \end{bmatrix} \quad (1.37)$$

and, removing the brackets, the actual equations are

$$\begin{aligned} j_1 - j_2 - j_4 &= 0 \\ j_4 + j_5 + j_6 &= 0 \\ -j_2 + j_3 + j_5 &= 0 \end{aligned} \quad (1.38)$$

The branch-voltage matrix is

$$[V_b] = [Q]^t \cdot [V_n] \quad (1.39)$$

where $[Q]^t$ is the transposed cut-set matrix. Thus,

$$\begin{bmatrix} v_1 \\ v_2 \\ v_3 \\ v_4 \\ v_5 \\ v_6 \end{bmatrix} = \begin{bmatrix} 1 & 0 & 0 \\ -1 & 0 & -1 \\ 0 & 0 & 1 \\ -1 & 1 & 0 \\ 0 & 1 & 1 \\ 0 & 1 & 0 \end{bmatrix} \cdot \begin{bmatrix} v_{n1} \\ v_{n6} \\ v_{n3} \end{bmatrix} = \begin{bmatrix} v_{n1} \\ -v_{n1} - v_{n3} \\ v_{n3} \\ -v_{n1} + v_{n6} \\ v_{n6} + v_{n3} \\ v_{n6} \end{bmatrix} \quad (1.40)$$

or

$$\begin{aligned} v_1 &= v_{n1} & v_4 &= -v_{n1} + v_{n6} \\ v_2 &= -v_{n1} - v_{n3} & v_5 &= v_{n6} + v_{n3} \\ v_3 &= v_{n3} & v_6 &= v_{n6} \end{aligned} \quad (1.41)$$

Writing now $j_1 = -i_1 + v_1 Y_1$, where i_1 is a current source in parallel with branch 1 as in sect. 2.2.2, and substituting the node-pair voltages from eqns. (1.41) in place of the branch voltages, eqns. (1.38) give

$$\begin{aligned} (Y_1 + Y_2 + Y_4)v_{n1} + Y_2 v_{n3} - Y_4 v_{n6} &= i_1 \\ -Y_4 v_{n1} + Y_5 v_{n3} + (Y_4 + Y_5 + Y_6)v_{n6} &= 0 \\ Y_2 v_{n1} + (Y_2 + Y_3 + Y_5)v_{n3} + Y_5 v_{n6} &= 0 \end{aligned} \quad (1.42)$$

4. TOPOLOGICAL RELATIONS AND CHOICE OF METHOD

It has been shown that the minimum number of independent equations to be solved is equal either to the number of links, in the case of loop-current analysis, or to the number of tree-branches, in the case of nodal-voltage analysis. In the illustration considered so far (Fig. 1-1 and the graph of Fig. 1-2), the number of equations is the same for both forms of analysis, and the choice of method is biassed only by the form in which the data is available. Either method will yield both the branch currents and voltages, for these are directly related by the branch impedances or admittances; but if, for example, the data for Fig. 1-1 is in the form of the branch impedances and source e.m.f., the nodal-voltage approach is less favourable because it requires conversion of the impedances into admittances, and the e.m.f. source into a current one (although this is not essential).

The number of tree-branches is, however, not always the same as the number of links. For a connected network of N nodes, B branches, B_t tree-branches, and L links,

$$\begin{aligned} L &= B - N + 1 \\ B_t &= B - L = N - 1 \end{aligned} \tag{1.43}$$

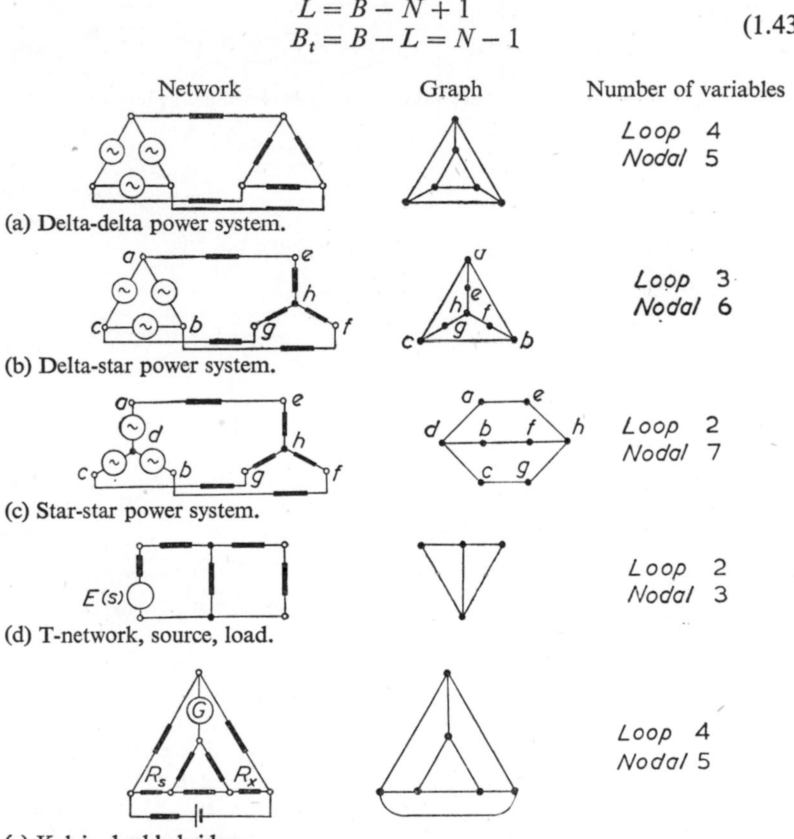

Fig. 1-10. Examples of practical networks topologically suited to loop-current analysis.

In Figs. 1-10 and 1-11 is shown a number of practical networks for which loop-current and nodal-voltage analysis are formally the optimum approaches. In some other cases, such as four and five arm bridges (the Anderson type) and parallel T-networks, the number of variables is the same for both methods of analysis.

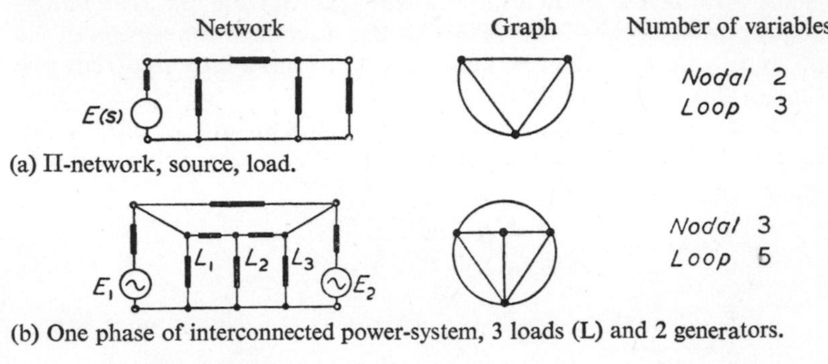

(a) Π-network, source, load.

(b) One phase of interconnected power-system, 3 loads (L) and 2 generators.

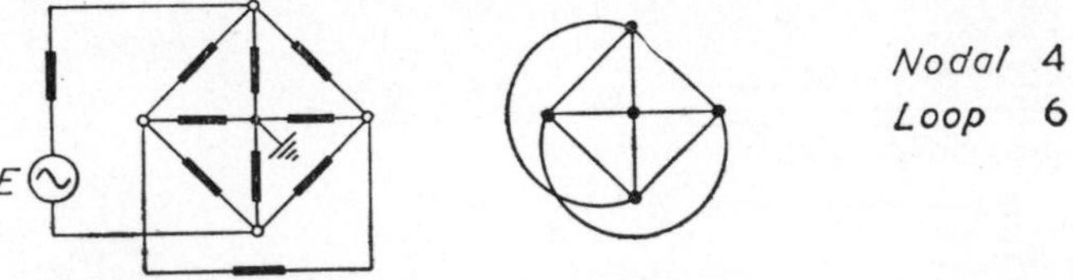

(c) General bridge, with admittances to earth (or star-quad cable capacitance network etc.)

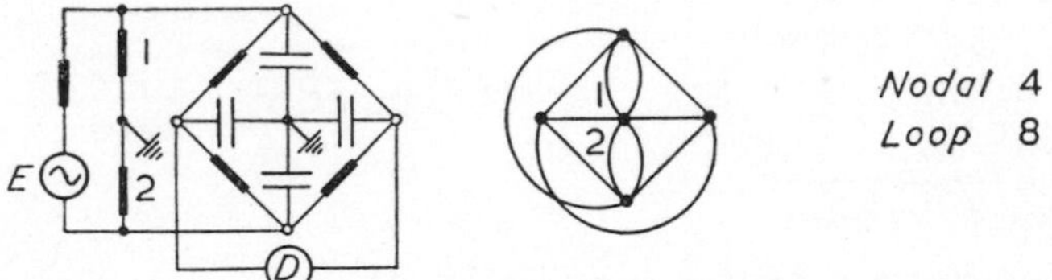

(d) Bridge with earth capacitances and Wagner earthing network (1, 2).

Fig. 1-11. Examples of practical networks topologically suited to nodal-voltage analysis.

In practice the choice implied formally by eqns. (1.43) is not necessarily the best, for simplification of the graph is often possible in various ways, including the use of theorems and equivalences. For example, consider Fig. 1-10 (b). In relation to the current flowing between node h and nodes a, b and c, nodes e, f and g might be regarded as superfluous, giving the simplified graph of Fig. 1-12 (a). Likewise, Fig. 1-10 (c) simplifies to Fig. 1-12 (b). This is particularly easy to solve as there are now only two nodes. Similar reasoning applies to Fig. 1-10 (d).

Fig. 1-12. Simplified graphs for Figs. 1-10 (b) and (c).

Often, in fact, the use of topology in a formal way is not occasioned at all, either because the network is well adapted to simplifying artifices and only a partial solution is required (as illustrated in subsequent chapters), or because it is simple and conforms to one of the basic patterns (star, delta, or T, Π; bridge, lattice, or bridged-T).

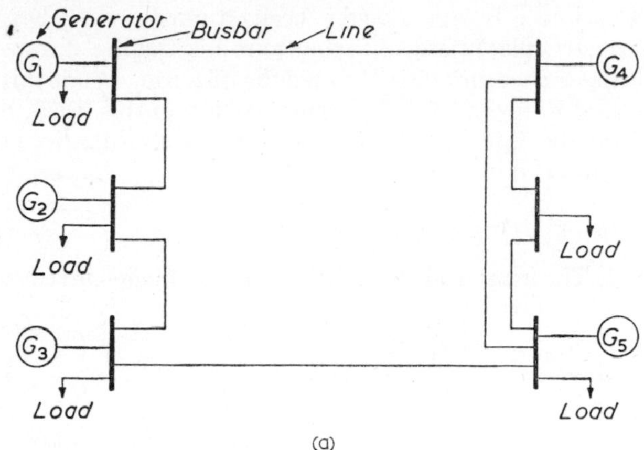

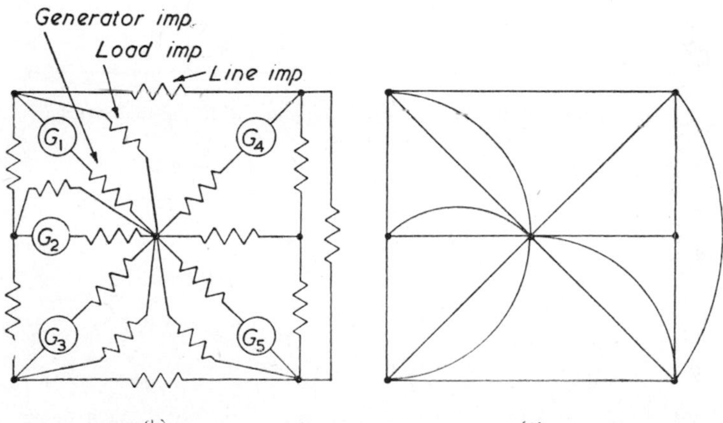

Fig. 1-13. Representations for a power-distribution system.

The distribution of electric power is one field in which complex networks are intrinsic, and in which a knowledge of currents and voltages at all points is generally required. An actual network for distributing power from five generating stations to five main loads is shown in block form in Fig 1-13(a). The system is three-phase, but as the current in each phase has the same magnitude under symmetrical loading conditions, it is sufficient to examine the network representing a single-phase of the system. For this purpose, the generators and loads are returned to a common point, the neutral of the system (corresponding to the star-point in a star-connected system). The single-phase network and its graph are illustrated in Figs. 1-14(b) and (c) respectively. Inspection of the graph reveals 7 nodes and 17 branches. In principle therefore the network should be soluble with 6 nodal-voltage or 11 loop-current equations. It has actually been studied by Nicholson and Lynn,[7] with particular reference to the economic loading of transmission systems, using the tensor analysis technique of Kron. While this mature matrix method is beyond detailed consideration in this book, it should be noted that the features of network topology and matrices included here are essential to it.

5. ILLUSTRATIVE EXAMPLES

Example 1.1. The numerical formulation of a set of loop-current equations

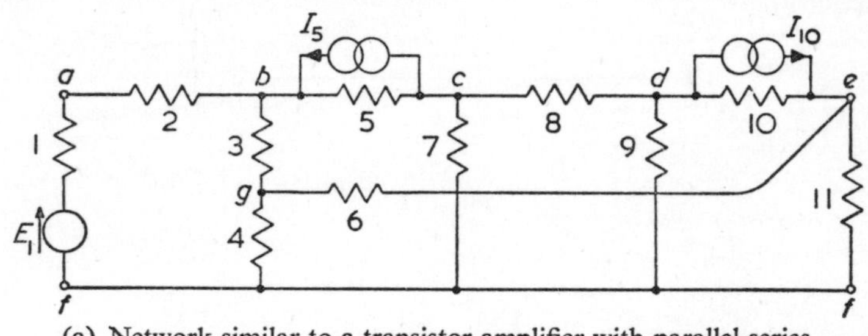

(a) Network similar to a transistor amplifier with parallel-series feedback.

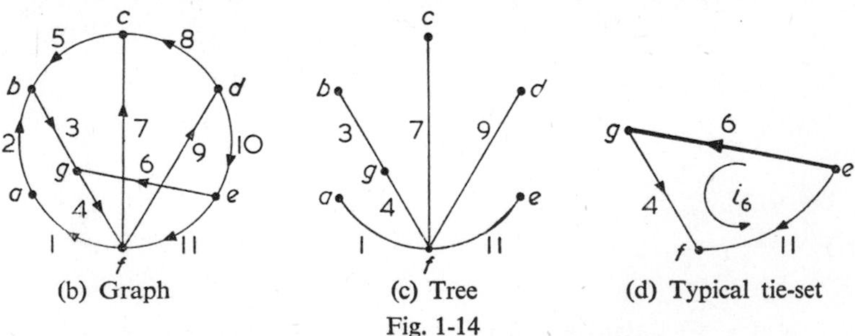

(b) Graph (c) Tree (d) Typical tie-set

Fig. 1-14

The network chosen is a practical one, being identified with the equivalent-circuit of a two-stage transistor amplifier with parallel-series feedback (branches 4, 6). However, for actual transistors the current-sources I_5 and I_{10} are functions of the currents in branches 2 and 8 respectively, and the resistances lie in too wide a range (20 Ω to 1 MΩ) to be convenient for the present objective of illustrating the formal procedure. The branches and sources will therefore be assigned values that are quite fictitious, but arithmetically convenient for this objective. Since the procedure is not a function of numerical values, the model may then be adapted by the reader to the parameters for an actual transistor circuit. If this is done, approximations may suggest themselves, occasioned by large differences between the practical values of some resistances.

For illustration, let the branch parameters be as follows:

Branch	Resistance, ohms	Branch	Resistance, ohms
1	5	7	10
2	4	8	5
3	2	9	3
4	5	10	10
5	8	11	8
6	10		

$$E_1 = 1\text{ V}, \quad I_5 = 2\text{ A}, \quad I_{10} = 4\text{ A}.$$

The graph is shown with arbitrary orientations in Fig. 1-14(b). There are 7 nodes and 11 branches, and by equations (1.43), 6 nodal-voltage or 5 loop-current equations are required for analysis. Fig. 1-14(c) is a convenient tree, and Fig. 1-14(d) illustrates a typical tie-set, with a loop-current i_6 identified with the current (j_6) in the link 6 that completes the tie-set with branches 4 and 11 of the tree.

By forming five tie-sets with links 2, 5, 6, 8, and 10, in which loop-currents i_2, i_5, i_6, i_8, and i_{10} are identified with the link-currents j_2, j_5, j_6, j_8, and j_{10}, the tie-set schedule of Table 1-4 is constructed.

Loop-Current, i	*Branch-current, j*										
	1	2	3	4	5	6	7	8	9	10	11
2	+1	+1	+1	+1	0	0	0	0	0	0	0
5	0	0	+1	+1	+1	0	+1	0	0	0	0
6	0	0	0	+1	0	+1	0	0	0	0	−1
8	0	0	0	0	0	0	−1	+1	+1	0	0
10	0	0	0	0	0	0	0	0	+1	+1	+1

Table 1-4. Tie-set schedule for Fig. 1-14.

From Table 1-4, the tie-set matrix is

$$[M] = \begin{bmatrix} 1 & 1 & 1 & 1 & 0 & 0 & 0 & 0 & 0 & 0 & 0 \\ 0 & 0 & 1 & 1 & 1 & 0 & 1 & 0 & 0 & 0 & 0 \\ 0 & 0 & 0 & 1 & 0 & 1 & 0 & 0 & 0 & 0 & -1 \\ 0 & 0 & 0 & 0 & 0 & 0 & -1 & 1 & 1 & 0 & 0 \\ 0 & 0 & 0 & 0 & 0 & 0 & 0 & 0 & 1 & 1 & 1 \end{bmatrix} \tag{1.44}$$

and the transposed matrix is

$$[M]^t = \begin{bmatrix} 1 & 0 & 0 & 0 & 0 \\ 1 & 0 & 0 & 0 & 0 \\ 1 & 1 & 0 & 0 & 0 \\ 1 & 1 & 1 & 0 & 0 \\ 0 & 1 & 0 & 0 & 0 \\ 0 & 0 & 1 & 0 & 0 \\ 0 & 1 & 0 & -1 & 0 \\ 0 & 0 & 0 & 1 & 0 \\ 0 & 0 & 0 & 1 & 1 \\ 0 & 0 & 0 & 0 & 1 \\ 0 & 0 & -1 & 0 & 1 \end{bmatrix} \tag{1.45}$$

Let $v_1 \dots v_{11}$ denote the net branch voltages, oriented in the same direction as the net branch currents $j_1 \dots j_{11}$. Then the matrix voltage-law equation is

$$[M]\cdot[V] = 0 \tag{1.46}$$

where $[V]$ denotes the column-matrix of voltages $V_1 \dots V_{11}$, and the branch-current matrix is expressed by

$$[J_b] = [M]^t\cdot[I_L] \tag{1.47}$$

where $[I_L]$ is the column-matrix of loop-currents $i_2, i_5, i_6, i_8, i_{10}$.

Substituting in eqn. (1.47) for $[M]^t$ from eqn. (1.45), multiplying by the column matrix $[I_L]$, and writing the result in normal equation form,

$$\begin{aligned} j_1 &= i_2 & j_7 &= i_5 - i_8 \\ j_2 &= i_2 & j_8 &= i_8 \\ j_3 &= i_2 + i_5 & j_9 &= i_8 + i_{10} \\ j_4 &= i_2 + i_5 + i_6 & j_{10} &= i_{10} \\ j_5 &= i_5 & j_{11} &= -i_6 + i_{10} \\ j_6 &= i_6 \end{aligned} \tag{1.48}$$

The incorporation of sources

(1) The e.m.f. E_1 in branch 1:

Introducing the branch resistance of 5 Ω and allowing for the sense of action of E_1 in relation to the orientation of j_1,

$$v_1 = 5j_1 - E_1 = 5j_1 - 1$$

(2) The current-source I_5 in parallel with branch 5:
The resistance is 8 Ω, and the net branch-current is

$$j_5 = I_5 + v_5/8 = 2 + v_5/8$$

Therefore,

$$v_5 = 8j_5 - 16$$

(3) The current-source I_{10} in parallel with branch 10:
In a similar way,

$$j_{10} = I_{10} + v_{10}/10 = 4 + v_{10}/10$$

whence

$$v_{10} = 10j_{10} - 40$$

Formulation of the final equations

Introducing the resistances of the remaining branches, and substituting from eqns. (1.48),

$$\begin{bmatrix} v_1 \\ v_2 \\ v_3 \\ v_4 \\ v_5 \\ v_6 \\ v_7 \\ v_8 \\ v_9 \\ v_{10} \\ v_{11} \end{bmatrix} = \begin{bmatrix} 5j_1 - 1 \\ 4j_2 \\ 2j_3 \\ 5j_4 \\ 8j_5 - 16 \\ 10j_6 \\ 10j_7 \\ 5j_8 \\ 3j_9 \\ 10j_{10} - 40 \\ 8j_{11} \end{bmatrix} = \begin{bmatrix} 5i_2 - 1 \\ 4i_2 \\ 2(i_2 + i_5) \\ 5(i_2 + i_5 + i_6) \\ 8i_5 - 16 \\ 10i_6 \\ 10(i_5 - i_8) \\ 5i_8 \\ 3(i_8 + i_{10}) \\ 10i_{10} - 40 \\ 8(i_{10} - i_6) \end{bmatrix} \tag{1.49}$$

Then, substituting in eqn. (1.46) for $[M]$ and $[V]$ from eqns. (1.44) and (1.49), multiplying the matrices and simplifying,

$$\begin{bmatrix} 16i_2 + 7i_5 + 5i_6 - 1 \\ 7i_2 + 25i_5 + 5i_6 - 10i_8 - 16 \\ 5i_2 + 5i_5 + 23i_6 - 8i_{10} \\ -10i_5 + 18i_8 + 3i_{10} \\ -8i_6 + 3i_8 + 21i_{10} - 40 \end{bmatrix} = 0$$

or,

$$\begin{aligned} 16i_2 + 7i_5 + 5i_6 &= 1 \\ 7i_2 + 25i_5 + 5i_6 - 10i_8 &= 16 \\ 5i_2 + 5i_5 + 23i_6 - 8i_{10} &= 0 \\ -10i_5 + 18i_8 + 3i_{10} &= 0 \\ -8i_6 + 3i_8 + 21i_{10} &= 40 \end{aligned}$$

or, more compactly,

$$\begin{bmatrix} 16 & 7 & 5 & 0 & 0 \\ 7 & 25 & 5 & -10 & 0 \\ 5 & 5 & 23 & 0 & -8 \\ 0 & -10 & 0 & 18 & 3 \\ 0 & 0 & -8 & 3 & 21 \end{bmatrix} \cdot \begin{bmatrix} i_2 \\ i_5 \\ i_6 \\ i_8 \\ i_{10} \end{bmatrix} = \begin{bmatrix} 1 \\ 16 \\ 0 \\ 0 \\ 40 \end{bmatrix} \tag{1.50}$$

Example 1.2. The numerical formulation of a set of nodal-voltage equations

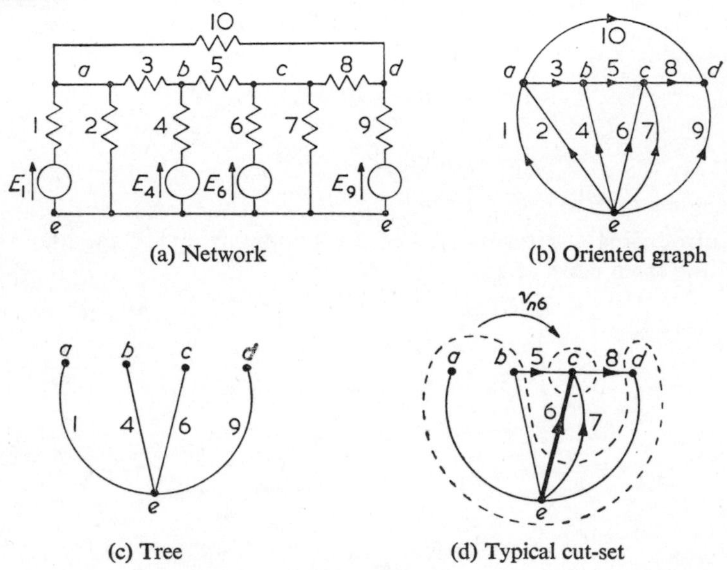

(a) Network

(b) Oriented graph

(c) Tree

(d) Typical cut-set

Fig. 1-15.

The network of Fig. 1-15(a) has arisen in connection with the analysis of a transistor differential amplifier.[8] For the present purpose, however, let the network be assigned fictitious convenient values as follows:

Branch	Conductance, mhos	Branch	Conductance, mhos
1	2	6	3
2	3	7	9
3	5	8	10
4	4	9	8
5	7	10	6

$E_1 = 2\text{ V};\quad E_4 = 3\text{ V};\quad E_6 = 2\text{ V};\quad E_9 = 4\text{ V}.$

The oriented graph of Fig. 1-15(b) has 5 nodes and 10 branches. Therefore, by eqn. (1.43), 6 loop-current or 4 nodal-voltage equations are required. A convenient tree is shown in Fig. 1-15(c), while Fig. 1-15(d) illustrates a typical cut-set. This has been formed by energising branch 6 of the tree, and adding links 5, 7, and 8 which also bridge the node-sets (the two dotted regions) linked by the energised branch.

By forming four such cut-sets, in which node-pair voltages v_{n1}, v_{n4}, v_{n6} and v_{n9} are identified with the tree-branch voltages v_1, v_4, v_6, and v_9, the cut-set schedule of Table 1-5 is constructed.

Node-pair voltage v_n	Branch voltage v.									
	1	2	3	4	5	6	7	8	9	10
1	+1	+1	−1	0	0	0	0	0	0	−1
4	0	0	+1	+1	−1	0	0	0	0	0
6	0	0	0	0	+1	+1	+1	−1	0	0
9	0	0	0	0	0	0	0	+1	+1	+1

Table 1-5. Cut-set schedule for Fig. 1-15.

From Table 1-5, the cut-set matrix is

$$[Q] = \begin{bmatrix} 1 & 1 & -1 & 0 & 0 & 0 & 0 & 0 & 0 & -1 \\ 0 & 0 & 1 & 1 & -1 & 0 & 0 & 0 & 0 & 0 \\ 0 & 0 & 0 & 0 & 1 & 1 & 1 & -1 & 0 & 0 \\ 0 & 0 & 0 & 0 & 0 & 0 & 0 & 1 & 1 & 1 \end{bmatrix} \tag{1.51}$$

and

$$[Q]^t = \begin{bmatrix} 1 & 0 & 0 & 0 \\ 1 & 0 & 0 & 0 \\ -1 & 1 & 0 & 0 \\ 0 & 1 & 0 & 0 \\ 0 & -1 & 1 & 0 \\ 0 & 0 & 1 & 0 \\ 0 & 0 & 1 & 0 \\ 0 & 0 & -1 & 1 \\ 0 & 0 & 0 & 1 \\ -1 & 0 & 0 & 1 \end{bmatrix} \tag{1.52}$$

Let $j_1 \dots j_{10}$ denote the branch currents, oriented in the same directions as the net branch voltages $v_1 \dots v_{10}$. Then the matrix current-law equation is

$$[Q]\cdot[J] = 0 \tag{1.53}$$

where $[J]$ denotes the column matrix of currents $j_1 \dots j_{10}$. The branch-voltage matrix is expressed by

$$[V] = [Q]^t \cdot [V_n] \tag{1.54}$$

where $[V_n]$ is the column matrix of node-pair voltages v_{n1}, v_{n4}, v_{n6}, v_{n9}.

Substituting in eqn. (1.54) for $[Q]^t$ from eqn. (1.52), multiplying by the column-matrix $[V_n]$, and writing the result in normal equation form

$$\begin{aligned} v_1 &= v_{n1}, & v_6 &= v_{n6} \\ v_2 &= v_{n1}, & v_7 &= v_{n6} \\ v_3 &= -v_{n1} + v_{n4}, & v_8 &= -v_{n6} + v_{n9} \\ v_4 &= v_{n4}, & v_9 &= v_{n9} \\ v_5 &= -v_{n4} + v_{n6}, & v_{10} &= -v_{n1} + v_{n9} \end{aligned} \tag{1.55}$$

The incorporation of sources

In this case there are e.m.f. sources only, and each acts in the same sense as the orientation assumed for the branch concerned. Thus, introducing the branch conductances and the e.m.f. values,

$$\begin{aligned} j_1 &= G_1(v_1 - E_1) = 2v_1 - 4 \\ j_4 &= G_4(v_4 - E_4) = 4v_4 - 12 \\ j_6 &= G_6(v_6 - E_6) = 3v_6 - 6 \\ j_9 &= G_9(v_9 - E_9) = 8v_9 - 32 \end{aligned}$$

Formulation of the final equations

Introducing the conductances of the remaining branches and substituting from eqns. (1.55),

$$\begin{bmatrix} j_1 \\ j_2 \\ j_3 \\ j_4 \\ j_5 \\ j_6 \\ j_7 \\ j_8 \\ j_9 \\ j_{10} \end{bmatrix} = \begin{bmatrix} 2v_1 - 4 \\ 3v_2 \\ 5v_3 \\ 4v_4 - 12 \\ 7v_5 \\ 3v_6 - 6 \\ 9v_7 \\ 10v_8 \\ 8v_9 - 32 \\ 6v_{10} \end{bmatrix} = \begin{bmatrix} 2v_{n1} - 4 \\ 3v_{n1} \\ -5v_{n1} + 5v_{n4} \\ 4v_{n4} - 12 \\ -7v_{n4} + 7v_{n6} \\ 3v_{n6} - 6 \\ 9v_{n6} \\ -10v_{n6} + 10v_{n9} \\ 8v_{n9} - 32 \\ -6v_{n1} + 6v_{n9} \end{bmatrix} \tag{1.56}$$

Then, substituting in eqn. (1.53) for $[Q]$ and $[J]$ from eqns. (1.51) and (1.56), multiplying the matrices and simplifying,

$$\begin{bmatrix} 16v_{n1} - 5v_{n4} - 6v_{n9} - 4 \\ -5v_{n1} + 16v_{n4} - 7v_{n6} - 12 \\ -7v_{n4} + 29v_{n6} - 10v_{n9} - 6 \\ -6v_{n1} - 10v_{n6} + 24v_{n9} - 32 \end{bmatrix} = 0$$

or,

$$\begin{bmatrix} 16 & -5 & 0 & -6 \\ -5 & 16 & -7 & 0 \\ 0 & -7 & 29 & -10 \\ -6 & 0 & -10 & 24 \end{bmatrix} \cdot \begin{bmatrix} v_{n1} \\ v_{n4} \\ v_{n6} \\ v_{n9} \end{bmatrix} = \begin{bmatrix} 4 \\ 12 \\ 6 \\ 32 \end{bmatrix} \tag{1.57}$$

Comments

(1) Step-by-step the procedure is absolutely dual with the procedure for formulating the loop-current equations in Example 1.1.

(2) The particular choice of tree has resulted in node-pairs that all include the same node, *e*. This is coincident, therefore, with the simpler procedure of node-datum analysis discussed in Chapter 2, sect. 3, in which one convenient node is selected as a datum to which the potentials of all other nodes may be referred. Fig. 1-15 is reconsidered in this light in Example 2.3.

REFERENCES

1. SESHU, S. and REED, M. B.: *Linear Graphs and Electrical Networks* (Addison-Wesley Publishing Company, Inc., Mass., U.S.A. 1961).
2. HOWE, G. W. O.: Editorials, *Wireless Engineer*, Oct. 1947 (XXIV No. 289) and Feb. 1948 (XXV No. 293).
3. BRYANT, P. R.: The Algebra and Topology of Electrical Networks, *Proceedings I.E.E.*, Monograph No. 414E, Nov. 1960 (C, 13, p. 215, Mar. 1961).
4. KRON, GABRIEL: *Tensor Analysis of Networks* (Chapman and Hall Ltd., London, 1939); *Diakoptics* (Macdonald, London, 1963).
5. AUSTEN STIGANT, S.: *The Elements of Determinants Matrices and Tensors for Engineers* (Macdonald, London, 1959).
6. BRANIN, F. H., Jr.: The Relation between Kron's Method and the Classical Methods of Network Analysis, *The Matrix and Tensor Quarterly*, Vol. 12, No. 3, Mar. 1962. (contains extensive bibliography).
7. NICHOLSON, H. and LYNN, J. W.: The Economic Loading of Transmission Systems, *Proceedings I.E.E.*, Monograph No. 294 S, Mar. 1958 (C, 8, p. 407, Sept. 1958).
8. NAMBIAR, K. P. P.: Transistor Differential Amplifier, *Electronic Technology*, Vol. 39, No. 4, April 1962.

2

PRACTICAL PROCEDURES FOR THE FORMATION AND SOLUTION OF NETWORK EQUATIONS

1. INTRODUCTION

The principles and procedures discussed in the last chapter are the fundamentals for systematically formulating independent sets of Kirchhoff-law equations. Now it is intended to illustrate extensions to these principles: the incorporation of all the network parameters into comprehensive matrix formulae; particularisations of loop-current and nodal-voltage analysis that are simple yet adaptable to most planar networks; and simplifications, including reduction of the network graph, based on the use of theorems and equivalences.

2. THE DEVELOPMENT OF COMPREHENSIVE MATRIX FORMULAE

The terms in the voltage and current-law equations are governed by the tie-set and cut-set matrices, $[M]$ and $[Q]$. While the necessary substitutions in terms of known branch impedances or admittances and sources, and branch currents or voltages, are numerically unique for a given network, the procedure is not unique and is readily generalised by resorting again to matrix formulation.

2.1 THE CONCEPT OF A BRANCH IMMITTANCE MATRIX

The term *immittance* is introduced here as a convenient generalisation embracing impedance and admittance.

Consider a network containing n branches, which in the first instance should be assumed to be entirely independent; that is, free from mutual coupling such as mutual inductance. When the sources are excluded, a list of the branch voltages displayed in matrix style is of the form

$$\begin{bmatrix} v_1 \\ v_2 \\ \cdot \\ \cdot \\ v_n \end{bmatrix} = \begin{bmatrix} Z_1 j_1 \\ Z_2 j_2 \\ \cdot \\ \cdot \\ Z_n j_n \end{bmatrix} \tag{2.1}$$

The right-hand side of eqn. (2.1), however, is consistent with the pre-multiplication of a column matrix representing the branch currents, by a rectangular matrix representing the impedances, provided the elements in this are zero except for those on the leading diagonal:

$$\begin{bmatrix} Z_1 & 0 & \cdot & \cdot & 0 \\ 0 & Z_2 & \cdot & \cdot & 0 \\ \cdot & \cdot & \cdot & \cdot & \cdot \\ \cdot & \cdot & \cdot & \cdot & 0 \\ 0 & 0 & \cdot & 0 & Z_n \end{bmatrix} \cdot \begin{bmatrix} j_1 \\ j_2 \\ \cdot \\ \cdot \\ j_n \end{bmatrix} = \begin{bmatrix} Z_1 j_1 \\ Z_2 j_2 \\ \cdot \\ \cdot \\ Z_n j_n \end{bmatrix} \tag{2.2}$$

Thus, eqn. (2.1) can be condensed into

$$[V_b] = [Z_b] \cdot [J_b] \tag{2.3}$$

where

$$[Z_b] = \begin{bmatrix} Z_1 & 0 & \cdot & \cdot & 0 \\ 0 & Z_2 & \cdot & \cdot & 0 \\ \cdot & \cdot & \cdot & \cdot & \cdot \\ \cdot & \cdot & \cdot & \cdot & 0 \\ 0 & 0 & \cdot & 0 & Z_n \end{bmatrix} \tag{2.4}$$

denotes the *branch impedance matrix*, consisting of diagonal elements only in the absence of mutual impedance between the branches.

Each branch current, as involved in nodal-voltage analysis, is of the form $j_k = Y_k v_k$. It therefore follows, by duality, that the *branch admittance matrix* is of the form

$$[Y_b] = \begin{bmatrix} Y_1 & 0 & . & . & 0 \\ 0 & Y_2 & . & . & 0 \\ . & . & . & . & . \\ . & . & . & . & 0 \\ 0 & 0 & . & . & Y_n \end{bmatrix} \tag{2.5}$$

in the absence of mutual admittance between the branches.

2.2 THE MATRIX PATTERNS FOR THE LOOP-CURRENT AND NODAL-VOLTAGE EQUATIONS

By eqn. (1.34), the column matrix of branch currents $[J_b]$ is related the column matrix of loop-currents $[I_L]$ by

$$[J_b]=[M]^t\cdot[I_L] \tag{2.6}$$

where $[M]^t$ denotes the transposed form (rows interchanged with columns) of the tie-set matrix, $[M]$. Substituting for $[J_b]$ in eqn. (2.3) then gives

$$[V_b]=[Z_b]\cdot[M]^t\cdot[I_L] \tag{2.7}$$

Now, $[V_b]$ is a column matrix representing all the branch voltages, and it has already been shown that the pattern of the voltage-law equations is set by $[M]$ in the form $[M]\cdot[V]=0$. Thus, referring to eqn. (2.7), the matrix pattern for the voltage-law equations incorporating all the branch impedances is

$$[M]\cdot[Z_b]\cdot[M]^t\cdot[I_L]=0 \tag{2.8}$$

By reference to Chapter 1, sect. 3.2, it follows by duality that the current-law matrix equation in terms of node-pair voltages is

$$[Q]\cdot[Y_b]\cdot[Q]^t\cdot[V_n]=0 \tag{2.9}$$

2.3 THE INCLUSION OF SOURCES: THE GENERAL FORMULAE

The network may be energised from e.m.f. or current sources, or both. A general representation combining both kinds of source is shown in Fig. 2-1.

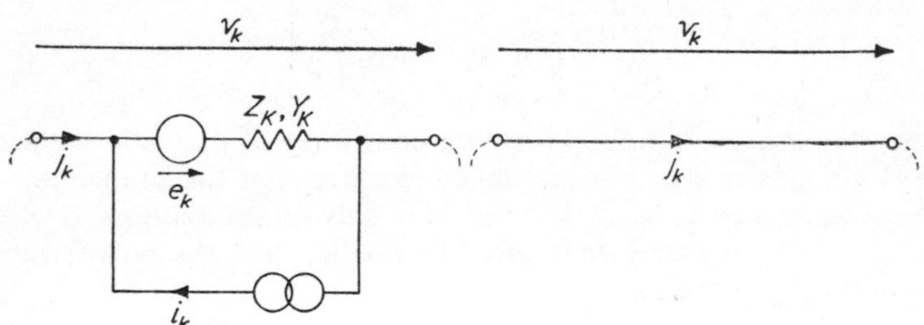

(a) Branch with both e.m.f. and current sources

(b) Graph equivalent

Fig. 2-1.

Referring to Fig. 2-1(a),

$$\begin{aligned} v_k &= Z_k(j_k+i_k)-e_k \\ &= Z_k j_k + Z_k i_k - e_k \end{aligned} \tag{2.10}$$

Transposing and writing $Y_k = 1/Z_k$,

$$\begin{aligned} j_k &= Y_k(v_k + e_k) - i_k \\ &= Y_k v_k + Y_k e_k - i_k \end{aligned} \tag{2.11}$$

As the branch currents for the whole network may be represented by a column matrix $[J_b]$, so also may the sources, numbered according to the branches, be represented in the matrix forms

$$[I] = \begin{bmatrix} i_1 \\ i_2 \\ \cdot \\ \cdot \\ \cdot \\ i_n \end{bmatrix} \text{ and } [E] = \begin{bmatrix} e_1 \\ e_2 \\ \cdot \\ \cdot \\ \cdot \\ e_n \end{bmatrix} \tag{2.12}$$

Then by reference to eqn. (2.10), the pattern of branch voltages for the whole network is

$$[M]\cdot[V] = [M]\cdot[Z_b]\cdot[J_b] + [M]\cdot[Z_b]\cdot[I] - [M]\cdot[E] \tag{2.13}$$

Now putting $[M]\cdot[V] = 0$ in accordance with Kirchhoff's voltage-law, and writing $[M]^t\cdot[I_L]$ for $[J_b]$, the comprehensive matrix equation for loop-current analysis becomes

$$[M]\cdot[Z_b]\cdot[M]^t\cdot[I_L] = [M]\{[E] - [Z_b]\cdot[I]\} \tag{2.14}$$

Again, it is sufficient merely to invoke the principle of duality in order to state the corresponding equation for nodal-voltage analysis:

$$[Q]\cdot[Y_b]\cdot[Q]^t\cdot[V_n] = [Q]\{[I] - [Y_b]\cdot[E]\} \tag{2.15}$$

It should be noted that while $[M]$ and $[Q]$ appear on both sides in eqns. (2.14) and (2.15) respectively, it is not permissible to cancel them.

2.4 THE GENERAL FORM FOR THE BRANCH IMMITTANCE MATRICES

The immittance matrices introduced in sect. 2.1 are limited to networks whose branches are linked at the nodes only and are otherwise independent. In practice, additional coupling may be distributed between branches in the form of capacitance or mutual inductance. When capacitance exists in this way, as the embodiment of stray electric fields, it is an impurity in the network; and while exact analysis of its effect may be intractable, it is usually possible to account for it, at least approximately, in terms of lumped equivalents between appropriate nodes. This is illustrated, for an un-earthed, un-shielded transformer or mutual inductor, in Fig. 2-2. The capacitances, which in general are distributed from each point on each winding to earth, from each point on each winding to every other point on the same winding (distributed self-capacitance), and from each point on either winding to every point on the other (distributed inter-winding capacitance), are effectively simulated by 10 inter-node capacitances. This capacitance network simplifies considerably if the windings are earthed.

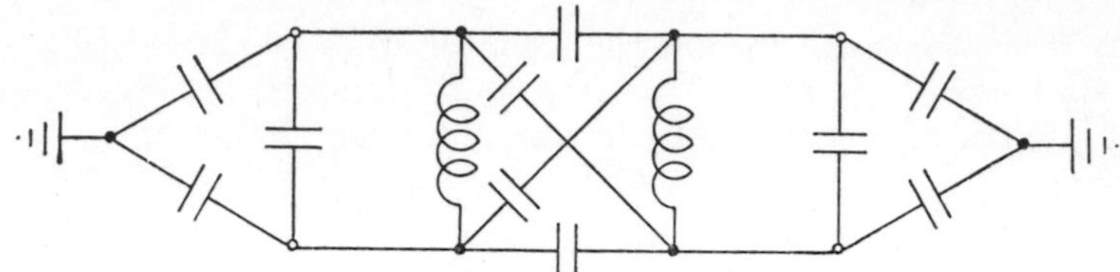

Fig. 2-2. Inter-nodal capacitances simulating distributed capacitances in an un-earthed, un-shielded transformer.

While mutual inductance may also exist as an impurity, it is often incorporated specifically to provide mutual coupling between branches that is non-physical and reversible in sign.

2.4.1 *A note on the sign of mutual inductance*

When branches are coupled by the windings of a mutual inductor, it is necessary to be able to determine the polarity of the e.m.f. induced in each winding, relative to the self-impedance voltage-drop of the branch in which it is connected.

Whether the induced voltages aid or oppose the self-impedance voltages can be decided by examining the relative senses of the self and mutual magnetic fluxes, for given senses of current traversal. This is illustrated by reference to Fig. 2-3, in which the interlinking or mutual fluxes ϕ_{21} and ϕ_{12} are proportions of ϕ_1 and ϕ_2, due to independent currents i_1 and i_2 respectively.

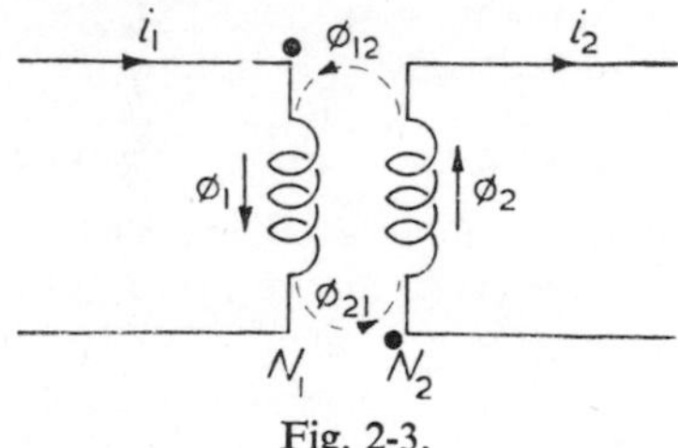

Fig. 2-3.

For the winding and current directions shown, both ϕ_1 and ϕ_2 are augmented by the mutual fluxes, so that the voltages across the coils of turns N_1 and N_2 become

$$\begin{aligned} v_1 &= N_1 \frac{d}{dt}(\phi_1 + \phi_{12}) \\ v_2 &= N_2 \frac{d}{dt}(\phi_2 + \phi_{21}) \end{aligned} \tag{2.16}$$

or in terms of the self and mutual inductances,

$$v_1 = L_1 \frac{di_1}{dt} + M \frac{di_2}{dt}$$
$$v_2 = L_2 \frac{di_2}{dt} + M \frac{di_1}{dt} \qquad (2.17)$$

Reversal of either winding or either current direction would reverse the mutual fluxes relative to the self-fluxes, thus reversing the signs of ϕ_{12} and ϕ_{21} in eqns. (2.16), and the sign of M in eqns. (2.17).

It is a convenient practice to mark with a dot, as indicated on Fig. 2-3, those ends of the coil at which currents should enter or leave in order to produce self and mutual fluxes that are additive. For a practical interpretation, consider Fig. 2-4.

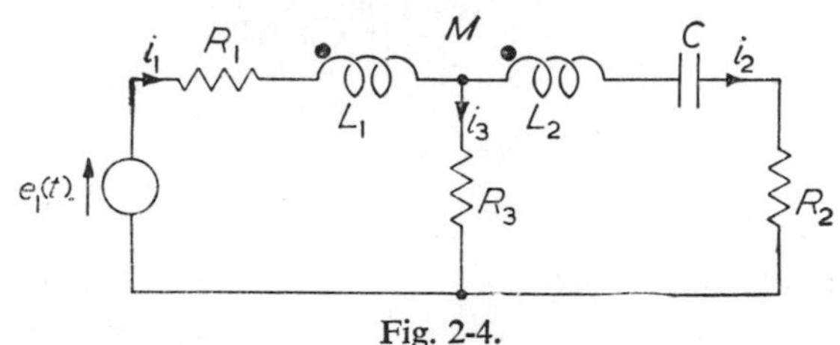

Fig. 2-4.

The currents i_1 and i_2 both enter the coils at the dotted ends and thus produce additive self and mutual fluxes. The voltage-law equations are therefore

$$-e_1(t) + i_1R_1 + L_1 \frac{di_1}{dt} + M \frac{di_2}{dt} + i_3R_3 = 0$$
$$i_2R_2 - i_3R_3 + L_2 \frac{di_2}{dt} + M \frac{di_1}{dt} + \frac{1}{C}\int i_2\, dt = 0 \qquad (2.18)$$

The equations would be unchanged if both coils were reversed, both dots being then on the right. But if one coil only were reversed, the coefficient M would become negative in both equations. This would also be so if, with the coil markings as in Fig. 2-4, the assumed direction of i_2 were reversed. While the direction shown in Fig. 2-4 is logical in relation to that of $e_1(t)$, it is nevertheless quite arbitrary at the onset. The solution may, in fact, be oscillatory.

2.4.2 *A unified symbolism for the transient and steady-states*

So far, the immittance symbols Z and Y have been associated, in a broad dimensional sense, with arbitrary voltages and currents. This has been desirable, for the topological properties of the network are independent of actual forms of excitation and response, and it has not been intended to particularise either the transient-state or the steady-state.

But more strictly, if v and j or i designate instantaneous values of time-varying quantities, then Z and Y are transient immittances, more formally represented by $Z(p)$ and $Y(p)$, where p symbolises the operation d/dt. For example, in the cases of an inductor and a capacitor,

$$v(t) = L\frac{di(t)}{dt} = Lpi(t)$$

and (2.19)

$$Z(p) = \frac{v(t)}{i(t)} = Lp$$

while

$$i(t) = C\frac{dv(t)}{dt} = Cpv(t)$$

and (2.20)

$$Y(p) = \frac{i(t)}{v(t)} = Cp$$

For sinusoidal steady-state variation, the currents and voltages are subject to simple vector representation in the exponential forms $I = |I| \cdot \exp[j(\omega t + \phi)]$, $V = |V| \cdot \exp[j(\omega t + \theta)]$. Then, $pI = j\omega I$ and $pV = j\omega V$. Therefore, for this special condition, p is equivalent to a multiplier $j\omega$, and

$$\begin{aligned} Z(p) &= Z(j\omega) = j\omega L \\ Y(p) &= Y(j\omega) = j\omega C \end{aligned} \tag{2.21}$$

Use of the operator p (here equivalent to the well-known operator D) renders a differential equation algebraic to the extent that a degree of manipulation is afforded, as in the example

$$Ri + Lpi + \frac{i}{Cp} = e(t) \tag{2.22}$$

which may be manipulated into

$$i = \frac{e(t)}{R + Lp + \dfrac{1}{Cp}} \tag{2.23}$$

But while this operational form may facilitate finding the particular integral or steady-state solution, through a number of operational rules and standard results, it does not yield the complete solution; for the transient part must be separately found by setting $e(t) = 0$. Moreover, the particular integral is difficult to obtain except for a limited range of excitation functions. The simple differential operator and notation $Z(p)$ cannot therefore be regarded as adequate in general for integrating the steady and transient states under a common symbolism.

A symbolism and technique of solution embracing both the transient and steady-states is afforded by the *Laplace transform.*[1,2] Through this, both the excitation and response are converted into functions of a new variable s, while differentiation and integration are replaced by multiplication and division by s, respectively. In the latter operations, s might seem indistinguishable from p* (or D): it is not the same, however; for while p and $1/p$ merely symbolise the operations of differentiation and integration, s and $1/s$ are the *transforms* of these operations, and behave as normal commutative algebraic symbols. Moreover, s is a complex frequency variable of form $s = \sigma + j\omega$, so that a differential equation in the *time-domain* (in which the excitation is a function of time) is entirely converted into a commutative algebraic equation in the *frequency* domain. Reversion to a complete solution in the time domain is then readily achieved by obtaining the *inverse transform* of the s-function, after the dependent variable—the response—has been expressed by algebraic manipulation as a convenient explicit function of s.

The most significant feature of the Laplace transform in the context of this treatise is that equation-forms for a given network in terms of the variable s are independent of the kind of excitation, if the excitation and response are attributed in general the forms $E(s)$ and $I(s)$. This implies that the forms may be regarded as universal, and adaptable to any particular excitation-function out of the wide variety that is Laplace-transformable. Equivalently, there is no need to distinguish between the transient and steady-state, or between sinusoidal and non-sinusoidal excitations. This will be clarified by the following simple illustration, for which the uninitiated reader is asked to accept the transform formulae as mathematical facts incidental to the main thesis: conversance with the Laplace transform in detail is not essential to the objectives of this book.

The Laplace transform of a function of time $f(t)$ is

$$F(s) = \int_0^\infty f(t)\, e^{-st}\, dt \tag{2.24}$$

where s is a complex-frequency variable, $s = \sigma + j\omega$. Here there is no occasion to be concerned with the components σ and ω: the point of

* Many British writers have used p as the complex-variable of the Laplace transform. The symbol s has, however, been recommended as the standard, and is almost universal in American publications.

principle is that eqn. 2.24 may be used to transform a function in which the variable is t into a new one in which it is s. For example, if

$$f(t) = e^{\alpha t}, \qquad F(s) = \frac{1}{s - \alpha} \tag{2.25}$$

$$f(t) = \sin \omega t, \qquad F(s) = \frac{\omega}{s^2 + \omega^2} \tag{2.26}$$

$$f(t) = H(t), \qquad F(s) = \frac{1}{s} \tag{2.27}$$

$H(t)$ denotes a unit step-function, $H(t) = 0$, $t < 0$ and $H(t) = 1$, $t > 0$. $H(t)\cdot E$ thus symbolises switching-on a constant e.m.f. E at an instant arbitrarily designated $t = 0$.

Changing to a new excitation formula with a new symbol, s, may alone seem pointless. But consider now the Laplace transforms ($\mathscr{L}$) of a derivative and an integral:

$$\mathscr{L}\, Df(t) = sF(s) - f(0+) \tag{2.28}$$

where $f(0+)$ indicates an initial value, such as the charge in a capacitor at $t = 0$, and

$$\mathscr{L}\left[\int_0^t f(t)\, dt\right] = \frac{F(s)}{s} \tag{2.29}$$

Thus, if a differential equation is Laplace-transformed on both sides, it is converted into an entirely algebraic one entirely in terms of s as the variable. Consider, for example, an initially passive circuit comprising a resistor R in series with an inductor L, to which is applied an excitation $e(t)$. Then,

$$L\frac{di}{dt} + Ri = e(t) \tag{2.30}$$

Transforming both sides, this becomes

$$LsI(s) + RI(s) = E(s) \tag{2.31}$$

where $I(s)$ and $E(s)$ denote the response and excitation as functions of s rather than t. From eqn. (2.31),

$$I(s) = \frac{E(s)}{R + Ls} \tag{2.32}$$

Eqn. (2.32) may now be particularised. Firstly, let $e(t) = H(t)\cdot E$. Then, $E(s) = E/s$ and

$$\begin{aligned} I(s) &= \frac{E}{s(R + Ls)} \\ &= \frac{E}{R}\left[\frac{1}{s} - \frac{1}{s + R/L}\right] \end{aligned} \tag{2.33}$$

Now, $1/s$ is recognised as the transform of $H(t)$, so that the inverse transform ($\mathscr{L}^{-1}$) of $1/s$ is 1; while $1/(s + R/L)$ may be compared with $1/(s - \alpha)$, which is the transform of $e^{\alpha t}$, so that $\mathscr{L}^{-1}\ 1/(s + R/L) = e^{-Rt/L}$. The complete solution in the time domain is therefore

$$f(t) = i(t) = \mathscr{L}^{-1}I(s) = \frac{E}{R}[1 - e^{-Rt/L}] \tag{2.34}$$

Secondly, let $e(t) = \hat{E} \sin \omega t$. Then $F(s) = \hat{E}\omega/(s^2 + \omega^2)$ and eqn. (2.32) becomes

$$I(s) = \frac{\hat{E}\omega}{(s^2 + \omega^2)(R + Ls)} \tag{2.35}$$

which, by partial fractions, may be put into the form

$$I(s) = \frac{\hat{E}\omega}{L(\alpha^2 + \omega^2)}\left[\frac{1}{s - \alpha} - \frac{s}{s^2 + \omega^2} - \frac{\alpha}{s^2 + \omega^2}\right] \tag{2.36}$$

where $\alpha = -R/L$. Then,

$$\begin{aligned} i(t) &= \mathscr{L}^{-1}I(s) \\ &= \frac{\hat{E}\omega}{L(\alpha^2 + \omega^2)}\left[e^{\alpha t} - \cos \omega t - \frac{\alpha}{\omega}\sin \omega t\right] \\ &= \frac{\hat{E}\sin(\omega t - \phi)}{\sqrt{[R^2 + \omega^2 L^2]}} + \frac{\hat{E}\omega L}{R^2 + \omega^2 L^2}\cdot e^{-Rt/L} \end{aligned} \tag{2.37}$$

where $\phi = \tan^{-1}\omega L/R$.

The first term is the steady-state sinusoidal current which could have been obtained from the vector equation

$$\begin{aligned} \hat{I}(j\omega) &= \frac{\hat{E}(j\omega)}{R + j\omega L} \\ &= \frac{\hat{E}\, e^{j\omega t}}{\sqrt{[R^2 + \omega^2 L^2]}\cdot e^{j\phi}} \\ &= \frac{\hat{E}[\cos(\omega t - \phi) + j \sin(\omega t - \phi)]}{\sqrt{[R^2 + \omega^2 L^2]}} \end{aligned} \tag{2.38}$$

Then, $i(t)$ is the imaginary part of $\hat{I}(j\omega)$, or

$$i(t) = \mathscr{I}m\ \hat{I}(j\omega) = \frac{\hat{E}\sin(\omega t - \phi)}{\sqrt{[R^2 + \omega^2 L^2]}} \tag{2.39}$$

Evidently, the sinusoidal steady-state is merely a special case of eqn. 2.32 in which $s = j\omega$.

The adaptability of the transformed equation to both the steady and transient states, here illustrated with reference to a simple circuit and two kinds of excitation only, is true for complicated networks and a wide range of excitations. Of particular importance is extension of the immittance concept to include both the transient and steady states, in the general forms

$$\begin{aligned} Z(s) &= E(s)/I(s) \\ Y(s) &= I(s)/E(s) \end{aligned} \tag{2.40}$$

The commonplace sinusoidal steady-state vector impedance Z, which is really $Z(j\omega)$, is merely a particularisation. Even when this state is known to prevail, there is algebraic advantage in writing s rather than $j\omega$. In respect of current, voltage and immittance, there is no need to write $I(s)$, $E(s)$, $Z(s)$ and $Y(s)$ throughout the text, on the understanding that in general these forms are implied in the abbreviated symbols I, E, Z and Y. Therefore, only where special emphasis is required will the formal functional notations be used.

2.4.3 *The general branch immittance matrix: inclusion of mutual immittances*

An illustrative network is shown in Fig. 2-5(a).

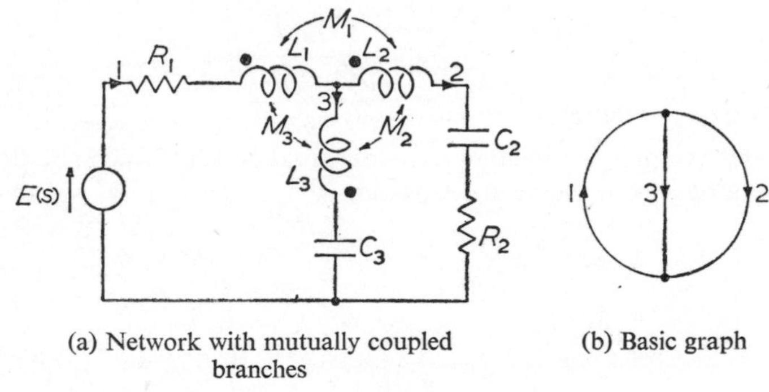

(a) Network with mutually coupled branches

(b) Basic graph

Fig. 2-5.

The branch voltage matrix is modified by the additional voltages induced through the mutual inductances M_1, M_2 and M_3, which in this case couple each branch to every other one. The graph, Fig. 2-5(b), is, however, unaltered by presence of the mutual coupling, for its function is to define the nodes and conducting paths only.

It is now orderly to denote branch impedances in the form Z_{kk} and mutual impedances associated with the mutual inductances in the form Z_{ik}. Thus, for Fig. 2-5,

$$\begin{aligned} Z_{11} &= Z_1 = R_1 + sL_1 \\ Z_{22} &= Z_2 = R_2 + sL_2 + 1/sC_2 \\ Z_{33} &= Z_3 = sL_3 + 1/sC_3 \\ Z_{12} &= Z_{21} = sM_1 \\ Z_{13} &= Z_{31} = sM_3 \\ Z_{23} &= Z_{32} = sM_2 \end{aligned} \tag{2.41}$$

where the signs of M_1, M_2 and M_3 are determined from the coil-senses as indicated by the dots.

With due regard for signs of induced voltages, the branch voltage-drops are

$$\begin{aligned} V_1 &= \quad Z_{11}I_1 + Z_{12}I_2 - Z_{13}I_3 \\ V_2 &= \quad Z_{21}I_1 + Z_{22}I_2 - Z_{23}I_3 \\ V_3 &= -Z_{31}I_1 - Z_{32}I_2 + Z_{33}I_3 \end{aligned} \tag{2.42}$$

which is consistent with

$$[V_b] = [Z_b]\cdot[I_b] \tag{2.43}$$

where

$$[Z_b] = \begin{bmatrix} Z_{11} & Z_{12} & -Z_{13} \\ Z_{21} & Z_{22} & -Z_{23} \\ -Z_{31} & -Z_{32} & Z_{33} \end{bmatrix}$$

$$[V_b] = \begin{bmatrix} V_1 \\ V_2 \\ V_3 \end{bmatrix}, \qquad [I_b] = \begin{bmatrix} I_1 \\ I_2 \\ I_3 \end{bmatrix}$$

In $[Z_b]$, the branch self-impedances constitute the leading diagonal, but new terms now exist off the diagonal to account for the coupling between the branches.

A matrix may be simplified by *partitioning*, which means dividing it into sub-matrices that are symbolically replaceable by single symbols. For example,

$$\left[\begin{array}{cc:cc} x_{11} & x_{12} & x_{13} & x_{14} \\ x_{21} & x_{22} & x_{23} & x_{24} \\ \hdashline x_{31} & x_{32} & x_{33} & x_{34} \\ x_{41} & x_{42} & x_{43} & x_{44} \end{array}\right] = \begin{bmatrix} A_{11} & A_{12} \\ & \\ A_{21} & A_{22} \end{bmatrix} \tag{2.44}$$

Partitioning in other ways is possible, provided partitioned matrices to be multiplied are conformable, as discussed in sect. 2.5.

In the present connection, partitioning of $[Z_b]$ into a diagonal form (which has computational advantages) is automatically achieved by reviewing the graph so that each element (L, R or C) is identified with one branch, while branches comprising the same kind of element are numbered in succession. This is illustrated in Fig. 2-6.

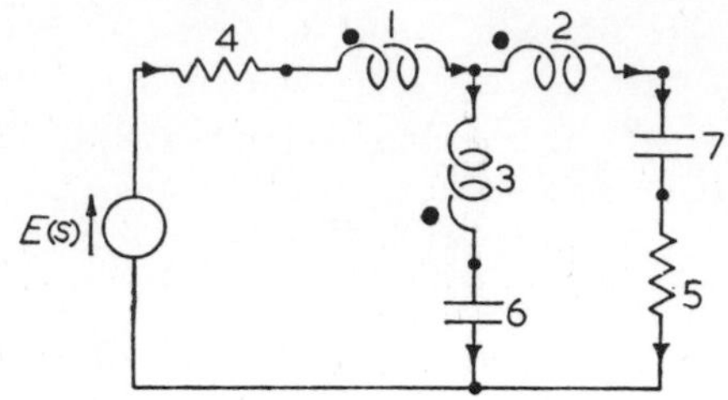

(a) Network, one branch assigned to each element.

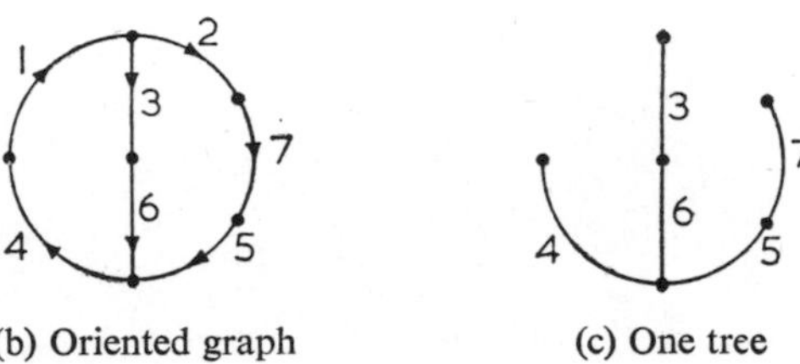

(b) Oriented graph (c) One tree

Fig. 2-6.

Writing L_{ik} in preference to M_{ik} for uniformity, the branch impedance matrix now becomes

$$[Z_b] = \begin{bmatrix} sL_{11} & sL_{12} & sL_{13} & 0 & 0 & 0 & 0 \\ sL_{21} & sL_{22} & sL_{23} & 0 & 0 & 0 & 0 \\ sL_{31} & sL_{32} & sL_{33} & 0 & 0 & 0 & 0 \\ 0 & 0 & 0 & R_{44} & 0 & 0 & 0 \\ 0 & 0 & 0 & 0 & R_{55} & 0 & 0 \\ 0 & 0 & 0 & 0 & 0 & \dfrac{1}{sC_{66}} & 0 \\ 0 & 0 & 0 & 0 & 0 & 0 & \dfrac{1}{sC_{77}} \end{bmatrix} \tag{2.45}$$

which partitions immediately into the form

$$[Z_b] = \begin{bmatrix} sL & 0 & 0 \\ 0 & R & 0 \\ 0 & 0 & 1/sC \end{bmatrix} \tag{2.46}$$

This partitioned form is typical of any linear network, regardless of complexity. It cannot contain more than three elements on the diagonal, since there are only three basic types of passive element—inductive, resistive and capacitative.

2.5 RULES FOR THE ADDITION, MULTIPLICATION, AND INVERSION OF MATRICES[3,4]

Equations 2.14 and 2.15 exemplify the involution of two of these basic processes. The third, inversion, is the matrix analogue of algebraic division : as a matrix is essentially a pattern, division in the normal algebraic sense is obviously precluded.

2.5.1 *Addition and subtraction*

These operations are possible only when the matrices are of the same order, $m \times n$ (m rows, n columns). Corresponding elements then add, as in

$$[A] + [B] = [a_{ij} + b_{ij}] \qquad \begin{matrix} i = 1 \ldots m \\ j = 1 \ldots n \end{matrix}$$

$$= \begin{bmatrix} a_{11} + b_{11} \ldots a_{1n} + b_{1n} \\ \ldots\ldots\ldots\ldots\ldots\ldots \\ a_{m1} + b_{m1} \ldots a_{mn} + b_{mn} \end{bmatrix} \tag{2.47}$$

Similarly,

$$[A] - [B] = [a_{ij} - b_{ij}] \tag{2.48}$$

Addition is both distributive and associative:

$$[A] + [B] = [B] + [A] \tag{2.49}$$

$$[A] + \{[B] + [C]\} = \{[A] + [B]\} + [C] \tag{2.50}$$

2.5.2 *Multiplication*

The principle of row-column multiplication introduced in Chapter 1, sect. 2.4, is extensible to the product of two matrices $[A]$ and $[B]$ of order $m_1 \times n_1$ and $m_2 \times n_2$ respectively, provided $m_2 = n_1$ when $[A]$ pre-multiplies $[B]$, or $m_1 = n_2$ when $[A]$ post-multiplies $[B]$, as exemplified by $[A]\cdot[B]$ and $[B]\cdot[A]$. Matrices meeting these requirements (which are consistent with the original idea of detaching variables from coefficients) are said to be *conformable*. Multiplication is non-commutative, or $[A]\cdot[B] \neq [B]\cdot[A]$. In the evolution of eqns. (2.14) and (2.15) for example, the order of the matrices, which is fundamental to the pattern of coefficients and variables, has been carefully preserved.

The rule for multiplying two conformable matrices is illustrated by

$$[A]\cdot[B] = \begin{bmatrix} a_{11} & a_{12} & a_{13} \\ a_{21} & a_{22} & a_{23} \\ a_{31} & a_{32} & a_{33} \end{bmatrix} \cdot \begin{bmatrix} b_{11} & b_{12} \\ b_{21} & b_{22} \\ b_{31} & b_{32} \end{bmatrix}$$

$$= \begin{bmatrix} a_{11}b_{11} + a_{12}b_{21} + a_{13}b_{31} & a_{11}b_{12} + a_{12}b_{22} + a_{13}b_{32} \\ a_{21}b_{11} + a_{22}b_{21} + a_{23}b_{31} & a_{21}b_{12} + a_{22}b_{22} + a_{23}b_{32} \\ a_{31}b_{11} + a_{32}b_{21} + a_{33}b_{31} & a_{31}b_{12} + a_{32}b_{22} + a_{33}b_{32} \end{bmatrix} \tag{2.51}$$

When matrices to be multiplied are partitioned, it is essential for the partitioned forms and the sub-matrices that they represent to be conformable. Thus, for example,

$$[A]\cdot[B]=\left[\begin{array}{cc:c} a_{11} & a_{12} & a_{13}\\ a_{21} & a_{22} & a_{23}\\ a_{31} & a_{32} & a_{33}\end{array}\right]\cdot\left[\begin{array}{cc} b_{11} & b_{12}\\ b_{21} & b_{22}\\ \hdashline b_{31} & b_{32}\end{array}\right]=[A_{11}\,A_{12}]\cdot\begin{bmatrix} B_{11}\\ \\ B_{21}\end{bmatrix} \quad (2.52)$$

The partitioned forms are conformable, giving

$$[A]\cdot[B]=[A_{11}B_{11}+A_{12}B_{21}] \quad (2.53)$$

Again, the sub-matrices are conformable, giving

$$A_{11}B_{11}=\begin{bmatrix} a_{11} & a_{12}\\ a_{21} & a_{22}\\ a_{31} & a_{32}\end{bmatrix}\cdot\begin{bmatrix} b_{11} & b_{12}\\ \\ b_{21} & b_{22}\end{bmatrix}$$

$$=\begin{bmatrix} a_{11}b_{11}+a_{12}b_{21} & a_{11}b_{12}+a_{12}b_{22}\\ a_{21}b_{11}+a_{22}b_{21} & a_{21}b_{12}+a_{22}b_{22}\\ a_{31}b_{11}+a_{32}b_{21} & a_{31}b_{12}+a_{32}b_{22}\end{bmatrix} \quad (2.54)$$

and

$$A_{21}B_{21}=\begin{bmatrix} a_{13}\\ a_{23}\\ a_{33}\end{bmatrix}\cdot[b_{31}\ b_{32}]$$

$$=\begin{bmatrix} a_{13}b_{31} & a_{13}b_{32}\\ a_{23}b_{31} & a_{23}b_{32}\\ a_{33}b_{31} & a_{33}b_{32}\end{bmatrix} \quad (2.55)$$

Adding the corresponding compound elements then gives the same result as eqn. (2.51). Though not commutative, matrix multiplication is associative and distributive. For example,

$$\begin{aligned}[A]\cdot[B]\cdot[C]\cdot[D] &= \{[A]\cdot[B]\}\cdot\{[C]\cdot[D]\}\\ &= [A]\cdot\{[B]\cdot[C]\cdot[D]\}\end{aligned} \quad (2.56)$$

and

$$[A]\cdot\{[B]+[C]+[D]\}=[A]\cdot[B]+[A]\cdot[C]+[A]\cdot[D] \quad (2.57)$$

2.5.3 *Inversion*

This operation is required for the solution of equations by matrix transposition, as distinct from ordinary algebraic elimination, and for converting a matrix from one form into another, such as $[Z]$ into $[Y]$, where the forms are of inverse kind.

Consider the equivalent equation-forms

$$[E]=[Z]\cdot[I] \quad (2.58)$$

$$\begin{bmatrix} E_1\\ E_2\\ \cdot\\ E_n\end{bmatrix}=\begin{bmatrix} Z_{11}Z_{12}\ldots Z_{1n}\\ Z_{21}Z_{22}\ldots Z_{2n}\\ \ldots\ldots\ldots\ldots\ldots\\ Z_{n1}Z_{n2}\ldots Z_{nn}\end{bmatrix}\cdot\begin{bmatrix} I_1\\ I_2\\ \cdot\\ I_n\end{bmatrix} \quad (2.59)$$

and

$$\begin{aligned} E_1 &= Z_{11}I_1 + Z_{12}I_2 + \ldots + Z_{1n}I_n \\ E_2 &= Z_{21}I_1 + Z_{22}I_2 + \ldots + Z_{2n}I_n \\ \cdot \quad & \ldots\ldots\ldots\ldots\ldots\ldots\ldots\ldots \\ E_n &= Z_{n1}I_1 + Z_{n2}I_2 + \ldots + Z_{nn}I_n \end{aligned} \tag{2.60}$$

The solution of eqns. (2.60) may likewise be expressed in matrix form. By determinants and Cramer's rule,

$$\begin{aligned} I_1 &= \frac{1}{\Delta}[E_1\Delta_{11} + E_2\Delta_{21} + \cdots + E_n\Delta_{n1}] \\ I_2 &= \frac{1}{\Delta}[E_1\Delta_{12} + E_2\Delta_{22} + \cdots + E_n\Delta_{n2}] \\ \cdot \quad & \cdot \ldots\ldots\ldots\ldots\ldots\ldots\ldots\ldots\ldots \\ I_n &= \frac{1}{\Delta}[E_1\Delta_{1n} + E_2\Delta_{2n} + \cdots + E_n\Delta_{nn}] \end{aligned} \tag{2.61}$$

where Δ denotes the determinant of the Z-coefficients and $\Delta_{11} \ldots \Delta_{nn}$ are cofactors of Δ (see sect. 4). Rewriting eqns. (2.61) in matrix form,

$$\begin{bmatrix} I_1 \\ I_2 \\ \cdot \\ I_n \end{bmatrix} = \begin{bmatrix} \frac{\Delta_{11}}{\Delta} & \frac{\Delta_{21}}{\Delta} & \cdots & \frac{\Delta_{n1}}{\Delta} \\ \frac{\Delta_{12}}{\Delta} & \frac{\Delta_{22}}{\Delta} & \cdots & \frac{\Delta_{n2}}{\Delta} \\ \cdot & \cdot & \cdots & \cdot \\ \frac{\Delta_{1n}}{\Delta} & \frac{\Delta_{2n}}{\Delta} & \cdots & \frac{\Delta_{nn}}{\Delta} \end{bmatrix} \cdot \begin{bmatrix} E_1 \\ E_2 \\ \cdot \\ E_n \end{bmatrix} \tag{2.62}$$

which by comparison with eqns. (2.59) and (2.58) may be compressed into the form

$$[I] = [Z]^{-1} \cdot [E] \tag{2.63}$$

where $[Z]^{-1}$ is the inverse of $[Z]$, and comprises admittance elements.

The elements of $[Z]^{-1}$, consistent with its form in eqn. (2.62), are given directly through the following procedure:

(1) Interchange rows with columns in $[Z]$ obtaining a *transpose matrix* $[Z]^t$. For example, if

$$[Z] = \begin{bmatrix} Z_{11} & Z_{12} & Z_{13} \\ Z_{21} & Z_{22} & Z_{23} \\ Z_{31} & Z_{32} & Z_{33} \end{bmatrix} \tag{2.64}$$

$$[Z]^t = \begin{bmatrix} Z_{11} & Z_{21} & Z_{31} \\ Z_{12} & Z_{22} & Z_{32} \\ Z_{13} & Z_{23} & Z_{33} \end{bmatrix} \tag{2.65}$$

(2) Replace each element in $[Z]^t$ by its cofactor in det. $[Z]^t$.

For a square matrix of order $n \times n$ having a determinant Δ, the cofactor C_{ij} of an element Z_{ij} is

$C_{ij} = (-1)^{i+j} \times$ (minor determinant formed by deleting from Δ the row and column containing Z_{ij}).

Thus

$$[Z]_c^t = \begin{bmatrix} C_{11} & C_{12} & C_{13} \\ C_{21} & C_{22} & C_{23} \\ C_{31} & C_{32} & C_{33} \end{bmatrix} \tag{2.66}$$

where, for example,

$$C_{32} = (-1)^{(3+2)} \begin{vmatrix} Z_{11} & Z_{31} \\ Z_{12} & Z_{32} \end{vmatrix}$$

$$= -(Z_{11}Z_{32} - Z_{12}Z_{31})$$

(3) Then,

$$[Z]^{-1} = \frac{[Z]_c^t}{\Delta} \tag{2.67}$$

where Δ is evaluated in any of the usual ways (see sect. 4).

The diagonal matrix, which has already arisen in the formulation of network equations (sect. 2.1), is very easily inverted. If

$$[Z] = \begin{bmatrix} Z_1 & 0 & \cdot & \cdot & 0 \\ 0 & Z_2 & \cdot & \cdot & 0 \\ \cdot & \cdot & \cdot & \cdot & \cdot \\ \cdot & \cdot & \cdot & \cdot & \cdot \\ 0 & 0 & \cdot & \cdot & Z_n \end{bmatrix} \tag{2.68}$$

then

$$[Z]^{-1} = \begin{bmatrix} 1/Z_1 & 0 & \cdot & \cdot & 0 \\ 0 & 1/Z_2 & \cdot & \cdot & 0 \\ \cdot & \cdot & \cdot & \cdot & \cdot \\ \cdot & \cdot & \cdot & \cdot & \cdot \\ 0 & 0 & \cdot & \cdot & 1/Z_n \end{bmatrix} \tag{2.69}$$

Several methods exist for diagonalising a square matrix. In principle the matrix is resolved into the form $[Z] = X \cdot \lambda \cdot X^{-1}$, where λ is a diagonal matrix while X, X^{-1} are inverse matrices. Then in general $[Z]^n = X\lambda^n X^{-1}$. This is shown in Chapter 4 sect. 2.4.2 along with a procedure applicable to a 2×2 matrix. The formal procedure, through the *eigenvalues* (latent roots) and *eigenvectors* of the matrix, is clearly illustrated in references 3 and 5.

2.6 FREQUENCY AND MAGNITUDE SCALING

Numerical values in a practical network are likely to be inconvenient for direct substitution into sets of equations, matrices or determinants. Powers of ten are required for conversions into henrys and farads, and along with 2π as factors of ω in the case of steady sinusoidal excitation.

The numbers become much more convenient when the network is scaled by wholly real and positive factors, to a 1-ohm standard of resistance or reactance at an angular frequency of 1 radian per second. Such scaling is valid, for while absolute magnitudes of currents and voltages depend on actual values in the real network at its working frequency, phases depend only on ratios of reactance to resistance. Thus, so long as these ratios are preserved in the scaled or *normalised* network, solutions for the network at its working frequency differ from solutions for the normalised network only by a magnitude factor, which by choice is a real, positive constant.

Consider an impedance of the form

$$Z(s) = R + sL + 1/sC \tag{2.70}$$

For excitation by a sinusoidal e.m.f. $E(s) = E(j\omega)$,

$$I(j\omega) = \frac{E(j\omega)}{R + j(\omega L - 1/\omega C)} \tag{2.71}$$

If now the frequency is divided by a real positive constant β, the current at the new angular frequency, $\omega_0 = \omega/\beta$, is unchanged in any respect, provided L and C are each multiplied by β, where $\beta = \omega/\omega_0$:

$$I(j\omega_0) = \frac{E(j\omega_0)}{R + j[\omega_0(L\beta) - 1/\omega_0(C\beta)]} = I(j\omega) \tag{2.72}$$

When additionally the impedance represented by eqn. (2.70) is divided by a real, positive constant α,

$$I_\alpha(j\omega_0) = \frac{E(j\omega_0)}{\dfrac{R}{\alpha} + j\dfrac{1}{\alpha}\left[\omega_0(L\beta) - 1/\omega_0(C\beta)\right]} \tag{2.73}$$

from which it follows that

$$\arg I_\alpha(j\omega_0) = \arg I(j\omega_0) = \arg I(j\omega)$$

but (2.74)

$$|I_\alpha(j\omega_0)| = \alpha|I(j\omega_0)| = \alpha|I(j\omega)|$$

If however the excitation magnitude at ω_0 is changed to $E_0 = E/\alpha$,

$$|I_\alpha(j\omega_0)| = |I(j\omega)| \tag{2.75}$$

$$(E_0 = E/\alpha)$$

For a fractional deviation $\pm\delta$ in frequency,

$$\frac{\omega'}{\omega} = \frac{\omega(1 \pm \delta)}{\omega} = \frac{\beta\omega_0(1 \pm \delta)}{\beta\omega_0} = \frac{\omega_0'}{\omega_0} \tag{2.76}$$

Thus, to the magnitude-scaled e.m.f. ($E_0 = E/\alpha$), the response of the magnitude and frequency-scaled network as ω_0 is varied is identical with the response of the real network as ω is correspondingly varied.

The scaling properties illustrated here by means of a simple *LCR* series circuit are true for linear networks in general. This is easily proved by reference to the determinantal form for the solution of an arbitrary linear network (see sect. 4).

The elements in the scaled network are

$$R_s = R/\alpha, \quad L_s = L\beta/\alpha, \quad C_s = C\beta\alpha \tag{2.77}$$

These values are normalised by setting $\beta = \omega$ so that $\omega_0 = 1$ radian/sec, while α is chosen by selecting a particular impedance element to be the 1-ohm reference. Examples of normalisation are shown in Fig. 2-7.

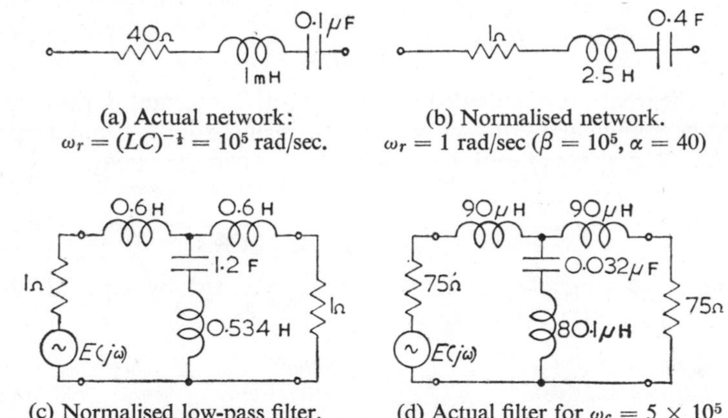

(a) Actual network: $\omega_r = (LC)^{-\frac{1}{2}} = 10^5$ rad/sec.

(b) Normalised network. $\omega_r = 1$ rad/sec ($\beta = 10^5$, $\alpha = 40$)

(c) Normalised low-pass filter. $\omega_c = 1$ rad/sec, terminating resistances 1-ohm.

(d) Actual filter for $\omega_c = 5 \times 10^5$ rad/sec and 75-ohm terminating resistances.

Fig. 2-7. Examples of normalised networks.

As an illustration of the arithmetical simplification afforded by normalisation, the output current $I_2(s)$ in the 1-ohm termination of the normalised filter of Fig. 2-7(c) is given by

$$I_2(s) = \frac{E(s)(1 + 0.64s^2)}{2(1 + 0.6s)(1 + 0.6s + s^2)} \tag{2.78}$$

From this the frequency characteristic for $s = j\omega$ can be easily calculated and plotted as a function of ω/ω_c, where $\omega_c = 1$ rad/sec. The characteristic thus obtained is identical with that for an actual filter such as Fig. 2-7(d), in which $\omega_c = 5 \times 10^5$ rad/sec.

Eqn. (2.78) is representative of the polynomial forms that are the basis of network synthesis.[6] Such polynomials may approximate specified responses, and network realisations in conformity with them are automatically in normalised forms. Viewed in reverse, eqn. (2.78) might have represented a desired response, and Fig. 2-7(c) the network realisation (actually, it is an ordinary *m*-derived low-pass filter).

In power engineering, scaling to *per unit* values is common.[7] The per unit value of a quantity is its actual value divided by a convenient reference or *base* value, in the same unit. The base value is often, but not necessarily, taken as the nominal rating in the unit, for the system. For example, in a 33 kV, 20 MVA, three-phase system, the voltage per phase is $V = 33/\sqrt{3} = 19.1$ kV, the MVA per phase is $20/3 = 6.67$, and the phase-current is accordingly $I = 6.67 \times 10^6/19.1 \times 10^3 = 350$ A. These ratings, 19.1 kV, 350 A and 6.67 MVA then serve as bases for the expression of other voltages, currents and powers in per unit terms, while the ratio $V/I = 54.6$ is the base for impedances.

A 33:6.6 kV, 20 MVA, 3-phase transformer having per phase an actual leakage reactance referred to its primary of 4.9 ohms, a magnetising current of 14.0 A, a copper-loss of 133 kW and a core-loss of 66.7 kW, has a leakage reactance of $4.9/54.6 = 0.09$ per unit, a magnetising current of $14/350 = 0.04$ per unit, a copper-loss of $133 \times 10^{-3}/6.67 = 0.02$ per unit, and a core-loss of $66.7 \times 10^{-3}/6.67 = 0.01$ per unit. The actual full-load primary current of 350 A is $350/350 = 1$ per unit, and similarly the primary voltage is $19.1/19.1 = 1$ per unit. The copper-loss per unit is $I_{pu}^2 R_{cpu} = 0.02$, or $R_{cpu} = 0.02/1^2 = 0.02$. Similarly, the equivalent core-loss resistance is given from $V_{pu}^2/R_{ipu} = 0.01$, whence $R_{ipu} = 100$ per unit. Finally, the shunt reactance per unit attributable to the magnetising current I_m is $X_{ipu} = V_{pu}/I_{mpu} = 1/0.04 = 25$ per unit. The ratio of the transformer is 33 kV : 6.6 kV = 5 :1, and this may be taken as the ratio of a perfect or ideal transformer to which the above

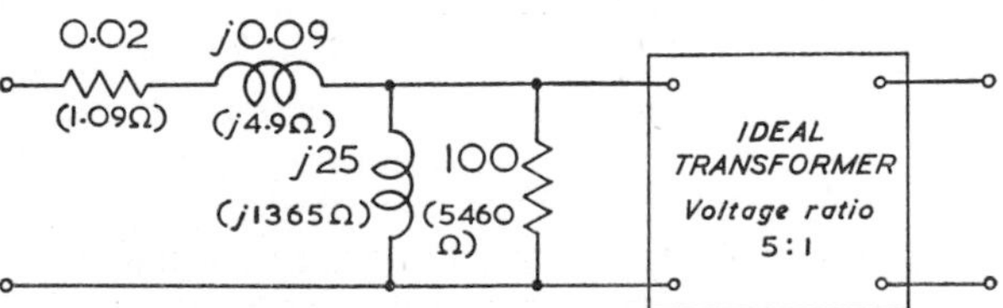

Fig. 2-8. Per unit and actual values in an equivalent representation for one phase of a power transformer.

parameters may be suitably appended to represent the actual, imperfect transformer. The equivalent representation is shown in Fig. 2-8 in per unit form, and with actual values indicated in brackets. These are given simply by multiplying the per unit impedance elements by the base, 54.6.

3. MESH-CURRENT AND NODE-DATUM ANALYSIS

These are particular forms of loop-current and nodal-voltage analysis, simpler to apply, yet generally suitable for planar networks, especially when the currents or voltages are not all required explicitly. This is a common practical situation, except in the case of power distribution systems.

In the formal procedures so far described, it is the tree that is chosen, and the tie-sets and cut-sets depend on the particular choice. But in *mesh-current* and *node-datum voltage analysis*, it is the loops that are chosen, to coincide with the meshes; and the nodes that are chosen, for reference to the most convenient datum of potential: a tree is not invoked at all. These techniques are common and far from new: mesh-current analysis has its origin in Maxwell's cyclic-current artifice, while nodal analysis on a node-datum basis has long been accepted (if perhaps with less facility) as an obviously valid alternative. Neither method is to be regarded as generally supplanted by the topological procedures, notwithstanding the emphasis these have received in recent times. On the contrary, both remain the most direct methods for solving a large proportion of the commonly encountered networks, which are not usually of great complexity, such as electrical measurement circuits, electronic inter-stage networks, individual networks in a communication system, etc.

Both methods are as economical in final equations as the formal topological approaches, for the number of loop-currents and node-pair voltages for any physical tree of the graph is the same as the number of mesh-currents and node-datum voltages. The merit in the methods lies in direct formulation of the final equations by inspection of the network, and only when this cannot readily be done are the methods to be regarded as supplanted by the formal topological procedures. These are quite general and independent of the complexity of the network. It is no more difficult, for example, to formulate the branch impedance matrix when multiple mutual inductance coupling exists between branches, than when it is absent (as exemplified by Fig. 2-5), and the procedures are applicable to networks that are non-planar, or otherwise complex in the sense that meshes cannot be clearly discerned. Moreover, the additional steps are insignificant when the simplicity of matrix calculations with a computer is borne in mind.

In mesh-current analysis, the assumed loop-currents are inserted in those loops of the network that are the meshes of its graph, and are assigned a common direction, which is usually taken as clockwise. In the dual procedure of node-datum analysis, the nodes are assigned potentials, of common polarity, relative to a common point or datum, which is one of the nodes themselves. These assumptions of common direction or polarity are conveniences justified by the fact that the related branch currents or voltages are themselves arbitrary. The methods are indicated in Fig. 2-9, in which the graph is similar to Fig. 1-2.

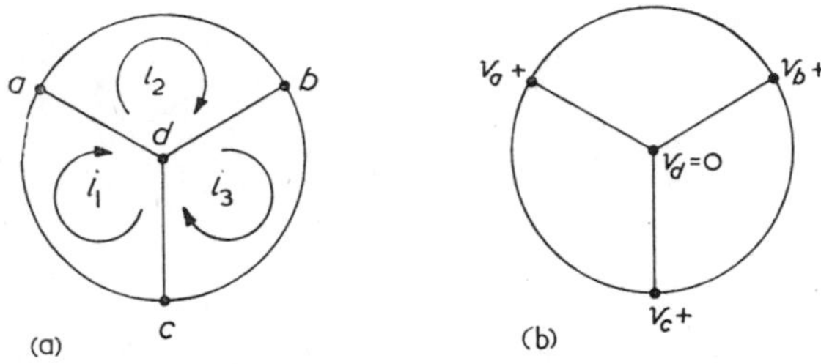

Fig. 2-9. Orientations for mesh-current (a) and node-datum (b) analysis.

Mesh-current and node-datum analysis are sometimes consistent with the choice of a particular tree, such that each tie-set is a mesh, and each cut-set is the group of branches meeting at a node. This is illustrated by Fig. 2-10, in which the particular choice of tree has resulted in loop-currents that circulate in the meshes of the graph, as in Fig. 2-9(a), and node-pair voltages that all radiate from a common node, *d*, which is the datum in Fig. 2-9(b).

Meshes and node-datum pairs are not, however, in general identifiable with the tie-sets and cut-sets of physical trees of the network. Fig. 2-11 is an illustration: whatever tree is tried, the tie-sets always give at least one loop that does not coincide with a mesh.

Practical interpretations of mesh and node-datum analysis are illustrated by Fig. 2-12. The two networks are the same, but in order to exploit the duality between loop-current and nodal-voltage analysis, the e.m.f. source E_1, Z_1 in (a) is transformed into a current equivalent, I_1, Y_1 in (b). The transformation is readily justified by reference to Figs. 1-4(a) and (c); but it is likely to be recognised as a simple application of the well-known *Norton's theorem* (the reverse transformation is afforded by the *Thévenin-Helmholtz theorem*, which is its dual).

In neither case is a graph necessary, for the meshes have obvious contour impedances, and the node-datum pairs have obvious junction

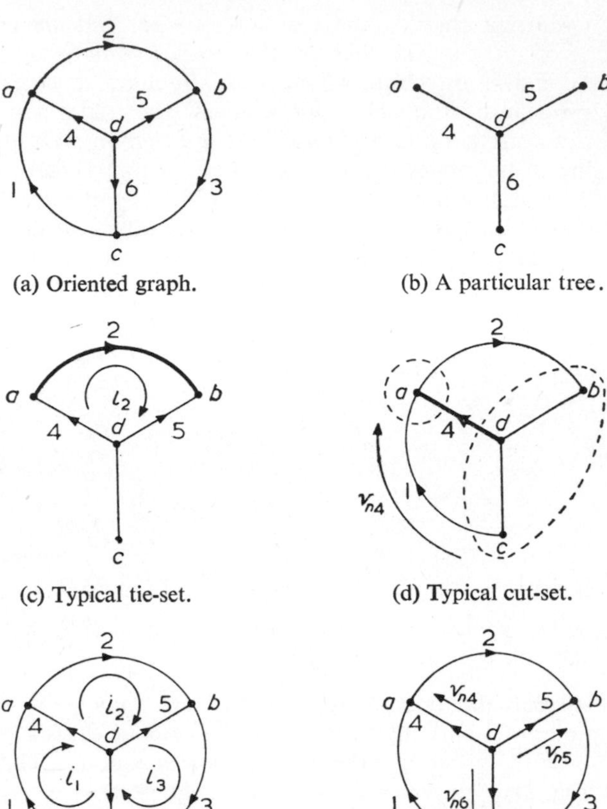

(a) Oriented graph.

(b) A particular tree.

(c) Typical tie-set.

(d) Typical cut-set.

(e) Superimposed tie-sets.

(f) Superimposed cut-sets.

Fig. 2-10. Pertaining to mesh and node-datum analysis.

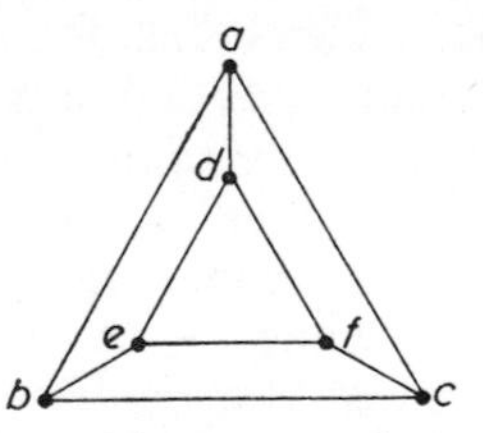

(a) Graph for a delta-connected power system.

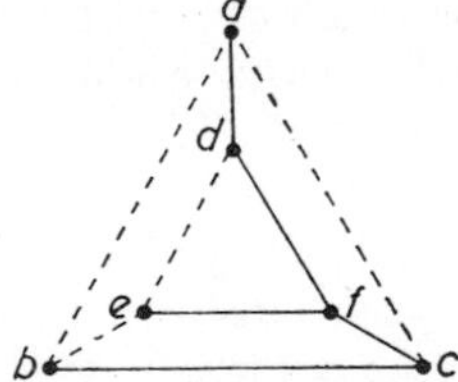

(b) Three loops of this tree coincide with meshes, but the fourth (a d f c b a) does not.

Fig. 2-11.

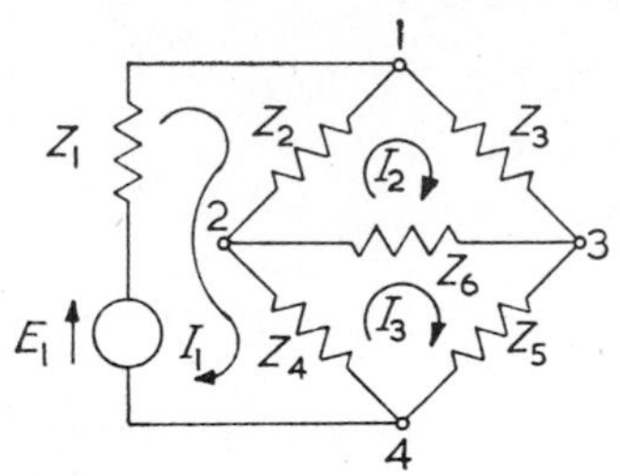

(a) Mesh-currents in a bridge.

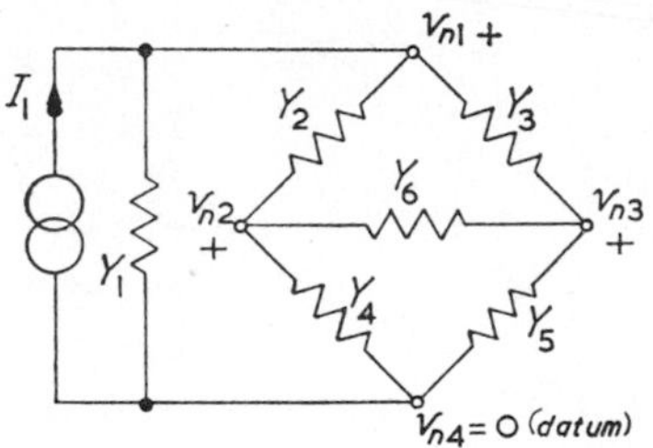

(b) Same network, source transformed for node-datum analysis ($I_1 = E_1/Z_1$)

Fig. 2-12.

admittances. Thus, by inspection, the mesh equations for (a) are

$$\begin{aligned}(Z_1+Z_2+Z_4)I_1 \quad - Z_2I_2 \quad - Z_4I_3 &= E_1\\ -Z_2I_1+(Z_2+Z_3+Z_6)I_2 \quad - Z_6I_3 &= 0\\ -Z_4I_1 \quad - Z_6I_2+(Z_4+Z_5+Z_6)I_3 &= 0\end{aligned} \tag{2.79}$$

or, more compactly and with positive signs throughout,

$$\begin{bmatrix} Z_{11} & Z_{12} & Z_{13}\\ Z_{21} & Z_{22} & Z_{23}\\ Z_{31} & Z_{32} & Z_{33}\end{bmatrix}\cdot\begin{bmatrix} I_1\\ I_2\\ I_3\end{bmatrix}=\begin{bmatrix} E_1\\ 0\\ 0\end{bmatrix} \tag{2.80}$$

where the mesh-contour impedances are

$$\begin{aligned}Z_{11}&=Z_1+Z_2+Z_4\\ Z_{22}&=Z_2+Z_3+Z_6\\ Z_{33}&=Z_4+Z_5+Z_6\end{aligned}$$

and the mutual (common) impedances are

$$\begin{aligned}Z_{12}&=Z_{21}=-Z_2\\ Z_{13}&=Z_{31}=-Z_4\\ Z_{23}&=Z_{32}=-Z_6\end{aligned}$$

Similarly, the node-datum equations for (b) are

$$\begin{aligned}(Y_1+Y_2+Y_3)V_{n1} \quad - Y_2V_{n2} \quad - Y_3V_{n3} &= I_1\\ -Y_2V_{n1}+(Y_2+Y_4+Y_6)V_{n2} \quad - Y_6V_{n3} &= 0\\ -Y_3V_{n1} \quad - Y_6V_{n2}+(Y_3+Y_5+Y_6)V_{n3} &= 0\end{aligned} \tag{2.81}$$

or,

$$\begin{bmatrix} Y_{11} & Y_{12} & Y_{13}\\ Y_{21} & Y_{22} & Y_{23}\\ Y_{31} & Y_{32} & Y_{33}\end{bmatrix}\cdot\begin{bmatrix} V_{n1}\\ V_{n2}\\ V_{n3}\end{bmatrix}=\begin{bmatrix} I_1\\ 0\\ 0\end{bmatrix} \tag{2.82}$$

where

$$\begin{aligned} Y_{11} &= Y_1 + Y_2 + Y_3 \\ Y_{22} &= Y_2 + Y_4 + Y_6 \\ Y_{33} &= Y_3 + Y_5 + Y_6 \\ Y_{12} &= Y_{21} = -Y_2 \\ Y_{13} &= Y_{31} = -Y_3 \\ Y_{23} &= Y_{32} = -Y_6 \end{aligned}$$

It will be seen that the sum of impedances forming the contour of a mesh has its dual in the sum of admittances meeting at a node, while a mutual impedance has its dual in an admittance linking two nodes.

4. OUTLINE OF DETERMINANTAL SOLUTION[3,4,8]

Whichever approach is used, the final equations are of the dual forms

$$[Z]\cdot[I] = [E] \tag{2.83}$$

or

$$[Y]\cdot[V] = [I] \tag{2.84}$$

$[Z]$ and $[Y]$ are either mesh-impedance and node-datum admittance matrices, which are evident on inspection of the network, or, in the case of general loop-current and nodal-voltage analysis, they are defined by eqns. (2.14) and (2.15) as

$$[Z] = [M]\cdot[Z_b]\cdot[M]^t \tag{2.85}$$

and

$$[Y] = [Q]\cdot[Y_b]\cdot[Q]^t \tag{2.86}$$

The role of matrices in network solution is primarily to systematise the evolution of a set of equations of minimum complexity. The matrices do not themselves yield the required solutions (except through the process of inversion), and it remains therefore to solve these equations by any valid method.

The solutions for the families of equations compactly represented by eqns. (2.83) and (2.84) may be expressed elegantly in terms of the determinant of the immittance matrix. Eqn. (2.83), for example, may be expanded into the generalised form

$$\begin{bmatrix} Z_{11} & Z_{12} \dots Z_{1n} \\ Z_{21} & Z_{22} \dots Z_{2n} \\ \dots & \dots \\ Z_{n1} & Z_{n2} \dots Z_{nn} \end{bmatrix} \cdot \begin{bmatrix} I_1 \\ I_2 \\ \vdots \\ I_n \end{bmatrix} = \begin{bmatrix} E_1 \\ E_2 \\ \vdots \\ E_n \end{bmatrix} \tag{2.87}$$

The square matrix of Z-coefficients has a determinant

$$\Delta = \begin{vmatrix} Z_{11} & Z_{12} \dots Z_{1n} \\ Z_{21} & Z_{22} \dots Z_{2n} \\ \dots & \dots \; \dots \; \dots \\ Z_{n1} & Z_{n2} \dots Z_{nn} \end{vmatrix} \tag{2.88}$$

A determinant of order n may be resolved, according to the *Laplace development*, into n simpler terms each of the form $Z_{ik}\Delta_{ik}$, where Δ_{ik} is the cofactor of the element Z_{ik}. This cofactor is $(-1)^{i+k}$ times the minor determinant, of order $n-1$, formed by deleting from Δ the ith. row and kth. column, which contain the element Z_{ik}. The resolution may be carried out in terms of the elements along any row or column. Then, along any row i or any column k,

$$\Delta = \sum_{k=1}^{n} Z_{ik}\Delta_{ik}$$

or (2.89)

$$\Delta = \sum_{i=1}^{n} Z_{ik}\Delta_{ik}$$

For example, if

$$\Delta = \begin{vmatrix} Z_{11} & Z_{12} & Z_{13} \\ Z_{21} & Z_{22} & Z_{23} \\ Z_{31} & Z_{32} & Z_{33} \end{vmatrix}$$

then resolving along the second row,

$$\Delta = -Z_{21}\begin{vmatrix} Z_{12} & Z_{13} \\ Z_{32} & Z_{33} \end{vmatrix} + Z_{22}\begin{vmatrix} Z_{11} & Z_{13} \\ Z_{31} & Z_{33} \end{vmatrix} - Z_{23}\begin{vmatrix} Z_{11} & Z_{12} \\ Z_{31} & Z_{32} \end{vmatrix}$$

The second-order minor determinants are evaluated by cross-multiplying the elements as indicated, and subtracting the upward products from the downward. This gives

$$\Delta = -Z_{21}(Z_{12}Z_{33} - Z_{32}Z_{13}) + Z_{22}(Z_{11}Z_{33} - Z_{31}Z_{13}) \\ - Z_{23}(Z_{11}Z_{32} - Z_{31}Z_{12})$$

The solution for any current I_k is given by Cramers's rule in the form

$$I_k = (E_1\Delta_{1k} + E_2\Delta_{2k} + \ldots + E_n\Delta_{nk})/\Delta \tag{2.90}$$

Similarly, the family of nodal-voltage equations symbolised by eqn. (2.84) have solutions of the form

$$V_k = (I_1\Delta_{1k} + I_2\Delta_{2k} + \ldots + I_n\Delta_{nk})/\Delta \tag{2.91}$$

where Δ is the determinant of the Y-matrix.

As an illustration, consider the numerical solution of Fig. 2-12(b) for V_{n3}. By eqn. (2.91),

$$V_{n3} = I_1\Delta_{13}/\Delta$$

$$= \frac{I_1\Delta_{13}}{Y_{11}\Delta_{11} + Y_{12}\Delta_{12} + Y_{13}\Delta_{13}} \tag{2.92}$$

where Δ has been resolved into cofactors of the elements in the first row of the Y-matrix in eqn. (2.82).

For simple arithmetic, let the admittances be pure conductances, in mhos,

$$G_1 = G_5 = 2 \times 10^{-3}, \qquad G_2 = 10^{-3},$$
$$G_3 = G_6 = 2.5 \times 10^{-3}, \qquad G_4 = 1.25 \times 10^{-3},$$

and let $I = 10$ mA.

It is convenient to scale these values by 10^3. If the current is scaled by the same factor, the correct result may be obtained. The scaled matrix parameters are

$$G_{11} = 5.5\,; \qquad G_{22} = 4.75\,; \qquad G_{33} = 7$$
$$G_{12} = G_{21} = -1\,; \qquad G_{13} = G_{31} = -2.5\,; \qquad G_{23} = G_{32} = -2.5$$

Then, referring to the Y-matrix in eqn. (2.82),

$$\Delta_{13} = \begin{vmatrix} G_{21} & G_{22} \\ G_{31} & G_{32} \end{vmatrix} = G_{21}G_{32} - G_{31}G_{22} = 14.375$$

$$\Delta_{11} = \begin{vmatrix} G_{22} & G_{23} \\ G_{32} & G_{33} \end{vmatrix} = G_{22}G_{33} - G_{32}G_{23} = 27.0$$

$$\Delta_{12} = -\begin{vmatrix} G_{21} & G_{23} \\ G_{31} & G_{33} \end{vmatrix} = -(G_{21}G_{33} - G_{31}G_{23}) = 13.25$$

Substituting these values into eqn. (2.92) and putting $I = 10$A as its scaled value, then gives

$$V_{n3} = \frac{10 \times 14.375}{5.5 \times 27.0 - 13.25 - 2.5 \times 14.375}$$
$$= 1.45 \text{ V}$$

5. REDUCTION OF THE GRAPH

There are several methods for simplifying the graph of a network. Firstly, in the case of mesh and node-datum analysis, it is appropriate to represent branches that are in series or parallel by a single immittance, as in eqns. (2.41), for example. Secondly, several branches and associated sources may be replaced by a single equivalent branch and source, in accordance with the *Thévenin-Helmholtz theorem* or its dual, *Norton's theorem*. Thirdly, the topology itself may be changed into a more convenient equivalent one, by means of the *star-mesh* or other *transformations*. The first simplification implies the elimination of meshes or nodes that are obviously superfluous. The others require elucidation.

5.1 MESH AND NODE ELIMINATION WITH THE THÉVENIN-HELMHOLTZ AND NORTON THEOREMS

Fig. 2-13 represents an arbitrary linear network containing sources, divided into two sets of branches and nodes at a node-pair *p-q*. The *active-set A* consists of branches and nodes which are connected to one or more sources; the *passive-set B* is free from sources, and is energised only when connected to set *A* through the node-pair *p-q*.

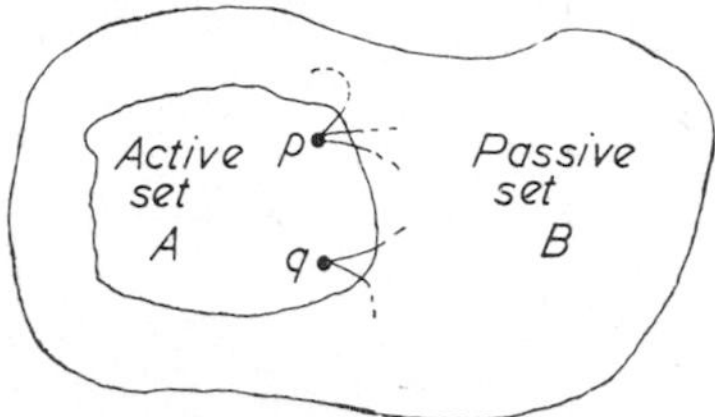

Fig. 2-13. Arbitrary linear network divided into active and passive (source-free) sets of nodes and branches.

According to the Thévenin-Helmholtz theorem,[8] the active-set *A* in Fig. 2-13 may be equivalently represented by a single e.m.f. source, equal to the potential between the node-pair *p-q* when disconnected from set *B*, acting in series with a single branch, whose impedance is that between *p* and *q* while set *B* is disconnected and all sources in set *A* are reduced to zero. Norton's theorem is the dual, in which the equivalent representation is a current-source equal to the current traversing *p-q* when short-circuited, acting in parallel with an admittance, which is the reciprocal of the impedance defined above. It is convenient to refer to these simple equivalent active networks as equivalent (constant) e.m.f. and (constant) current generators, respectively.

The excitation in the active-set or network may be from e.m.f. or current sources, or from both. The conversion of one kind into the other is illustrated by Figs. 2-14(a) and (b), while the replacement of active networks by equivalent simple generators is shown for the common and important cases of the star and delta topologies. Note that T and Π networks are merely four-terminal versions of these structures.

In Fig. 2-14(c), Z is the impedance between the terminals or nodes 2 and 3 when E_1 is reduced to zero, while E equals the voltage between them under open-circuit conditions.* By inspection,

$$Z = Z_4 + \frac{Z_3(Z_1 + Z_2)}{Z_1 + Z_2 + Z_3}$$

and

$$E = V^0_{2-3} = \frac{E_1 Z_3}{Z_1 + Z_2 + Z_3} \tag{2.93}$$

* When desirable, parameters between specific terminals under open or short-circuit conditions at others will be indicated respectively by an indicial *o* or *s*, in conjunction with appropriate subscripts, as in eqns. (2.93) and (2.94).

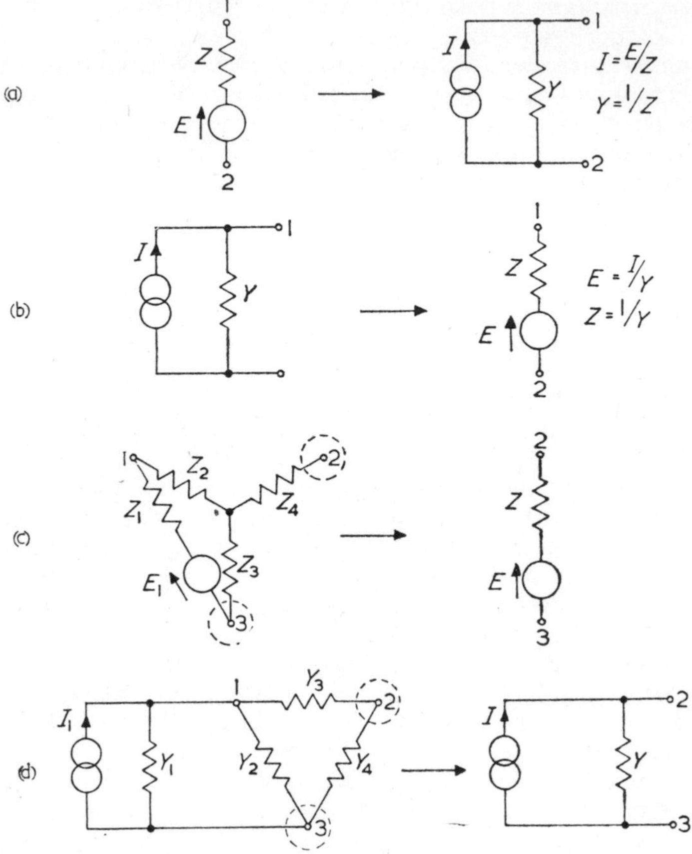

Fig. 2-14. Source transformations, and applications of the Thévenin-Helmholtz and Norton theorems.

Fig. 2-14(d) is the dual case, in which I is the current traversing terminals 2-3 when short-circuited, while Y is the admittance between these terminals when I_1 is reduced to zero, its path under this condition being regarded as an open-circuit. Current divides between admittances in parallel as does voltage across impedances in series, while admittances in series combine like impedances in parallel. Then, by inspection,

$$Y = Y_4 + \frac{Y_3(Y_1 + Y_2)}{Y_1 + Y_2 + Y_3}$$

$$I = I^s_{2-3} = \frac{I_1 Y_3}{Y_1 + Y_2 + Y_3} \tag{2.94}$$

These equations are the duals of eqns. (2.93).

Fig. 2-15 illustrates the reduction of an active network containing both e.m.f. and current sources. It corresponds to a representation for a transistor. In this case, it is expedient to transform the current-source in (a) into an e.m.f. source as in (b), for this leads by inspection to the equivalent e.m.f. generator in (c), which may be transformed into the alternative current generator, as indicated.

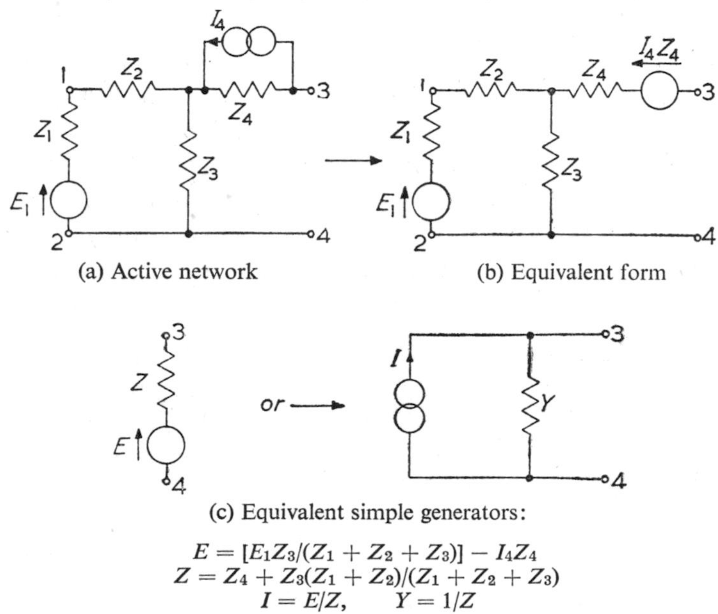

(a) Active network (b) Equivalent form

(c) Equivalent simple generators:

$$E = [E_1Z_3/(Z_1 + Z_2 + Z_3)] - I_4Z_4$$
$$Z = Z_4 + Z_3(Z_1 + Z_2)/(Z_1 + Z_2 + Z_3)$$
$$I = E/Z, \qquad Y = 1/Z$$

Fig. 2-15. Reduction of 2-source active network.

Fig. 2-16 illustrates the partial reduction of a complex network in the context of Fig. 2-13, in two stages.

5.1.1 *A note on the choice of theorem*

The value of both theorems depends on the ease with which the simple equivalent generators may be derived. This is governed by the topology of the active network and the kinds of source in it. It is the current generator that is likely to be the easier to derive if the network contains current sources and its topology is favourable for nodal-voltage analysis (fewer tree-branches B_t than links L), and the e.m.f. generator if it contains e.m.f. sources and is favourable for loop-current analysis ($L < B_t$). These cases are exemplified in Fig. 2-17 by the topologies involved in finding the open-circuit voltage of a T-network and the

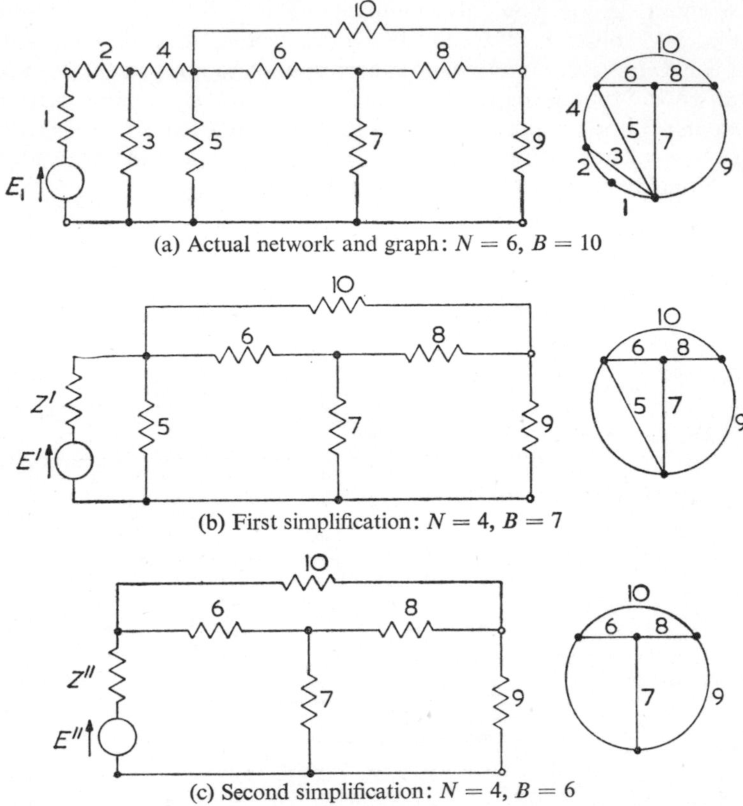

(a) Actual network and graph: $N = 6$, $B = 10$

(b) First simplification: $N = 4$, $B = 7$

(c) Second simplification: $N = 4$, $B = 6$

Fig. 2-16. Partial reduction of a complex network.

short-circuit current of a Π network. The effective graphs (b) and (d) are in fact dual (see Chapter 3), which is consistent with the duality between the expressions for E and I in eqns. (2.93) and (2.94).

The choice of equivalent generator should also take account of the topology of the network that follows it. It is, however, simple to change the generator from either form into the other, as indicated in Figs. 2-14(a) and (b).

5.2 TOPOLOGICAL TRANSFORMATIONS

These depend on equivalences[8] that may exist between networks having the same number of terminals or nodes for external connection, but different internal configurations. Two networks are equivalent if the replacement of one of them by the other, in a fixed electrical system, causes no change whatsoever in the current and potential conditions external to the networks.

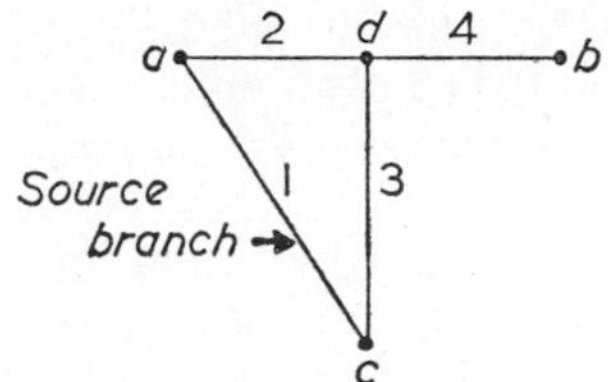

(a) Graph of open-circuited T-network.

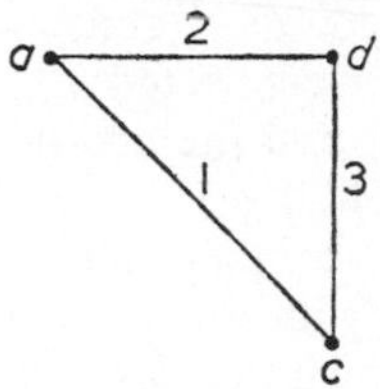

(b) Effective graph for finding open-circuit voltage (branch 4 redundant). $L = 1$, $B_t = 2$

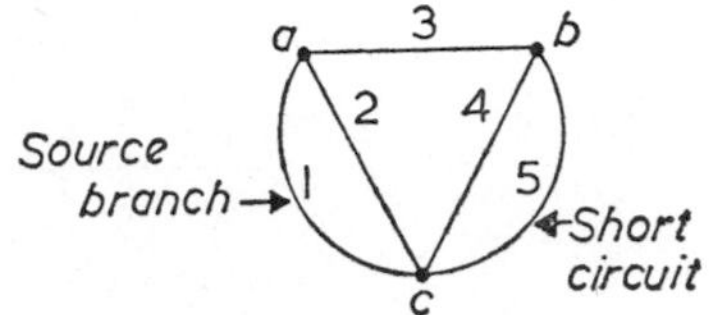

(c) Graph of short-circuited Π-network.

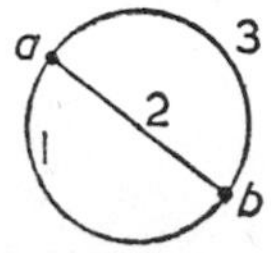

(d) Effective graph for finding short-circuit current (branch 4 redundant). $B_t = 1$, $L = 2$

Fig. 2-17.

5.2.1 *The general star-mesh transformation*[8]

An important fundamental equivalence is that between an arbitrary system of n terminals interconnected by n immittances in the form of a star, and the same system of terminals interconnected by $n(n-1)/2$ immittances linking each terminal to every other one. If the admittances from each terminal to the common point of the star are Y_1, Y_2, ... Y_n, then the equivalent system consists of admittances $Y_iY_1/\Sigma Y$, $Y_iY_2/\Sigma Y$, ... $Y_iY_n/\Sigma Y$ linking each terminal ($i = 1, 2, \ldots n$) to every other one. The equivalence is illustrated for the case $n = 4$ in Fig. 2-18. A proof is given in Example 3.5.

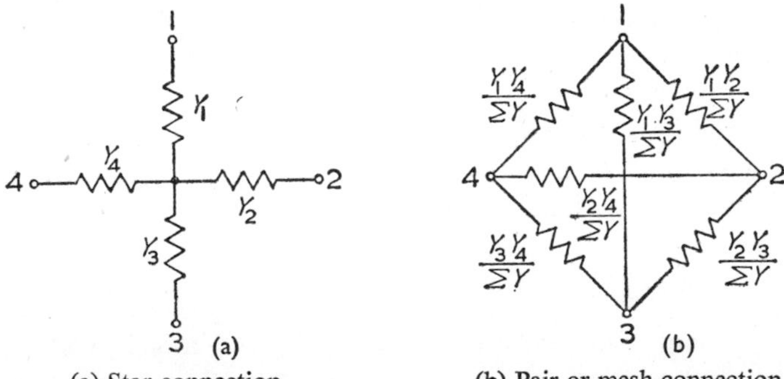

(a) Star connection.

(b) Pair or mesh-connection.

Fig. 2-18. Illustrating equivalence relationships.

The topological consequence of the transformation from the star into the pair-connected arrangement is the elimination of one node (the star-point), and the creation of $[n(n-1)/2]-n+1$ (see eqn. (1.43)), or $[n(n-3)/2]+1$ loops.

In practice, the n terminals will be closed by external immittances. Fig. 2-19(a) illustrates the capacitance network in a four-conductor cable, in which the star comprises the capacitances from each conductor to earth (the cable sheath), and Fig. 2-19(b) shows the result of transforming the star and merging those capacitances that are in parallel. The graphs are shown in Figs. 2-19(c) and (d) with the external source and load-loops added.

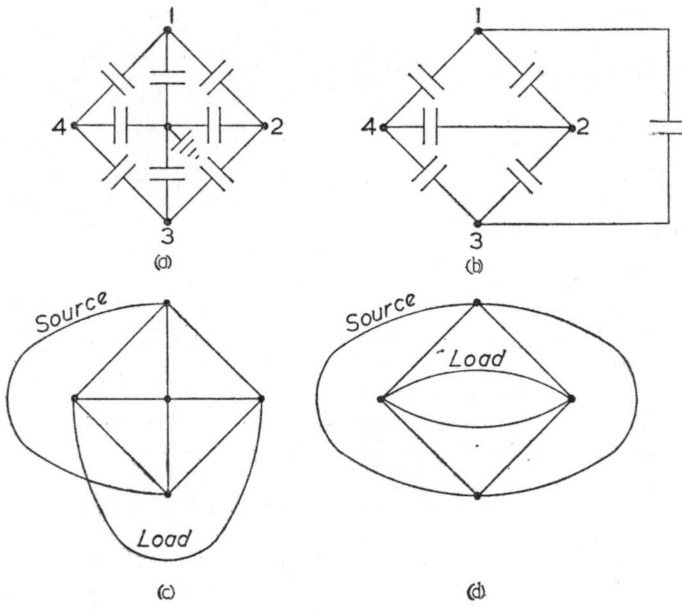

Fig. 2-19.

Fig. 2-19(c) requires 4 nodal-voltage equations and 6 loop-current. Fig. 2-19(d) requires only 3 nodal-voltage and 5 loop-current, or 4 loop-current if the immittance in parallel with the load is merged with it.

5.2.2 *The star-delta transformation*

A very important special case is the three-branch star, whose equivalent is the delta network. The equivalence relationships are easily derived independently.

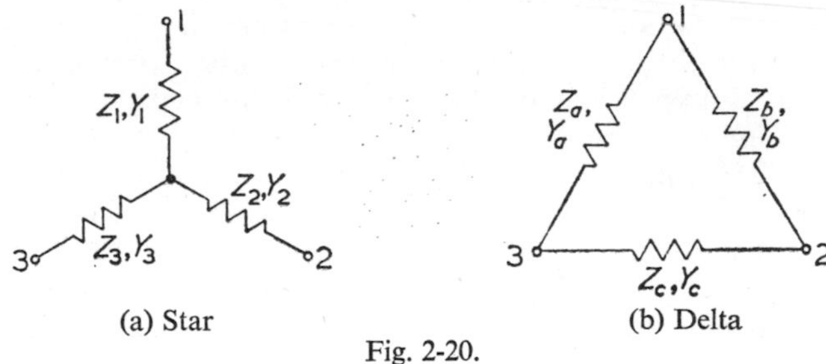

(a) Star (b) Delta

Fig. 2-20.

Referring to Fig. 2-20, equating impedances between corresponding terminal-pairs gives

$$Z_1 = Z_a Z_b/\Sigma Z, \quad Z_2 = Z_b Z_c/\Sigma Z, \quad Z_3 = Z_a Z_c/\Sigma Z \qquad (2.95)$$

Similarly, equating admittances under short-circuit conditions imposed on one corresponding terminal-pair at a time gives the dual relations

$$Y_a = Y_1 Y_3/\Sigma Y, \quad Y_b = Y_1 Y_2/\Sigma Y, \quad Y_c = Y_2 Y_3/\Sigma Y \qquad (2.96)$$

By repeated use of the star-delta or delta-star transformation, a complicated network can, in principle, be reduced to a simple one. But when the immittances are complex (of form $R + jX$, $G - jB$), the arithmetical work involved detracts from the advantage gained through the simplicity of the reduced network.

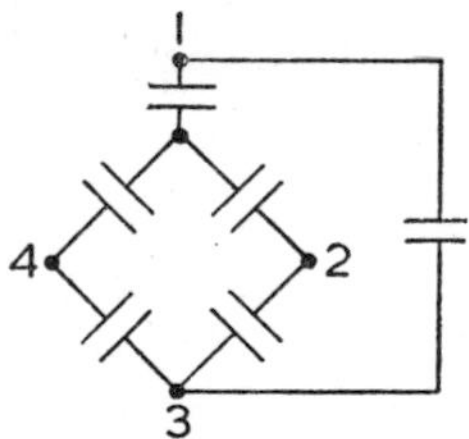

(a) Fig. 2-19(b) after delta-star transformation at terminals 1, 2, 4.

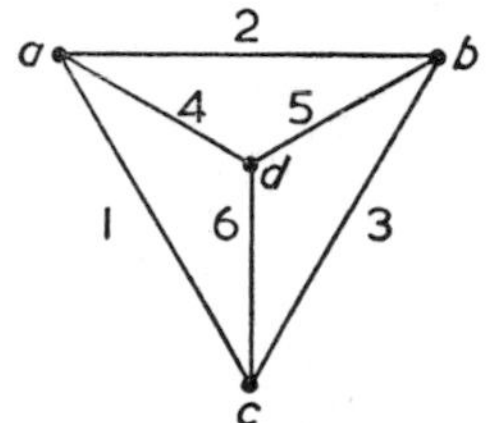

(b) General graph for bridge-type networks.

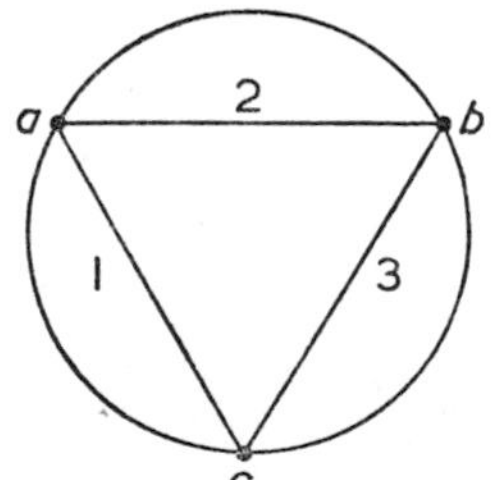

(c) Graph of (b) after star-delta transformation (branches 4, 5, 6).

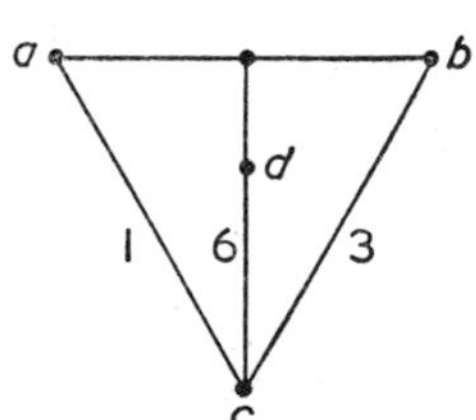

(d) Graph of (b) after delta-star transformation (branches 2, 4, 5).

Fig. 2-21.

The transformations are most useful when one kind of element only is involved, for then the arithmetic is very simple. For example, in Fig. 2-19(b) it is impossible to calculate the effective capacitance between terminals 1 and 3 in terms of series-parallel combinations. But a delta-star transformation is easily made at terminals 1, 2 and 4, and this changes the topology to that of Fig. 2-21(a). The calculation is then simple. In Fig. 2-21(b) is shown the general graph for bridged-T, bridge and lattice networks; while Figs. 2-21(c) and (d) illustrate the changes in topology arising from star-delta and delta-star transformations.

5.2.3 *Other transformations*

Equivalence formulae can generally be found by equating a sufficient set of immittances at corresponding terminal-pairs, under like conditions such as open-circuit or short-circuit, at all others.

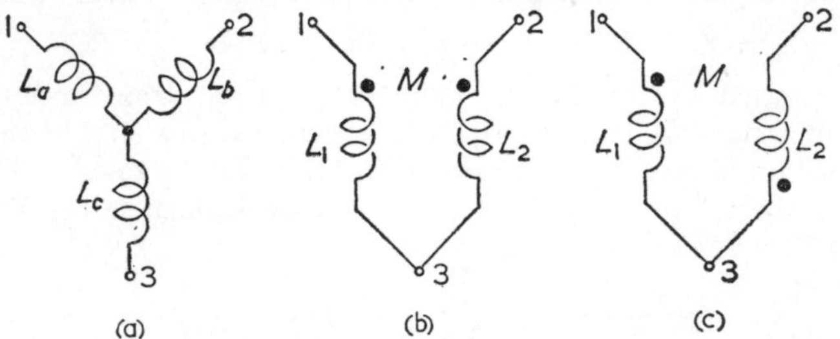

Fig. 2-22. Pertaining to mutual-inductor transformation.

The first of two further equivalences is illustrated by Fig. 2-22. Let L_{1-2} denote the effective inductance between terminals 1 and 2. Then, in the case of Fig. 2-22(b), a current i traversing these terminals enters by one dot but leaves by the other, so that the self and mutual fluxes are in opposition. Thus,

$$L_{1-2}\frac{di}{dt} = L_1\frac{di}{dt} - M\frac{di}{dt} + L_2\frac{di}{dt} - M\frac{di}{dt}$$

$$= (L_1 + L_2 - 2M)\frac{di}{dt}$$

whence

$$L_{1-2} = L_1 + L_2 - 2M \tag{2.97}$$

Now equating inductances at corresponding terminal-pairs for Figs. 2-22(a) and (b),

$$L_{1-2} = L_a + L_b = L_1 + L_2 - 2M$$
$$L_{1-3} = L_a + L_c = L_1$$
$$L_{2-3} = L_b + L_c = L_2$$

whence

$$\begin{aligned} L_a &= L_1 - M \\ L_b &= L_2 - M \\ L_c &= M \end{aligned} \tag{2.98}$$

Thus, so long as $M<(L_1, L_2)$, two coils coupled by mutual inductance and having the orientations of Fig. 2-22(b) are replaceable by a star network of three real, positive self-inductors. In the case of Fig. 2-22(c) however,

$$L_{1-2} = L_1 + L_2 + 2M \tag{2.99}$$

which gives

$$\begin{aligned} L_a &= L_1 + M \\ L_b &= L_2 + M \\ L_c &= -M \end{aligned} \tag{2.100}$$

The equivalence is then physically unrealisable, as L_c is negative. With sinusoidal excitation at a fixed frequency, however, a capacitor of the same reactance value could be substituted.

The transformation from Fig. 2-22(a) to 2-22(b) does not reduce the number of loops in a network, but replaces a physical mutual impedance by a non-physical one. While this is a useful economy in physical inductors, the equivalence is important in several other respects. Firstly, it permits coupling between loops without physical contact if desired: topologically this implies changing from a *connected* graph to an *unconnected* one. Secondly, the transformation from Fig. 2-22(b) into 2-22(a) may exhance perception of network behaviour: for example, such a transformation in the *Carey Foster* bridge resolves it into the *Wheatstone* pattern, with obvious balance conditions. Thirdly, and perhaps most important, it may permit the practical realisation of a network that would otherwise be unrealisable. This is illustrated by Fig. 2-23, which is an example from network synthesis. Fig. 2-23(a) has been synthesised to have the impedance

$$Z(s) = \frac{s^3 + 19s^2 + 20s + 28}{4s^2 + 12s + 16}$$

In this form, however, the network requires a negative inductor ($-1/4H$), and is therefore unrealisable. But the three inductors may be replaced by two positive ones coupled by mutual inductance, with a coupling coefficient $k = M/\sqrt{(L_1 L_2)} = 2/\sqrt{5}$. Since $k < 1$, the network of Fig. 2-23(b) is fully realisable.

The second equivalence is that between a symmetrical lattice or bridge network, and any other symmetrical (and, strictly, balanced) four-terminal network. It is exemplified by Fig. 2-24.

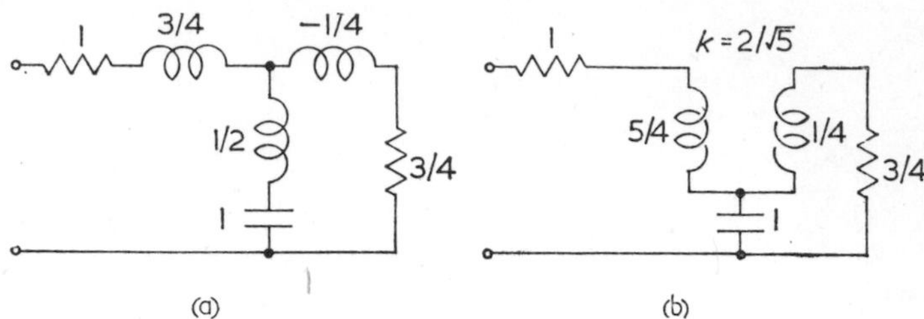

Fig. 2-23. Physical realisation of a network containing a negative inductor.

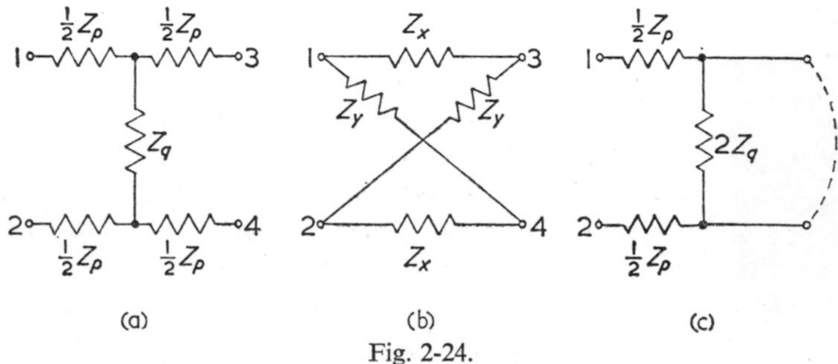

Fig. 2-24.

Equating impedances at terminals 1–2 under open and short-circuit conditions at terminals 3–4 for Figs. 2-24(a) and (b),

$$Z^0_{1-2} = Z_p + Z_q = \tfrac{1}{2}(Z_x + Z_y)$$
$$Z^s_{1-2} = Z_p + Z_pZ_q/(Z_p + Z_q) = 2Z_xZ_y/(Z_x + Z_y)$$

whence

$$\begin{aligned} Z_x &= Z_p \\ Z_y &= Z_p + 2Z_q \end{aligned} \tag{2.101}$$

or

$$\begin{aligned} Z_p &= Z_x \\ Z_q &= \tfrac{1}{2}(Z_y - Z_x) \end{aligned} \tag{2.102}$$

Fig. 2-24(c) is the half-network or half-section formed by bisecting Fig. 2-24(a) at Z_q. Eqns. (2.101) are now identifiable respectively with the obvious short-circuit and open-circuit impedances of the half-section at terminals 1–2. This property is generalised in *Bartlett's bisection theorem*,[8,9] according to which the branches Z_x and Z_y of the lattice network are equal to the input impedances of the half-section of the equivalent network, under respectively short and open-circuit conditions on the side corresponding to the bisection.

In relation to network solution, transformation from the lattice into the equivalent form of Fig. 2-24(a) is of special interest, for it effects a reduction in the graph. This is illustrated by Fig. 2-25, which includes source and load.

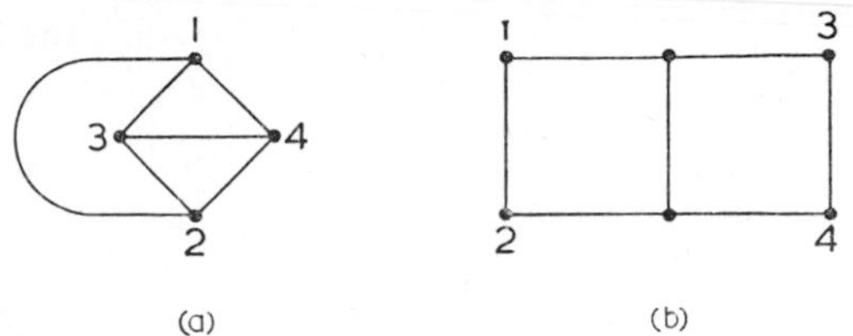

Fig. 2-25. Graphs, (a) for a symmetrical lattice, and (b) for an equivalent network.

6. ILLUSTRATIVE EXAMPLES

Example 2.1. The formulation of loop-current and nodal-voltage equations by means of the branch-immittance matrix

For this illustration, the loop-current equations for Example 1.1 will be developed in detail by the alternative means of eqn. (2.14), and then the dual procedure leading to the nodal voltage equations for Example 1.2 will be outlined.

Loop-current equations

Referring to Example 1.1, the initial topological procedure leading to the tie-set matrix $[M]$ will be assumed. By eqns. (1.44) and (1.45),

$$[M] = \begin{bmatrix} 1 & 1 & 1 & 1 & 0 & 0 & 0 & 0 & 0 & 0 & 0 \\ 0 & 0 & 1 & 1 & 1 & 0 & 1 & 0 & 0 & 0 & 0 \\ 0 & 0 & 0 & 1 & 0 & 1 & 0 & 0 & 0 & 0 & -1 \\ 0 & 0 & 0 & 0 & 0 & 0 & -1 & 1 & 1 & 0 & 0 \\ 0 & 0 & 0 & 0 & 0 & 0 & 0 & 0 & 1 & 1 & 1 \end{bmatrix}$$

and

$$[M]^t = \begin{bmatrix} 1 & 0 & 0 & 0 & 0 \\ 1 & 0 & 0 & 0 & 0 \\ 1 & 1 & 0 & 0 & 0 \\ 1 & 1 & 1 & 0 & 0 \\ 0 & 1 & 0 & 0 & 0 \\ 0 & 0 & 1 & 0 & 0 \\ 0 & 1 & 0 & -1 & 0 \\ 0 & 0 & 0 & 1 & 0 \\ 0 & 0 & 0 & 1 & 1 \\ 0 & 0 & 0 & 0 & 1 \\ 0 & 0 & -1 & 0 & 1 \end{bmatrix}$$

By eqn. (2.14), the loop-current equations are arrived at by evaluating

$$[M]\cdot[Z_b]\cdot[M]^t\cdot[I_L] = [M]\cdot\{[E] - [Z_b]\cdot[I]\}$$

As mutual inductance is absent, the branch-impedance matrix, $[Z_b]$ is diagonal (see, for comparison, Example 2.2). Writing the numerical values along the diagonal in the order 1 to 11 in which the branches are numbered in Fig. 1-14,

$$[Z_b] = \begin{bmatrix} 5 & 0 & \cdot & \cdot & \cdot & \cdot & \cdot & \cdot & \cdot & \cdot & 0 \\ 0 & 4 & \cdot & \cdot & \cdot & \cdot & \cdot & \cdot & \cdot & \cdot & \cdot \\ \cdot & \cdot & 2 & \cdot & \cdot & \cdot & \cdot & \cdot & \cdot & \cdot & \cdot \\ \cdot & \cdot & \cdot & 5 & \cdot & \cdot & \cdot & \cdot & \cdot & \cdot & \cdot \\ \cdot & \cdot & \cdot & \cdot & 8 & \cdot & \cdot & \cdot & \cdot & \cdot & \cdot \\ \cdot & \cdot & \cdot & \cdot & \cdot & 10 & \cdot & \cdot & \cdot & \cdot & \cdot \\ \cdot & \cdot & \cdot & \cdot & \cdot & \cdot & 10 & \cdot & \cdot & \cdot & \cdot \\ \cdot & \cdot & \cdot & \cdot & \cdot & \cdot & \cdot & 5 & \cdot & \cdot & \cdot \\ \cdot & \cdot & \cdot & \cdot & \cdot & \cdot & \cdot & \cdot & 3 & \cdot & \cdot \\ \cdot & \cdot & \cdot & \cdot & \cdot & \cdot & \cdot & \cdot & \cdot & 10 & 0 \\ 0 & \cdot & \cdot & \cdot & \cdot & \cdot & \cdot & \cdot & \cdot & 0 & 8 \end{bmatrix}$$

Then,

$$[M]\cdot[Z_b] = \begin{bmatrix} 5 & 4 & 2 & 5 & 0 & 0 & 0 & 0 & 0 & 0 & 0 \\ 0 & 0 & 2 & 5 & 8 & 0 & 10 & 0 & 0 & 0 & 0 \\ 0 & 0 & 0 & 5 & 0 & 10 & 0 & 0 & 0 & 0 & -8 \\ 0 & 0 & 0 & 0 & 0 & 0 & -10 & 5 & 3 & 0 & 0 \\ 0 & 0 & 0 & 0 & 0 & 0 & 0 & 0 & 3 & 10 & 8 \end{bmatrix}$$

The loop-current matrix $[I_L]$ is a column-matrix of the currents i_2, i_5, i_6, i_8, i_{10}. Thus,

$$[M]\cdot[Z_b]\cdot[M]^t\cdot[I_L] = \begin{bmatrix} 16 & 7 & 5 & 0 & 0 \\ 7 & 25 & 5 & -10 & 0 \\ 5 & 5 & 23 & 0 & -8 \\ 0 & -10 & 0 & 18 & 3 \\ 0 & 0 & -8 & 3 & 21 \end{bmatrix} \cdot \begin{bmatrix} i_2 \\ i_5 \\ i_6 \\ i_8 \\ i_{10} \end{bmatrix} \tag{2.103}$$

This is in agreement with the left-hand side of eqn. (1.50).

The matrix of voltages arising from e.m.f. and current-sources and balancing the loop voltage-drops in eqn. (2.103) is determined by $[M]\cdot\{[E] - [Z_b]\cdot[I]\}$. In formulating the column matrices $[E]$ and $[I]$, correct signs must, however, be attached to their elements. These can be decided by the orientations of the sources relative to the loop-currents for the loops in which they act. The orientation of an e.m.f. represents a direction of potential rise, while the orientation of a loop-current represents also the direction of potential fall around its loop. Thus, an e.m.f. acting in a loop and oriented in the same direction as the loop-current is negative with respect to the potential fall. It is therefore reckoned negative in the loop, as exemplified by

$$I(Z_1 + Z_2 + \cdots + Z_n) - E = 0$$

but positive when transferred to the right hand side of the equilibrium equation. On the other hand, a current-source feeding a loop in the same sense as the loop-current is positive with respect to it, and becomes negative when transferred to the excitation or source-side of an equilibrium equation.

In this case there is an e.m.f. E_1 in branch 1 oriented in the same direction as the loop-current i_2; a current-source I_5 in parallel with branch 5, feeding the loop in the same sense as i_5; and a further current-source I_{10} in parallel with branch 10, feeding the loop in the same sense as i_{10}. $[E]$ and $[I]$ are therefore column-matrices of elements $E_1\,0000000000$ and $0000 -I_5\,0000 -I_{10}0$. Thus,

$$[E]-[Z_b]\cdot[I]=\begin{bmatrix}E_1\\0\\0\\0\\0\\0\\0\\0\\0\\0\\0\end{bmatrix}-\begin{bmatrix}0\\0\\0\\0\\-R_5I_5\\0\\0\\0\\0\\-R_{10}I_{10}\\0\end{bmatrix}=\begin{bmatrix}E_1\\0\\0\\0\\R_5I_5\\0\\0\\0\\0\\R_{10}I_{10}\\0\end{bmatrix}=\begin{bmatrix}1\\0\\0\\0\\16\\0\\0\\0\\0\\40\\0\end{bmatrix}$$

and then

$$[M]\cdot\{[E]-[Z_b]\cdot[I]\}=\begin{bmatrix}1\\16\\0\\0\\40\end{bmatrix} \tag{2.104}$$

By reference to eqn. (2.103), the final matrix equation is therefore

$$\begin{bmatrix}16 & 7 & 5 & 0 & 0\\ 7 & 25 & 5 & -10 & 0\\ 5 & 5 & 23 & 0 & -8\\ 0 & -10 & 0 & 18 & 3\\ 0 & 0 & -8 & 3 & 21\end{bmatrix}\cdot\begin{bmatrix}i_2\\i_5\\i_6\\i_8\\i_{10}\end{bmatrix}=\begin{bmatrix}1\\16\\0\\0\\40\end{bmatrix} \tag{2.105}$$

which is identical with eqn. (1.50).

Nodal-voltage equations

The procedure for arriving at the nodal-voltage equations for Example 1.2 is precisely dual with that just illustrated in respect of loop-current equations. By eqn. (2.15), the nodal-voltage equations are arrived at by evaluating

$$[Q]\cdot[Y_b]\cdot[Q]^t\cdot[V_n]=[Q]\cdot\{[I]-[Y_b]\cdot[E]\}$$

Referring to Fig. 1-15 and the schedule of branch conductances,

$$[Y_b] = \begin{bmatrix} 2 & 0 & \cdot & \cdot & \cdot & \cdot & \cdot & \cdot & \cdot & 0 \\ 0 & 3 & \cdot & \cdot & \cdot & \cdot & \cdot & \cdot & \cdot & \cdot \\ \cdot & \cdot & 5 & \cdot & \cdot & \cdot & \cdot & \cdot & \cdot & \cdot \\ \cdot & \cdot & \cdot & 4 & \cdot & \cdot & \cdot & \cdot & \cdot & \cdot \\ \cdot & \cdot & \cdot & \cdot & 7 & \cdot & \cdot & \cdot & \cdot & \cdot \\ \cdot & \cdot & \cdot & \cdot & \cdot & 3 & \cdot & \cdot & \cdot & \cdot \\ \cdot & \cdot & \cdot & \cdot & \cdot & \cdot & 9 & \cdot & \cdot & \cdot \\ \cdot & \cdot & \cdot & \cdot & \cdot & \cdot & \cdot & 10 & \cdot & \cdot \\ \cdot & \cdot & \cdot & \cdot & \cdot & \cdot & \cdot & \cdot & 8 & 0 \\ 0 & \cdot & \cdot & \cdot & \cdot & \cdot & \cdot & \cdot & 0 & 6 \end{bmatrix}$$

The node-pair voltage matrix is a column matrix of the node-pair voltages v_{n1}, v_{n4}, v_{n6}, v_{n9}. Then, substituting for the matrices $[Q]$ and $[Q]^t$ as given by eqns. (1.51) and (1.52) and multiplying in strict order,

$$[Q]\cdot[Y_b]\cdot[Q]^t\cdot[V_n] = \begin{bmatrix} 16 & -5 & 0 & -6 \\ -5 & 16 & -7 & 0 \\ 0 & -7 & 29 & -10 \\ -6 & 0 & -10 & 24 \end{bmatrix} \cdot \begin{bmatrix} v_{n1} \\ v_{n4} \\ v_{n6} \\ v_{n9} \end{bmatrix} \qquad (2.106)$$

In this case there are e.m.f. sources only. The sign of each element in $[E]$ is decided by its orientation relative to the node-pair voltage for the cut-set to which it belongs. If it is the same, it is reckoned negative when transferred to the excitation side of an equilibrium equation (this is the dual of the case for a current-source in a tie-set). $[E]$ is therefore a column-matrix of elements $-E_1\,0\,0 - E_4\,0 - E_6\,0\,0 - E_9\,0$. Then, making the appropriate substitutions,

$$[Q]\cdot\{-[Y_b]\cdot[E]\} = \begin{bmatrix} 4 \\ 12 \\ 6 \\ 32 \end{bmatrix} \qquad (2.107)$$

and by reference to eqn. (2.106), the final matrix equation is therefore

$$\begin{bmatrix} 16 & -5 & 0 & -6 \\ -5 & 16 & -7 & 0 \\ 0 & -7 & 29 & -10 \\ -6 & 0 & -10 & 24 \end{bmatrix} \cdot \begin{bmatrix} v_{n1} \\ v_{n4} \\ v_{n6} \\ v_{n9} \end{bmatrix} = \begin{bmatrix} 4 \\ 12 \\ 6 \\ 32 \end{bmatrix} \qquad (2.108)$$

which accords with eqn. (1.57).

Example 2.2. The matrix analysis of a network with mutually-coupled branches

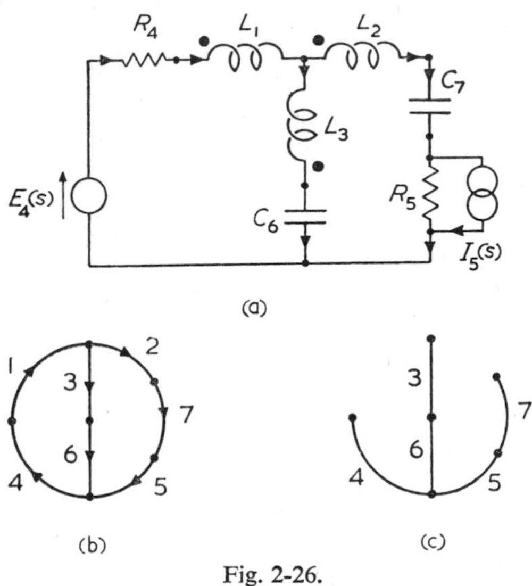

Fig. 2-26.

The network is similar to that discussed in sect. 2.4.3, but includes an additional source, the current source $I_5(s)$ in parallel with branch 5. The oriented graph is shown in Fig. 2-26(b), and a tree in Fig. 2-26(c).

Let the network have the following normalised parameters:

Self-inductance	Mutual inductance
$L_{11} = L_1 = 4\text{H}$	$L_{12} = L_{21} = 3\text{H}$
$L_{22} = L_2 = 3\text{H}$	$L_{13} = L_{31} = -2\text{H}$
$L_{33} = L_3 = 2\text{H}$	$L_{23} = L_{32} = -1\text{H}$
Resistance	**Capacitance**
$R_{44} = R_4 = 2\Omega$	$C_{66} = C_6 = 2\text{F}$
$R_{55} = R_5 = 3\Omega$	$C_{77} = C_7 = 3\text{F}$

Constructing tie-sets by adding link 1 and then link 2 to the tree of Fig. 2-26(c) gives the tie-set schedule,

Loop-current	Branch-current						
	1	2	3	4	5	6	7
I_1	1	0	1	1	0	1	0
I_2	0	1	−1	0	1	−1	1

The tie-set matrix is therefore

$$[M] = \begin{bmatrix} 1 & 0 & 1 & 1 & 0 & 1 & 0 \\ 0 & 1 & -1 & 0 & 1 & -1 & 1 \end{bmatrix}$$

and

$$[M]^t = \begin{bmatrix} 1 & 0 \\ 0 & 1 \\ 1 & -1 \\ 1 & 0 \\ 0 & 1 \\ 1 & -1 \\ 0 & 1 \end{bmatrix}$$

The impedance-parameter matrices are

$$[L] = \begin{bmatrix} L_{11} & L_{12} & L_{13} \\ L_{21} & L_{22} & L_{23} \\ L_{31} & L_{32} & L_{33} \end{bmatrix} = \begin{bmatrix} 4 & 3 & -2 \\ 3 & 3 & -1 \\ -2 & -1 & 2 \end{bmatrix}$$

$$\left[\frac{1}{C}\right] = \begin{bmatrix} \dfrac{1}{C_{66}} & 0 \\ 0 & \dfrac{1}{C_{77}} \end{bmatrix} = \begin{bmatrix} \frac{1}{2} & 0 \\ 0 & \frac{1}{3} \end{bmatrix}$$

$$[R] = \begin{bmatrix} R_{44} & 0 \\ 0 & R_{55} \end{bmatrix} = \begin{bmatrix} 2 & 0 \\ 0 & 3 \end{bmatrix}$$

The branch impedance matrix is therefore

$$[Z_b] = \begin{bmatrix} Ls & 0 & 0 \\ 0 & R & 0 \\ 0 & 0 & \dfrac{1}{Cs} \end{bmatrix}$$

$$= \begin{bmatrix} 4s & 3s & -2s & . & . & 0 & 0 \\ 3s & 3s & -s & . & . & . & 0 \\ -2s & -s & 2s & . & . & . & . \\ . & . & . & 2 & . & . & . \\ . & . & . & . & 3 & . & . \\ 0 & . & . & . & . & \dfrac{1}{2s} & . \\ 0 & 0 & . & . & . & . & \dfrac{1}{3s} \end{bmatrix}$$

By eqn. (2.14), the product $[M]\cdot[Z_b]\cdot[M]^t\cdot[I_L]$ is now required. Substituting for the matrices as listed above and multiplying in strict order,

$$[M]\cdot[Z_b] = \begin{bmatrix} 2s & 2s & 0 & 2 & 0 & \frac{1}{2}s & 0 \\ 5s & 4s & -3s & 0 & 3 & -\frac{1}{2}s & \frac{1}{3}s \end{bmatrix}$$

$$[M]\cdot[Z_b]\cdot[M]^t = \begin{bmatrix} 2s+\dfrac{1}{2s}+2 & 2s-\dfrac{1}{2s} \\ 2s-\dfrac{1}{2s} & 7s+\dfrac{5}{6s}+3 \end{bmatrix}$$

and therefore

$$[M]\cdot[Z_b]\cdot[M]^t\cdot[I_L] = \begin{bmatrix} Z_{11} & Z_{12} \\ Z_{21} & Z_{22} \end{bmatrix}\cdot\begin{bmatrix} I_1 \\ I_2 \end{bmatrix} \tag{2.109}$$

where

$$\begin{aligned} Z_{11} &= 2+2s+1/2s \\ Z_{22} &= 3+7s+5/6s \\ Z_{12} &= Z_{21} = 2s-1/2s \end{aligned} \tag{2.110}$$

Referring to eqn. (2.14), the matrix of excitation voltages is found by evaluating $[M]\cdot\{[E(s)]-[Z_b]\cdot[I(s)]\}$. The e.m.f. $E_4(s)$ and the current-source $I_5(s)$ are oriented in the directions of the respective loop-currents, I_1 and I_2. Therefore, $[E(s)]$ is a column-matrix of elements $0\,0\,0\,E_4(s)\,0\,0\,0$ and $I(s)$ is a column-matrix of elements $0\,0\,0\,0\,-I_5\,0\,0$. Then,

$$[M]\cdot\{[E(s)]-[Z_b]\cdot[I(s)]\} = \begin{bmatrix} E_4(s) \\ R_5I_5(s) \end{bmatrix} = \begin{bmatrix} E_4(s) \\ 3I_5(s) \end{bmatrix}$$

Referring to eqn. (2.109), the final matrix equation is therefore

$$\begin{bmatrix} Z_{11} & Z_{12} \\ Z_{21} & Z_{22} \end{bmatrix}\cdot\begin{bmatrix} I_1 \\ I_2 \end{bmatrix} = \begin{bmatrix} E_4(s) \\ 3I_5(s) \end{bmatrix} \tag{2.111}$$

where the elements of the Z-matrix are defined by eqns. (2.110).

The solutions for I_1 and I_2 in eqn. (2.111) are given by

$$I_1 = (E_4(s)\Delta_{11}+3I_5(s)\Delta_{21})/\Delta \tag{2.112}$$

$$I_2 = (E_4(s)\Delta_{12}+3I_5(s)\Delta_{22})/\Delta \tag{2.113}$$

where Δ is the determinant of the Z-matrix, given by

$$\Delta = Z_{11}Z_{22}-Z_{21}Z_{12}$$

and

$$\Delta_{11}=Z_{22},\qquad \Delta_{21}=-Z_{12},\qquad \Delta_{22}=Z_{11},\qquad \Delta_{12}=-Z_{21}$$

are cofactors of Δ.

The forms of the solutions as functions of time depend on the forms of the excitations $E_4(s)$ and $I_5(s)$. If, for example, these are sinusoidal functions of time, as generated by vectors of constant magnitudes rotating with the same constant angular velocity ω, and steady-state conditions are assumed, s is everywhere replaced by $j\omega$. For simplicity, let $\omega = 1$ rad/sec. so that $s = j1$. Then, referring to eqns. (2.110),

$$\begin{aligned} Z_{11} &= 2 + j(2 - 1/2) = 2 + j3/2 \\ Z_{22} &= 3 + j(7 - 5/6) = 3 + j37/6 \\ Z_{12} &= Z_{21} = j(2 + 1/2) = j5/2 \end{aligned}$$

and therefore in eqns. (2.112) and (2.113),

$$\begin{aligned} \Delta &= Z_{11}Z_{22} - Z_{21}Z_{12} &&= (18 + j101)/6 \\ \Delta_{11} &= Z_{22} &&= (18 + j37)/6 \\ \Delta_{12} &= \Delta_{21} = -Z_{12} &&= -j5/2 \\ \Delta_{22} &= Z_{11} &&= 2 + j3/2 \end{aligned}$$

It is convenient to represent the sources vectorially as cisoidal functions of time, in the forms

$$\begin{aligned} E_4(t) &= E_4 \operatorname{cis}(\omega t + \phi_1) \\ &= E_4 [\cos(\omega t + \phi_1) + j \sin(\omega t + \phi_1)] \\ &= E_4\, e^{j(\omega t + \phi_1)} \end{aligned}$$

and similarly

$$\begin{aligned} I_5(t) &= I_5 \operatorname{cis}(\omega t + \phi_2) \\ &= I_5\, e^{j(\omega t + \phi_2)} \end{aligned}$$

where a value at any instant t_1 is exemplified by

$$e_4(t_1) = \mathscr{I}m\, E_4(t_1) = E_4 \sin(\omega t_1 + \phi_1)$$

To provide a simple illustration, let $E_4(t)$ and $I_5(t)$ be in-phase, and let $E_4 = 1$ volt and $I_5 = 1$ amp, so that $E_4(t) = e^{jt}$ and $I_5(t) = e^{jt}$. Then, by eqn. (2.112),

$$\begin{aligned} I_1(t) &= e^{jt}(18 - j8)/(18 + j101) \\ &= 0.192\, e^{j(t - 0.577\pi)} \text{ amp} \end{aligned} \tag{2.114}$$

Similarly, by eqn. (2.113),

$$\begin{aligned} I_2(t) &= e^{jt}(36 + j12)/(18 + j101) \\ &= 0.37\, e^{j(t - 0.342\pi)} \text{ amp} \end{aligned} \tag{2.115}$$

Example 2.3. The reduction of Fig. 1-15 (Example 1.2), and its node-datum equations

Referring to Fig. 1-15, the graph may be reduced either by Thévenin's theorem, through which E_1 and branches 1, 2, and E_6 and branches 6, 7 are replaced by equivalent single branches 1′ and 6′ containing e.m.fs.

E_1' and E_6' respectively; or by Norton's theorem, through which the e.m.fs. and branches are replaced by constant-current sources in parallel with single branches. Either way, the branches in the graph are reduced by 2, though the number of essential nodes is unchanged. This reduces the necessary number of loop-current equations to 4, which is also the necessary number of nodal-voltage equations.

For convenience in setting-up node-datum voltage equations, constant-current sources are preferred. The network of Fig. 1-15(a) is shown with constant-current sources, and with its topology reduced, in Fig. 2-27(a). The corresponding reduced graph is shown in Fig. 2-27(b).

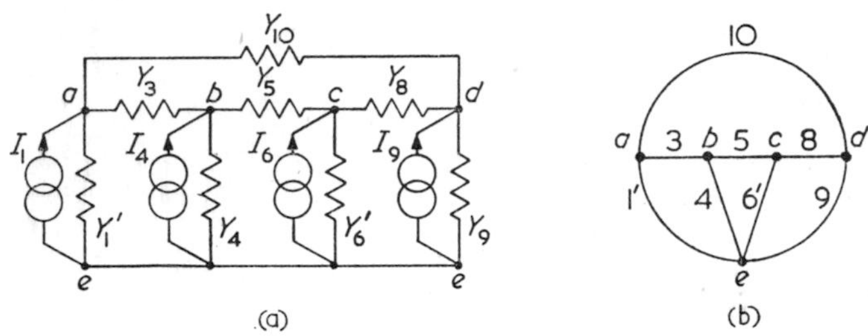

Fig. 2-27. Transformed and reduced versions of Figs. 1-15(a) and (b).

The branches 1 to 10 in Fig. 1-15(a) are here assigned admittances Y_1 to Y_{10}. Then in Fig. 2-27(a),

$$\begin{aligned} I_1 &= E_1 Y_1 \quad \text{and} \quad Y_1' = Y_1 + Y_2 \\ I_4 &= E_4 Y_4 \\ I_6 &= E_6 Y_6 \quad \text{and} \quad Y_6' = Y_6 + Y_7 \\ I_9 &= E_9 Y_9 \end{aligned}$$

Let V_{n1}, V_{n4}, V_{n6}, V_{n9}, denote respectively the potentials of nodes a, b, c, and d relative to the datum e. Then, by inspection, the node-datum equations are

$$\begin{aligned} (Y_1' + Y_3 + Y_{10})V_{n1} - Y_3 V_{n4} - Y_{10} V_{n9} &= I_1 \\ (Y_3 + Y_4 + Y_5)V_{n4} - Y_3 V_{n1} - Y_5 V_{n6} &= I_4 \\ (Y_5 + Y_6' + Y_8)V_{n6} - Y_5 V_{n4} - Y_8 V_{n9} &= I_6 \\ (Y_8 + Y_9 + Y_{10})V_{n9} - Y_8 V_{n6} - Y_{10} V_{n1} &= I_9 \end{aligned}$$

Substituting for Y_1', Y_6' and I_1', I_4, I_6, and I_9, these equations may be put in the ordered form

$$\begin{bmatrix} Y_{11} & Y_{12} & Y_{13} & Y_{14} \\ Y_{21} & Y_{22} & Y_{23} & Y_{24} \\ Y_{31} & Y_{32} & Y_{33} & Y_{34} \\ Y_{41} & Y_{42} & Y_{43} & Y_{44} \end{bmatrix} \cdot \begin{bmatrix} V_{n1} \\ V_{n4} \\ V_{n6} \\ V_{n9} \end{bmatrix} = \begin{bmatrix} E_1 Y_1 \\ E_4 Y_4 \\ E_6 Y_6 \\ E_9 Y_9 \end{bmatrix} \qquad (2.116)$$

where

$$Y_{11} = Y_1 + Y_2 + Y_3 + Y_{10}; \qquad Y_{22} = Y_3 + Y_4 + Y_5$$
$$Y_{33} = Y_5 + Y_6 + Y_7 + Y_8; \qquad Y_{44} = Y_8 + Y_9 + Y_{10}$$
$$Y_{12} = Y_{21} = -Y_3; \qquad Y_{13} = Y_{31} = 0$$
$$Y_{14} = Y_{41} = -Y_{10}; \qquad Y_{23} = Y_{32} = -Y_5$$
$$Y_{24} = Y_{42} = 0; \qquad Y_{34} = Y_{43} = -Y_8$$

By substituting the numerical values used in Example 1.2, eqn. (2.116) may be shown to be identical with eqn. (1.57). This verifies that node-datum analysis is consistent with the choice of a particular tree in general node-pair analysis. Where such a tree is obvious, there is little point in following the formal topological procedure illustrated in Example 1.2.

Example 2.4

Determine the current flowing in the branch *BD* of Fig. 2-28, in which the conductances of the branches in mhos are as shown.

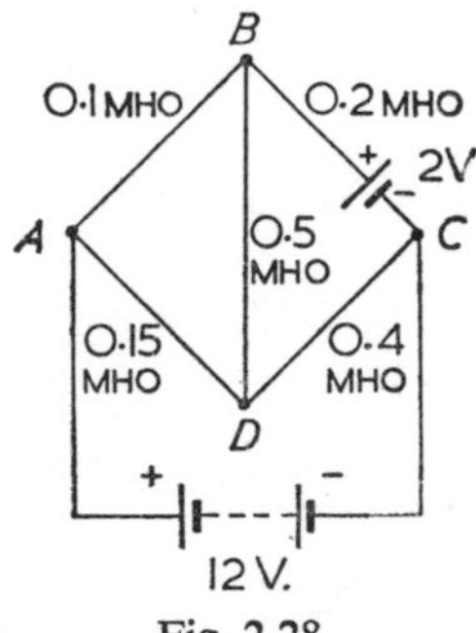

Fig. 2-28.

(I.E.E., Part 2, Electrical Engineering 2)

The graph has the same number of links as tree-branches, and therefore the same number of equations is required for loop-current as for nodal-voltage analysis. The choice is governed, therefore, by the form in which the data is given. As branch admittances are quoted, the preference is for nodal-voltage analysis in the node-datum form, to which they are directly adaptable.

For a numerical problem as simple as this one, there is no advantage in employing the formal double-subscript notation: it is easy to write the equations directly with numerical coefficients.

If node *C* is chosen as datum, the potential V_A of node *A* is identifiable with the 12V battery. This might be compared with Fig. 2-12, in which it is the presence of series impedance in the e.m.f. source that merits transformation into the constant-current form.

Let the current flowing into node A from the 12V battery be I_A and let V_E denote the potential of the positive pole of the 2V battery relative to node C. Then, summing currents at nodes A, B, and D, with C as datum,

$$\begin{aligned}
(0.1 + 0.15)V_A - 0.1V_B - 0.15V_D &= I_A \\
(0.1 + 0.2 + 0.5)V_B - 0.1V_A - 0.5V_D - 0.2V_E &= 0 \\
(0.15 + 0.4 + 0.5)\,V_D - 0.15V_A - 0.5V_B &= 0
\end{aligned}$$

Since $V_A = +12$ and $V_E = +2$, these reduce to

$$\begin{aligned}
I_A + 0.1V_B + 0.15V_D &= 3 \\
0.8V_B - 0.5V_D &= 1.6 \\
0.5V_B - 1.05V_D &= -1.8
\end{aligned}$$

or

$$\begin{bmatrix} 1 & 0.1 & 0.15 \\ 0 & 0.8 & -0.5 \\ 0 & 0.5 & -1.05 \end{bmatrix} \cdot \begin{bmatrix} I_A \\ V_B \\ V_D \end{bmatrix} = \begin{bmatrix} 3 \\ 1.6 \\ -1.8 \end{bmatrix}$$

Expanding the determinant of the admittance-matrix along the first column (which contains two zeros) gives simply

$$\Delta = \begin{bmatrix} 0.8 & -0.5 \\ 0.5 & -1.05 \end{bmatrix} = -0.59$$

Then, by Cramer's rule,

$$\begin{aligned}
V_B &= (3\Delta_{12} + 1.6\Delta_{22} - 1.8\Delta_{32})/\Delta \\
&= (0 + 1.6 \times -1.05 - 1.8 \times 0.5)/-0.59 \\
&= 4.37 \text{ V}
\end{aligned}$$

Similarly,

$$\begin{aligned}
V_D &= (0 + 1.6 \times -0.5 - 1.8 \times 0.8)/-0.59 \\
&= 3.79 \text{ V}
\end{aligned}$$

Then,

$$I_{BD} = (V_B - V_D)G_{BD} = 0.58 \times 0.5 = 0.29 \text{ A}$$

Example 2.5

When a null condition only is required, a cofactor of the determinant Δ of the immittance-matrix is alone sufficient. As this is one order less than Δ, it is likely to be easy to evaluate, as illustrated by Fig. 2-29.

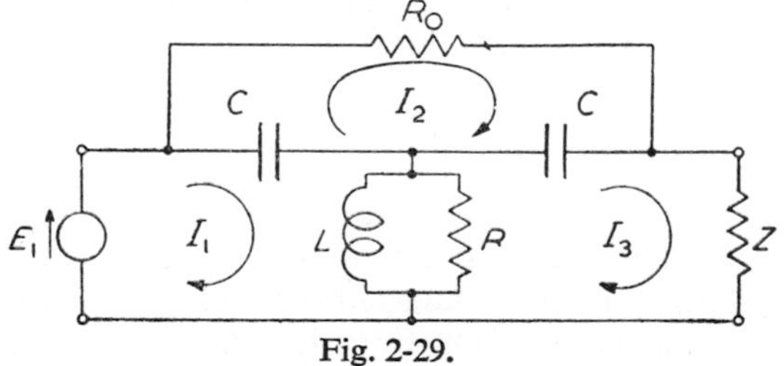

Fig. 2-29.

By Cramer's rule,

$$I_3 = E_1\Delta_{13}/\Delta$$

where Δ is the determinant of the mesh-impedance matrix,

$$\Delta = \begin{vmatrix} Z_{11} & Z_{12} & Z_{13} \\ Z_{21} & Z_{22} & Z_{23} \\ Z_{31} & Z_{32} & Z_{33} \end{vmatrix}$$

and

$$\Delta_{13} = \begin{vmatrix} Z_{21} & Z_{22} \\ Z_{31} & Z_{32} \end{vmatrix}$$

where

$$\begin{aligned} Z_{21} &= Z_{32} = -1/sC \\ Z_{22} &= R_0 + 2/sC \\ Z_{31} &= -1/[(1/R) + (1/sL)] = -sLR/(R + sL) \end{aligned}$$

$I_3 = 0$ when

$$\Delta_{13} = Z_{21}Z_{32} - Z_{31}Z_{22} = 0$$

or,

$$\frac{R}{s^2C^2} + \frac{L}{sC^2} + sLRR_0 + \frac{2LR}{C} = 0$$

For $s = j\omega$, this becomes

$$-\frac{R}{\omega^2C^2} - j\frac{L}{\omega C^2} + j\omega LRR_0 + \frac{2LR}{C} = 0$$

whence, by setting real parts and imaginary parts separately to zero,

$$\begin{aligned} L &= 1/2\omega^2C \\ R &= 1/\omega^2C^2R_0 \end{aligned}$$

A comparison should be made with the approaches used in Examples 4.7 and 4.9, in Chapter 4.

Example 2.6. Transistor equivalent-circuit calculations

The transistor exemplifies a network that violates the reciprocity theorem (Chapter 3, sect. 2.1.2). For operation under approximately linear (*small signal*) conditions, however, it may be represented in the form of a T or Π network of passive elements in association with an e.m.f. or current-source that is a function of the input current (to the base electrode), as indicated in Chapter 4, sect. 2.5.

The graph of a T-network (basically a three-branch four-node star) with source and load contains two loops but three node-pairs; that for a Π-network (basically a three-branch three-node delta) with source and load contains two node-pairs but three loops. Therefore, mesh-current analysis is more economical for the T-network, and node-datum voltage analysis for the Π-network.

For low-frequencies, at least, a transistor is more commonly represented in the T-form, conventionally with a current-source as the active element as exemplified by Fig. 2-30(a). But a current-source is ill-adapted to the voltage-law equations of mesh-current analysis. It is therefore an advantage to make the simple transformation into an equivalent e.m.f. source, as illustrated in Fig. 2-30(b) with reference to analysis of the common-collector (*emitter-follower*) circuit arrangement.

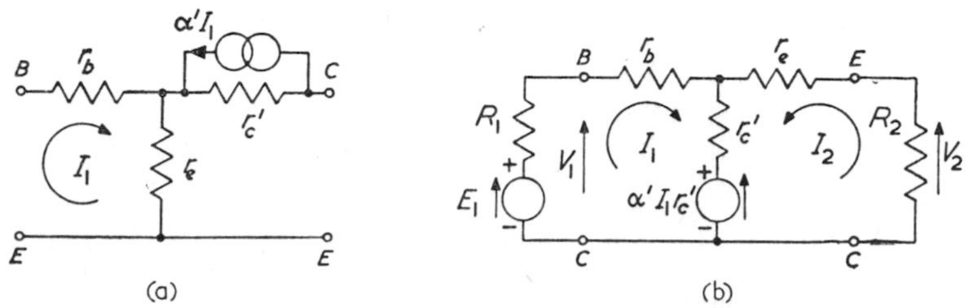

Fig. 2-30. (a) Transistor common-emitter equivalent circuit. (b) A common-collector equivalent circuit based on (a), but with the current-source $\alpha' I_1$, r_c' transformed for convenience in mesh analysis.

In Fig. 2-30(b), the mesh-currents are oriented according to the convention now usual for the matrix analysis of four-terminal or two-port networks, including transistors (see Chapter 4, sect. 2.1). Then,

$$(R_1 + r_b + r_c')I_1 + I_2 r_c' = E_1 - \alpha' I_1 r_c'$$

and (2.117)

$$(R_2 + r_e + r_c')I_2 + r_c' I_1 = -\alpha' I_1 r_c'$$

The equivalent T-parameters for a transistor are, however, usually specified with reference to the common-base circuit arrangement. While r_b and r_e are shared by both arrangements, the current amplification factor α' and collector resistance r_c' for the common-emitter arrangement must be calculated from the corresponding common-base parameters through the relations

$$\alpha' = \alpha/(1 - \alpha)$$

and (2.118)

$$r_c' = r_c(1 - \alpha)$$

Making these substitutions in eqns. (2.117), simplifying and re-arranging in matrix form,

$$\begin{bmatrix} R_{11} & R_{12} \\ R_{21} & R_{22} \end{bmatrix} \cdot \begin{bmatrix} I_1 \\ I_2 \end{bmatrix} = \begin{bmatrix} E_1 \\ 0 \end{bmatrix} \tag{2.119}$$

where

$$\begin{aligned} R_{11} &= R_1 + r_b + r_c \\ R_{12} &= r_c(1-\alpha) \\ R_{21} &= r_c \\ R_{22} &= R_2 + r_e + r_c(1-\alpha) \end{aligned}$$

Note that $R_{12} \neq R_{21}$, which contrasts with the properties of a reciprocal network composed of normal linear, bilateral* resistances (or in general, immittances).

The determinant of the R-matrix is

$$\begin{aligned} \Delta &= R_{11}R_{22} - R_{21}R_{12} \\ &= [R_1 + r_b][R_2 + r_e + r_c(1-\alpha)] + r_c(R_2 + r_e) \end{aligned}$$

and by Cramer's rule the solutions are

$$I_1 = E_1\Delta_{11}/\Delta = E_1R_{22}/\Delta$$

and

$$I_2 = E_1\Delta_{12}/\Delta = -E_1R_{21}/\Delta$$

The current-ratio is therefore

$$\begin{aligned} I_2/I_1 &= -R_{21}/R_{22} \\ &= -r_c/[R_2 + r_e + r_c(1-\alpha)] \end{aligned} \tag{2.120}$$

The negative sign implies that the true direction of I_2 is the reverse of that assumed.

The input current I_1 is

$$\begin{aligned} I_1 &= E_1R_{22}/\Delta \\ &= \frac{E_1[R_2 + r_e + r_c(1-\alpha)]}{[R_1 + r_b][R_2 + r_e + r_c(1-\alpha)] + r_c(R_2 + r_e)} \end{aligned}$$

Then, putting $R_1 = 0$ so that $V_1 = E_1$, the transistor input resistance is

$$R_{in} = \frac{V_1}{I_1} = r_b + \frac{r_c(R_2 + r_e)}{R_2 + r_e + r_c(1-\alpha)} \tag{2.121}$$

The voltage gain can then be written as

$$\begin{aligned} V_2/V_1 &= -I_2R_2/I_1R_{in} \\ &= \frac{r_cR_2}{R_2 + r_e + r_c(1-\alpha)} \cdot \frac{R_2 + r_e + r_c(1-\alpha)}{r_b[R_2 + r_e + r_c(1-\alpha)] + r_c(R_2 + r_e)} \\ &= \frac{r_cR_2}{r_b[R_2 + r_e + r_c(1-\alpha)] + r_c(r_2 + r_e)} \end{aligned} \tag{2.122}$$

* If the term linear is meant to include currents and voltages over the range $-\infty$ to $+\infty$, the qualification bilateral becomes superfluous.

Finally, the output resistance of the transistor at terminals *E-C* may be calculated by removing R_2, reducing E_1 to zero while leaving terminals *B-C* closed by R_1, and regarding V_2 as an externally applied voltage. The matrix equation then becomes

$$\begin{bmatrix} R_{11} & R_{12} \\ R_{21} & R_{22} \end{bmatrix} \cdot \begin{bmatrix} I_1 \\ I_2 \end{bmatrix} = \begin{bmatrix} 0 \\ V_2 \end{bmatrix} \tag{2.123}$$

which gives

$$I_2 = V_2 \Delta_{22}/\Delta, \text{ where } \Delta \text{ excludes } R_2.$$

Then,

$$\begin{aligned} R_{out} &= V_2/I_2 \\ &= \frac{[R_1 + r_b][r_e + r_c(1-\alpha)] + r_c r_e}{R_1 + r_b + r_c} \\ &= r_e + \frac{r_c(1-\alpha)(R_1 + r_b)}{R_1 + r_b + r_c} \end{aligned} \tag{2.124}$$

General formulae such as eqns. (2.121), (2.122) and (2.124) are more useful for reference than for practical calculations. These are more commonly made by substituting numerical values directly into the Kirchhoff-law equations appropriate to the particular problem. While approximations are usually justified by the wide divergence in parameter values, care is nevertheless necessary in their choice. This is illustrated by the following example of the common-collector circuit.

Typical common-base parameters are $r_b = 500\Omega$, $r_e = 20\Omega$, $r_c = 1\text{M}\Omega$, and $\alpha = 0.98$. Let $R_1 = 5{,}000\Omega$ and $R_2 = 500\Omega$. Then, to four figures,

$$\begin{aligned} R_{11} &= R_1 + r_b + r_c = 1.006 \times 10^6 \\ R_{12} &= r_c(1-\alpha) = 2 \times 10^4 \\ R_{21} &= r_c = 10^6 \\ R_{22} &= R_2 + r_e + r_c(1-\alpha) = 2.052 \times 10^4 \end{aligned}$$

The determinant of the *R*-matrix in equation (2.119) is therefore

$$\begin{aligned} \Delta &= R_{11}R_{22} - R_{21}R_{12} \\ &= 10^{10}(2.064 - 2.000) \\ &= 6.4 \times 10^8 \end{aligned}$$

Since in this case Δ is the difference between two nearly equal quantities, great errors can result from indiscriminate approximations. For example, $R_1 + r_b$ is only 0.5% of r_c, and $R_2 + r_e$ is only 2.5% of

$r_c(1 - \alpha)$. But if $R_1 + r_b$ and $R_2 + r_e$ were neglected on this basis, the entirely fallacious result $\Delta = 0$ would be obtained.

The numerical solution might proceed as follows, using $\Delta = 6.4 \times 10^8$:

Current gain

$$\frac{I_2}{I_1} = \frac{\Delta_{12}}{\Delta_{11}} = -\frac{R_{21}}{R_{22}} = -48.7$$

Voltage gain, relative to E_1

$$\frac{V_2}{E_1} = \frac{-I_2R_2}{E_1} = -\frac{\Delta_{12}R_2}{\Delta} = \frac{R_{21}R_2}{\Delta} = 0.781$$

Transistor base-collector input resistance

$$R_{in} = \frac{E_1}{I_1} - R_1 = \frac{\Delta}{\Delta_{11}} - R_1 = 2.61 \times 10^4 \text{ ohms}$$

Transistor voltage gain

$$\frac{V_2}{V_1} = \frac{-I_2R_2}{I_1R_{in}} = 48.7 \times \frac{R_2}{R_{in}} = 0.932$$

Transistor emitter-collector output resistance

Reducing E_1 to zero, removing R_2 and applying an e.m.f. E_2 in its place:

$$I_2 = E_2\Delta_{22}/\Delta,$$

and

$$R_{out} = \frac{E_2}{I_2} = \frac{\Delta}{\Delta_{22}} = \frac{\Delta}{R_{11}} = 636 \text{ ohms.}$$

Example 2.7. Mesh-current analysis of a common-emitter transistor circuit with parallel-series or bridge feedback

The graph shown in Fig. 2-31(c) has 7 nodes (N) and 9 branches (B), and the links (L) and tree-branches (B_t) are $L = B - N + 1 = 3$ and $B_t = B - L = 6$. Thus, 3 loop-current or 6 nodal-voltage equations are required. However, if nodes 1, 2, and 7 are regarded as superfluous, the nodal-voltage equations also reduce to 3.

In Fig. 2-31(d), which shows the network re-arranged for mesh-current analysis, the e.m.f. generator E_2, r_c' replaces the less convenient current-generator $\alpha' I_1$, r_c' which appears in Fig. 2-31(b).

Let $R_1 = 1{,}000\Omega$, $R_2 = 100\Omega$, $R_3 = 10{,}000\Omega$, $R_4 = 500\Omega$, and $R_5 = 10{,}000\Omega$. Typical common-base parameters for the transistor are

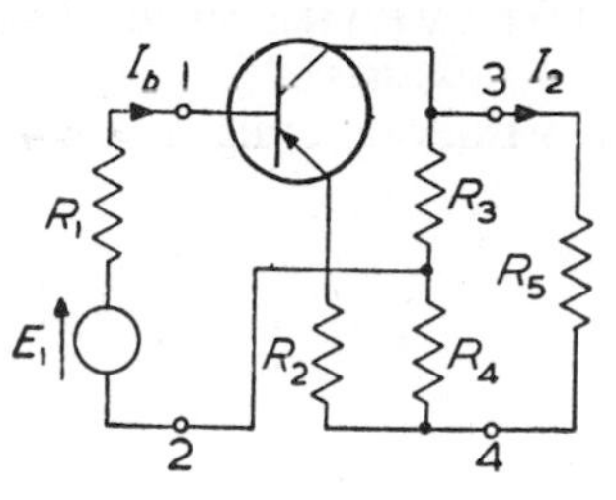

(a) Basic circuit

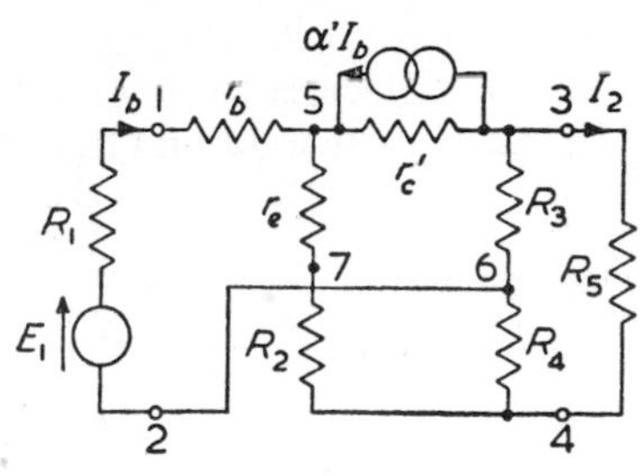

(b) Equivalent circuit

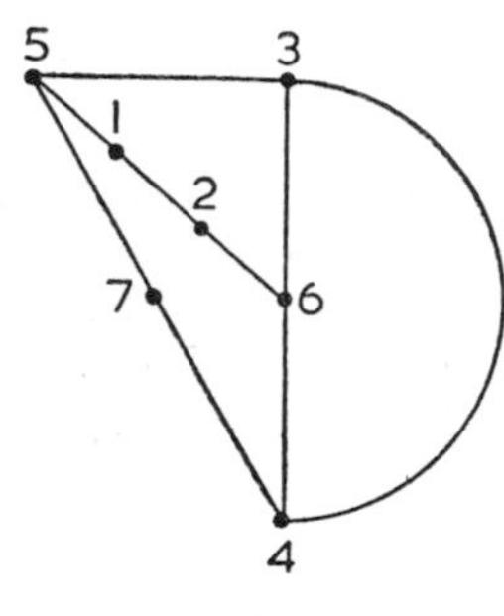

(c) Graph

(d) Network for mesh-analysis

Fig. 2-31.

$r_e = 20\Omega$, $r_b = 500\Omega$, $r_c = 1\text{M}\Omega$, and $\alpha = 0.98$. The parameters r_c' and $\alpha' I_b$ which replace r_c and αI_b in the common-emitter arrangement are then

$$r_c' = r_c(1 - \alpha) = 2 \times 10^4\Omega$$
$$\alpha' I_b = I_b\alpha/(1 - \alpha) = 49 I_b$$

Referring now to Fig. 2-31(d),

$$E_2 = \alpha' r_c' I_b = \alpha r_c I_b = 98 \times 10^4 I_b$$
$$r_c' = 2 \times 10^4\Omega$$
$$r_1 = r_b + R_1 = 1{,}500\Omega$$
$$r_2 = r_e + R_2 = 120\Omega$$
$$R_3 = R_5 = 10^4\Omega \quad \text{and} \quad R_4 = 500\Omega$$

Then,

$$\begin{bmatrix} R_{11} & R_{12} & R_{13} \\ R_{21} & R_{22} & R_{23} \\ R_{31} & R_{32} & R_{33} \end{bmatrix} \cdot \begin{bmatrix} I_1 \\ I_2 \\ I_3 \end{bmatrix} = \begin{bmatrix} E_1 - E_2 \\ 0 \\ -E_1 \end{bmatrix}$$

where

$$\begin{aligned}
R_{11} &= r_1 + r_c' + R_3 &&= 31.5 \times 10^3 \\
R_{22} &= R_3 + R_4 + R_5 &&= 20.5 \times 10^3 \\
R_{33} &= r_1 + r_2 + R_4 &&= 2.12 \times 10^3 \\
R_{12} &= R_{21} = -R_3 &&= -10 \times 10^3 \\
R_{13} &= R_{31} = -r_1 &&= -1.5 \times 10^3 \\
R_{23} &= R_{32} = -R_4 &&= -0.5 \times 10^3
\end{aligned}$$

To obtain both the input and output currents I_b and I_c for Fig. 2-31(a), it is necessary to solve for the three mesh-currents, since $I_b = I_1 - I_3$. It is therefore worth considering solution by matrix inversion, for this gives the three solutions simultaneously in the form

$$[I] = [Z]^{-1} \cdot [E]$$

Scaling each element in $[R]$ by 10^{-3} and writing $[R_s]$ to denote the scaled matrix,

$$[R_s] = \begin{bmatrix} 31.5 & -10 & -1.5 \\ -10 & 20.5 & -0.5 \\ -1.5 & -0.5 & 2.12 \end{bmatrix}$$

Then, following the procedure of sect. 2.5.3,

$$[R_s]^t = \begin{bmatrix} 31.5 & -10 & -1.5 \\ -10 & 20.5 & -0.5 \\ -1.5 & -0.5 & 2.12 \end{bmatrix}$$

Note that the pattern of numerical elements is unchanged by transposition since $R_{12} = R_{21}$, $R_{13} = R_{31}$, and $R_{23} = R_{32}$.

$$[R_s]_c^t = [C] = \begin{bmatrix} C_{11} & C_{12} & C_{13} \\ C_{21} & C_{22} & C_{23} \\ C_{31} & C_{32} & C_{33} \end{bmatrix} = \begin{bmatrix} 43.3 & 22 & 35.8 \\ 22 & 64.6 & 30.8 \\ 35.8 & 30.8 & 546 \end{bmatrix}$$

where, for example,

$$C_{23} = -[31.5 \times -0.5 - (-1.5 \times -10)] = 30.75$$

The determinant Δ_s of the scaled matrix $[R_s]$ is

$$\Delta_s = \begin{vmatrix} 31.5 & -10 & -1.5 \\ -10 & 20.5 & -0.5 \\ -1.5 & -0.5 & 2.12 \end{vmatrix} = 1{,}090$$

Dividing each element in $[C]$ by Δ_s gives $[R_s]^{-1}$, and then the scaled currents are expressed by

$$[I_s] = [R_s]^{-1} \cdot [E]$$

The currents are restored to their correct proportions by dividing each element in [E] by 10^3, giving

$$\begin{bmatrix} I_1 \\ \\ I_2 \\ \\ I_3 \end{bmatrix} = \begin{bmatrix} \frac{39.8}{10^3} & \frac{20.2}{10^3} & \frac{32.9}{10^3} \\ \\ \frac{20.2}{10^3} & \frac{59.4}{10^3} & \frac{28.3}{10^3} \\ \\ \frac{32.9}{10^3} & \frac{28.3}{10^3} & \frac{501}{10^3} \end{bmatrix} \cdot \begin{bmatrix} \frac{E_1 - E_2}{10^3} \\ \\ 0 \\ \\ -\frac{E_1}{10^3} \end{bmatrix}$$

Multiplying the admittance and e.m.f. matrices, and removing the brackets and simplifying:

$$I_1 = 6.9E_1 - 39.8E_2 \ \ \mu\text{A}$$
$$I_2 = -8.1E_1 - 20.2E_2 \ \ \mu\text{A}$$
$$I_3 = -468E_1 - 32.9E_2 \ \ \mu\text{A}$$

For I_b in μA, $E_2 = 0.98I_b$. Then,

$$I_b = I_1 - I_3 = 475E_1 - 6.9 \times 0.98I_b \ \ \mu\text{A}$$

whence

$$I_b = 475E_1/7.76 = 61.1E_1 \ \ \mu\text{A}$$

and

$$E_2 = 0.98I_b = 59.9E_1 \ \ \mu\text{V}$$

Substituting for E_2,

$$I_2 = -1.218E_1 \ \ \mu\text{A}$$
$$= -1.218E_1 \times 10^{-3} \ \ \text{A}$$

The voltage-gain relative to E_1 is

$$V_2/E_1 = -I_2R_5/E_1 = -1.218 \times 10^{-3} \times 10^4 = -12.18$$

The input resistance at terminals 1-2 is

$$R_{in} = (E_1/I_b) - R_1$$
$$= 15{,}400 \text{ ohms.}$$

This is much higher than the order to be expected without feedback, but is consistent with the high total amount of negative feedback present.

Example 2.8. An application of Bartlett's bisection theorem.

In Fig. 2–32 is shown an equivalence of special importance in the design of lattice filters. In that case, Z may represent equalised loss resistances included in Z_x and Z_y. According to the equivalence, these equalised resistances may be extracted from the lattice and absorbed into the terminating resistances, leaving a lattice network whose behaviour is wholly reactive or non-dissipative.

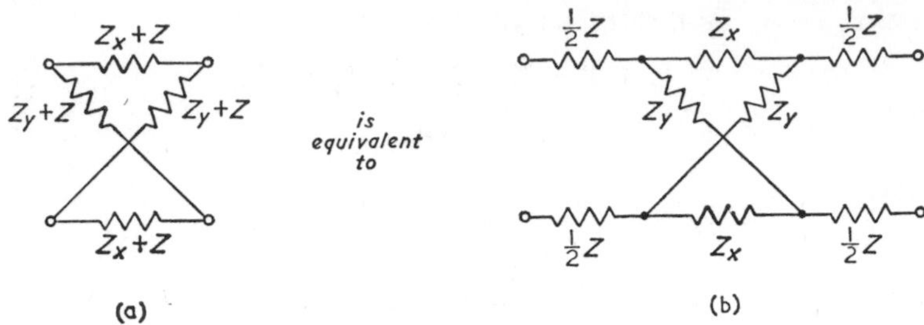

Fig. 2-32.

The equivalence may be verified by equating impedances at either pair of terminals under open-circuit and short-circuit conditions at the other. But the short-circuit impedance cannot be found in the case of Fig. 2-32(a) until the delta-star transformation has been applied to change its topology: this is evident when the network is drawn in the form of a bridge.

Bartlett's bisection theorem, however, affords a very simple proof of the equivalence. Applying eqns. (2.102) to Fig. 2-32(a) gives Fig. 2-33(a); but this may be re-drawn as in Fig. 2-33(b), in which the demarcated section is the equivalent of a lattice network of branches Z_x and Z_y. Fig. 2-33(b) is therefore equivalent to Fig. 2-32(b); but as Figs. 2-33(a) and (b) are both equivalent to Fig. 2-32(a), Figs. 2-32(a) and (b) must be equivalent.

The dual case is that of a lattice network in which the impedance Z

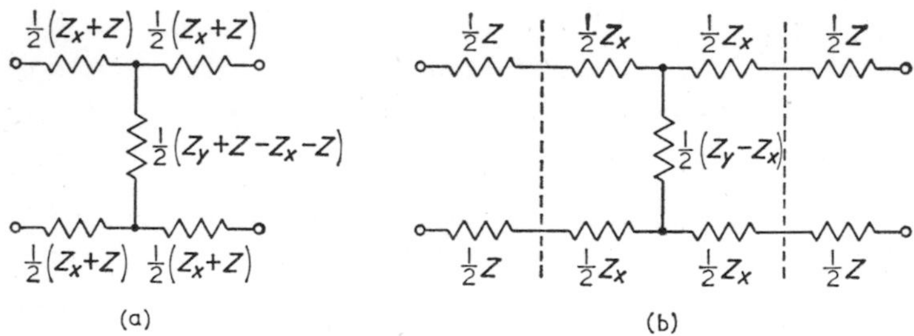

Fig. 2-33.

is connected in parallel with Z_x and Z_y. This arrangement is equivalently represented by a lattice of branches Z_x and Z_y, with an impedance Z in parallel with both the input and output terminals. In this case the proof is furnished through the equivalent O-network (balanced Π), a half-section of which is shown in Fig. 2-34(a). Working in admittances and applying first a short-circuit and then an open-circuit at the bisection $a-a'$, Bartlett's theorem gives

$$Y_x + Y = Y_q + 2/Z_p = Y_q + 2Y_p$$

and

$$Y_y + Y = Y_q$$

whence

$$Y_q = Y_y + Y$$

and

$$Y_p = \tfrac{1}{2}(Y_x + Y - Y_y - Y)$$
$$= \tfrac{1}{2}(Y_x - Y_y)$$

The equivalent O-network may therefore be represented as in Fig. 2-34(b). But as the demarcated section is the equivalent of a lattice network of branches $Z_x = 1/Y_x$ and $Z_y = 1/Y_y$, the stated equivalence is proved.

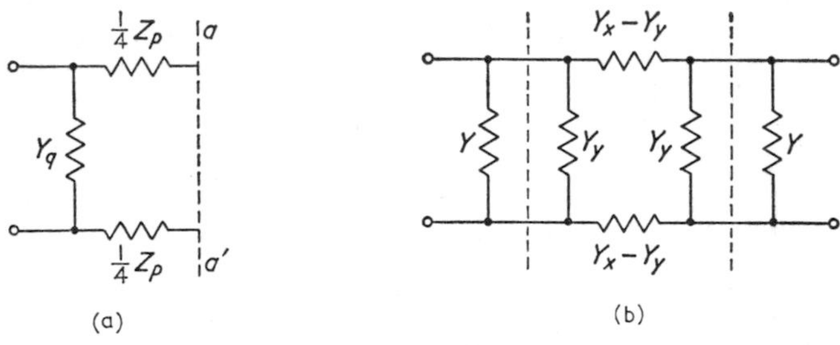

Fig. 2-34.

Example 2-9.

An impedance Z is extracted from each of the four arms of a symmetrical lattice network, and Z is placed in series with one of the input and also one of the output terminals of the network. Show that the resulting arrangement is electrically identical with the original lattice.

Hence indicate how this re-arrangement might be used to obtain the equivalent T-network for a given symmetrical lattice network.

(*I.E.E., Part* 3, *Advanced Electrical Engineering*)

For the first part, see Example 2.8. Note, however, that whereas the lattice is a balanced structure, the equivalent structure for Z extracted as stated is not formally balanced. It is in order to preserve the structural balance that the author has derived the equivalence in terms of the H-network (balanced-T).

The re-arranged network has the form of Fig. 2-35(a). This reduces to Fig. 2-35(b) when $Z = Z_x$. But Fig. 2-35(a) is the equivalent of a lattice network of branches $(Z_x - Z) + Z = Z_x$ and $(Z_y - Z) + Z = Z_y$. Therefore, Fig. 2-35(b) is the equivalent of a lattice network of branches Z_x and Z_y.

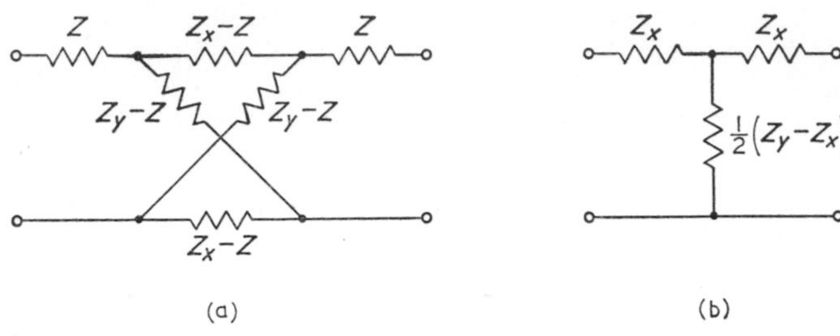

Fig. 2-35.

The equivalence between Fig. 2-35(b) and a lattice network is limited in the sense that, while the T-network can operate in an unbalanced system, i.e. a system grounded on one side or having otherwise one common connection, the lattice cannot: the formal equivalent of the lattice is a symmetrical and balanced H-network, the topology of which can be re-cast in the form of a T when unbalanced operation is required.

REFERENCES

1. CHENG, D. K.: *Analysis of Linear Systems* (Addison-Wesley Publishing Company Inc., Mass., U.S.A., 1959).
2. DAY, W. D.: *Introduction to Laplace Transforms for Radio and Electronic Engineers* (Iliffe and Sons Ltd., London; Interscience Publishers, Inc., New York, 1960).
3. TROPPER, A. MARY: *Matrix Theory for Electrical Engineering Students* (George G. Harrap and Co. Ltd., London, 1962).
4. AUSTEN STIGANT, S.: *The Elements of Determinants, Matrices and Tensors for Engineers* (Macdonald, London, 1959).
5. MARGENEAU, H. and MURPHY, G. M.: *The Mathematics of Physics and Chemistry* (D. Van Nostrand Company, Inc., New York, 1943).
6. VAN VALKENBURG, M. E.: *Introduction to Modern Network Synthesis* (John Wiley and Sons, Inc., New York, 1960).
7. MORTLOCK, J. R. and HUMPHREY DAVIES, M. W.: *Power System Analysis* (Chapman and Hall Ltd., London, 1952).
8. ROGERS, F. E.: *The Theory of Networks in Electrical Communication and Other Fields* (Macdonald, London; D. Van Nostrand, New York, 1957).
9. BARTLETT, A. C.: *The Theory of Electrical Artificial Lines and Filters* (Chapman and Hall Ltd., London, 1930, p. 28).

3

ON THEOREMS, DUALITY AND OTHER PRINCIPLES

1. INTRODUCTION

It has been shown that the complexity of a network graph is reducible with the aid of simple theorems; that a graph may be transformed into a more convenient topology by means of equivalences; and that relationships for techniques based on the alternatives of loop-current and nodal-voltage analysis are generally dual, which aids the assimilation of ideas and the prediction of results. This chapter is devoted to enlarging on such theorems and principles as are complementary to the fundamental Kirchhoff-law procedures.

2. THE THEOREMS

These are divisible into fundamental ones, implicit in the generalised solutions of the Kirchhoff-law equations, and subsidiary ones, which are corollaries appropriate to particular network arrangements or kinds of problem. Both classes have been illustrated extensively by the author in another work.[1]

2.1 THE FUNDAMENTAL THEOREMS

These are considered to be the *Superposition* and *Reciprocity* theorems, the *Thévenin-Helmholtz* theorem already demonstrated in Chapter 2, sect. 5, and the *Compensation* theorem.

2.1.1 *The superposition theorem*

When several e.m.f. sources act in a network of linear elements, the current in any branch is the sum of the currents which would flow in that branch due to the independent action of each e.m.f.

By duality, an equivalent statement applies to the voltage across any branch due to the action of several current sources. Thus, for the kth. branch of an arbitrary linear network the solutions have the dual forms

$$I_k = I_{k(1)} + I_{k(2)} \cdots + I_{k(n)} \tag{3.1}$$

and

$$V_k = V_{k(1)} + V_{k(2)} + \cdots + V_{k(n)} \tag{3.2}$$

where $I_{k(1)} \ldots I_{k(n)}$ are the currents due respectively to e.m.f. sources $E_1 \ldots E_n$ when acting alone, while $V_{k(1)} \ldots V_{k(n)}$ are the voltages due respectively to current sources $I_1 \ldots I_n$ when acting alone. Eqns. (3.1) and (3.2) are readily verified by reference to eqns. (2.90) and (2.91), in which each term represents the contribution of current or voltage due respectively to each e.m.f. or current source alone.

Simple practical interpretations of the superposition theorem are illustrated by Fig. 3-1.

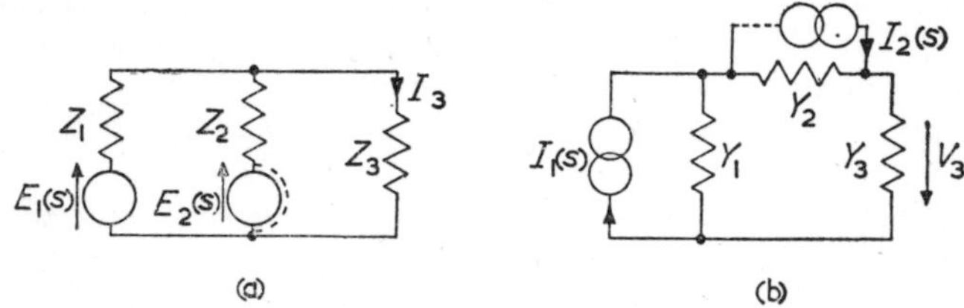

Fig. 3-1. Illustrating the superposition theorem.

In Fig. 3-1(a), let $I_{3(1)}$ be the current in Z_3 due to $E_1(s)$ alone, $E_2(s)$ being at the time reduced to zero and bridged as indicated, and let $I_{3(2)}$ be similarly the current due to $E_2(s)$.

When $E_2(s)$ is zero, the voltage across the parallel combination of Z_2 and Z_3 is, by inspection,

$$V_{(1)} = E_1(s)\,\frac{Z_2Z_3/(Z_2+Z_3)}{Z_1 + Z_2Z_3/(Z_2+Z_3)}$$

and then

$$I_{3(1)} = \frac{V_{(1)}}{Z_3} = \frac{E_1(s)Z_2}{Z_1(Z_2+Z_3)+Z_2Z_3} \tag{3.3}$$

By symmetry, $I_{3(2)}$ may be stated merely by interchanging symbols in eqn. (3.3), which gives

$$I_{3(2)} = \frac{E_2(s)Z_1}{Z_2(Z_1+Z_3)+Z_1Z_3} \tag{3.4}$$

The total current, according to the theorem, is thus

$$I_3 = I_{3(1)} + I_{3(2)}$$
$$= \frac{E_1(s)Z_2 + E_2(s)Z_1}{Z_1(Z_2 + Z_3) + Z_2Z_3} \quad (3.5)$$

In the case of a current-source, its circuit must be regarded as open when the source is rendered inactive. Thus in Fig. 3-1(b), when $I_2(s)$ is zero and its circuit is opened as indicated, the current traversing the series combination of Y_2 and Y_3 is

$$I_{(1)} = I_1(s) \frac{Y_2Y_3/(Y_2 + Y_3)}{Y_1 + Y_2Y_3/(Y_2 + Y_3)}$$

and then

$$V_{3(1)} = \frac{I_{(1)}}{Y_3} = \frac{I_1(s)Y_2}{Y_1(Y_2 + Y_3) + Y_2Y_3} \quad (3.6)$$

Again by symmetry,

$$V_{3(2)} = \frac{I_2(s)Y_1}{Y_2(Y_1 + Y_3) + Y_1Y_3} \quad (3.7)$$

Eqns. (3.6) and (3.7) are the duals of eqns. (3.3) and (3.4). That Fig. 3-1(b) is the dual of Fig. 3-1(a) might have been recognised from the topology (as discussed in sect. 3), and eqns. (3.6) and (3.7) might have been predicted from the knowledge of eqns. (3.3) and (3.4).

One advantage of the superposition theorem for multi-source problems is the simplicity with which current or voltage directions are defined: the direction of each superposed current or voltage is decided by that of each corresponding source. For example, reversal of $E_2(s)$ in Fig. 3-1(a) would reverse $I_{3(2)}$, giving clearly a subtraction rather than an addition of the superposed currents.

2.1.2 *The reciprocity theorem*

Let the current at a point y in a network be due to an e.m.f. at a point x. Then, provided the network comprises linear and bilateral elements only, the same current would flow at the point x if the e.m.f. were transferred to the point y.

This statement is consistent with the symmetry of the network determinant. Referring to eqn. (2.90), the current in the mth. mesh of a generalised linear network due to one e.m.f. in the kth. mesh is

$$I_m = E_k\Delta_{km}/\Delta$$

Similarly, when the e.m.f. and current positions are interchanged,

$$I_k = E_m\Delta_{mk}/\Delta$$

But for a bilateral linear system, $\Delta_{km} = \Delta_{mk}$ and therefore $I_k = I_m$ when $E_m = E_k$.

The theorem is illustrated by Fig. 3-2, in which the equality of currents for the two arrangements is easily verified. It is striking to evaluate a numerical example in which Z_1, Z_2 and Z_3 are resistances of widely different values, such as 1,000Ω, 10Ω and 1Ω.

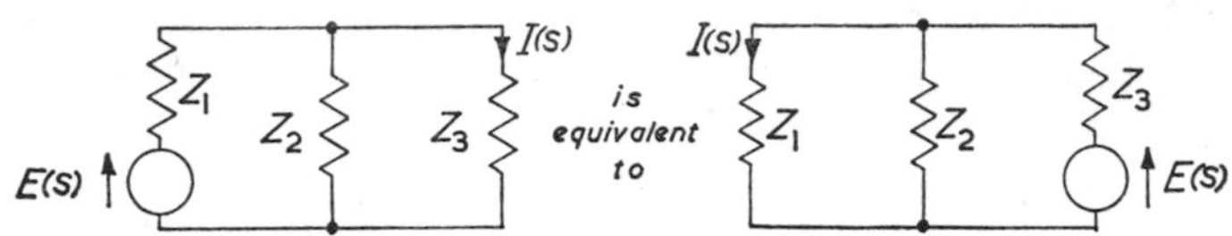

Fig. 3-2. Illustrating the reciprocity theorem.

The reciprocity theorem is of great fundamental importance, for it has implications in all network calculations. Nevertheless, it is consciously invoked much more often as a powerful premise for theoretical reasoning than as an expedient for the practical solution of a network (as compared, for example, with the Thévenin or superposition theorems). It is important to note that the theorem is valid only for an interchange in the points of action of e.m.f. and current: it is not valid for an interchange that includes also the impedances existing at the points concerned, unless they happen to be equal. Thus, the theorem cannot be expected to apply exactly to a physical network, in which transference of the physical source is accompanied by transference of its intrinsic impedance.

Violation of the reciprocity theorem is characteristic of a network containing thermionic valves, rectifiers, transistors, etc. It is shown in Chapter 4, sect. 2.5, however, that such a non-reciprocal network can be resolved into a normal reciprocal one, plus an e.m.f. or current source, which is additional to the source of excitation but a function of it.

2.1.3 *The Thévenin-Helmholtz theorem*

This and its dual, Norton's theorem, have been illustrated adequately in the context of topology in Chapter 2, sects. 5 and 6. The only extension necessary is a proof, which is now readily derived from the principle of superposition.

Consider an active network having a pair of output terminals, similar to the active set A in Fig. 2-13. Let $V_o(s)$ denote the arbitrary open-circuit output voltage, and $Z_o(s)$ denote the impedance between the output terminals when all the internal sources are reduced to zero. Now suppose that an external e.m.f. identical with $V_o(s)$ is caused to act in opposition to $V_o(s)$, in series with the network terminals. The total voltage $V_o(s) + (-V_o(s))$ is zero, so that the current traversing the external circuit if then closed by a short-circuit (or any finite impedance) must also be zero. But if the network were rendered passive by reducing all sources within it to zero, the current in the external short-circuit due to the e.m.f. $-V_o(s)$ alone would be $-V_o(s)/Z_o(s)$. Therefore, in order for the current to be zero when the network is active as well, the superposed current due to it alone must be $V_o(s)/Z_o(s)$. The active network may therefore be represented by an equivalent simple generator of e.m.f. equal to $V_o(s)$ and intrinsic impedance $Z_o(s)$.

2.1.4 *The compensation theorem*

This also has been attributed to Helmholtz,[3] and is regarded here as fundamental because it is a direct inference from Kirchhoff's voltage-law, as illustrated by Fig. 3-3.

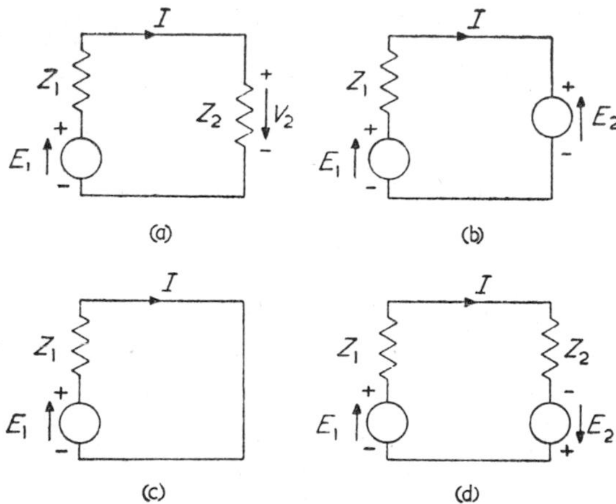

Fig. 3-3. Pertaining to the compensation theorem.

Referring to (a), the voltage-law equation $E_1 - IZ_1 - IZ_2 = 0$ is unaltered by the removal of Z_2, provided Z_2 is replaced as in (b) by an e.m.f. E_2 identical with V_2, where $V_2 = -IZ_2$. Similarly for (c), the equation $E_1 - IZ_1 = 0$ is unaltered by the addition of Z_2, provided an e.m.f. $E_2 = IZ_2$ is introduced as in (d), which gives $E_1 - IZ_1 - IZ_2 + IZ_2 = E_1 - IZ_1 = 0$ as before.

Since E_2 compensates either for the removal or addition of Z_2, the change in current in the actual circuit due to decreasing or increasing the impedance by Z_2 must be equal but opposite to the current that would be caused by E_2 acting alone in the modified circuit. Denoting the current due to E_2 by $I_{(2)}$, the change ΔI due, for example, to increasing the circuit impedance by Z_2, is

$$\begin{aligned}\Delta I &= -I_{(2)}\\ &= -IZ_2/(Z_1+Z_2)\\ &= -E_1\,Z_2/Z_1(Z_1+Z_2)\end{aligned}$$

What has been demonstrated above for a rudimentary circuit extends by superposition to any complex linear network, for which the following is a general statement of the compensation theorem:

If in a linear network a branch that carries a current I be altered an amount ΔZ, the current is changed everywhere by amounts corresponding to the currents which would result from an e.m.f. $-I\Delta Z$ acting independently in series with the modified branch.

2.2 A USEFUL SUBSIDIARY THEOREM: THE PARALLEL E.M.F. GENERATOR THEOREM AND ITS DUAL

This is a corollary to the superposition theorem, first recognised for its practical utility by Millman.[4] Many problems are solvable by it either directly or after simple modifications have been made.

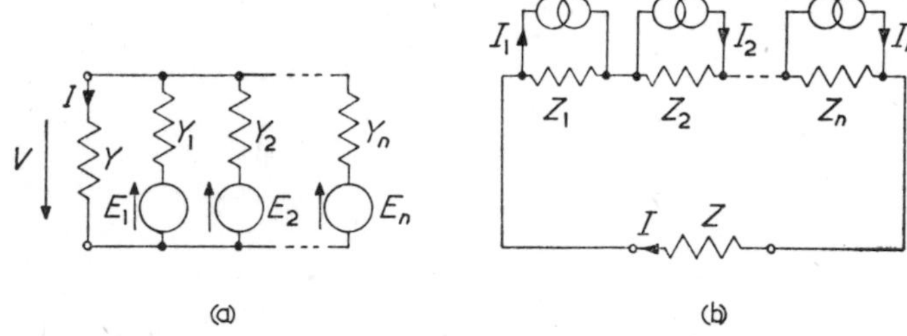

Fig. 3-4. (a) Arrangement conforming to the parallel e.m.f. generator theorem, and (b) to its dual.

In Fig. 3-4(a), let each generator be transformed into its constant-current equivalent. Then in terms of the corresponding constant-currents $I_1 \ldots I_n$,

$$V = (I_1 + I_2 + \cdots + I_n)/\Sigma Y$$

or

$$V = (E_1 Y_1 + E_2 Y_2 + \cdots + E_n Y_n)/\Sigma Y \tag{3.8}$$

where

$$\Sigma Y = Y + Y_1 + Y_2 + \cdots + Y_n$$

Eqn. (3.8) is an algebraic statement of the theorem.

By duality, Fig. 3-4(b) gives

$$I = (I_1 Z_1 + I_2 Z_2 + \cdots + I_n Z_n)/\Sigma Z \tag{3.9}$$

3. DUALITY

This section is an extension to the examples already given following the introduction in Chapter 1, sect. 2.3. In particular, it outlines formally the principles governing the construction of a dual network, and the interpretation of quantitative relationships between a given network and its dual.

3.1 THE REALISATION OF A DUAL NETWORK

The dual of a given network has a topology and distribution of sources such that its nodal-voltage (or loop-current) equations have an algebraic pattern identical with that of the loop-current (or nodal-voltage) equations for the given network. It has actual elements, sources, and variables that are, branch for branch, the duals of those in the given network, so that, regardless of complexity, the one set of equations is transformed into the other merely by the exchange of these dual parameters in corresponding terms. The first feature requires the graph of the dual network to be the dual of that for the given network, while the second requires a correlation between the individual branches in the two graphs.

The key to the topology of the dual graph lies in the dualities between tie-sets and cut-sets, links and tree branches, loops and node-pairs, and Kirchhoff's voltage and current laws.

For identical equation patterns, the number of branch voltages (or currents) in the dual network must equal the number of branch currents (or voltages) in the given network. Therefore, both networks must contain the same total number of branches. Moreover, by reference to Chapter 1, sect. 3.2, the number of branches to any tree of the dual graph must equal the number of links in the given graph and vice versa.

Let N, B, L, and B_t denote the nodes, branches, links, and tree-branches in the given network graph, and N', B', L', and B_t' those in the dual network graph. Then,

$$B' = B, \qquad L' = B_t \quad \text{and} \quad B_t' = L$$

By eqn. (1.43),

$$B_t = B - L = N - 1 \tag{3.10}$$

and

$$B_t' = B' - L' = N' - 1 \tag{3.11}$$

From eqn. (3.11),

$$N' = B_t' + 1 = L + 1 \tag{3.12}$$

Substituting then for L from eqn. (3.10),

$$N' = B + 2 - N \tag{3.13}$$

The dual graph, having by eqn. (3.12) one more node than the given graph has links, has therefore one more node than the given graph has loops.

For planar networks, loop-current and nodal-voltage analysis may take the forms of mesh-current and node-datum voltage analysis. The dual of a loop-current is a node-pair voltage, and the dual of a mesh-current is a node-datum voltage or simply a node-voltage, since the datum node may be assumed to be at zero potential. The dual of a mesh is therefore a node. This is confirmed also by eqns. (2.79)–(2.82), in which the sum of impedances forming the contour of a mesh is shown to have its dual in the sum of admittances meeting at a node. Thus, of the $n + 1$ nodes in the graph that is the dual of another having n meshes, the $(n + 1)$th. may be regarded as the datum node, while each of the remaining n nodes may be allotted to one mesh as its dual, as illustrated in Fig. 3-5.

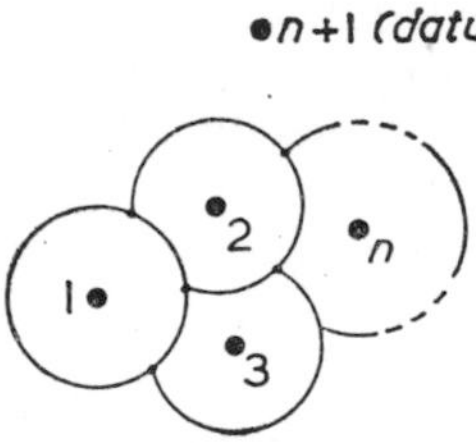

Fig. 3-5. Arbitrary system of meshes, and distribution of nodes in dual graph.

Consider now the example of Fig. 3-6(a). The voltage-law equation for mesh 1 is

$$Z_1I_1 + Z_2(I_1 - I_2) + Z_3(I_1 - I_3) = 0 \tag{3.14}$$

In Fig. 3-6(b), the node potentials, V_1, V_2, and V_3 are the duals of I_1, I_2, and I_3. Therefore, the current-law dual of eqn. (3.14) is realised by impressing voltages V_1, $V_1 - V_2$, and $V_1 - V_3$ on admittances Y_1, Y_2, and Y_3 to give

$$Y_1V_1 + Y_2(V_1 - V_2) + Y_3(V_1 - V_3) = 0 \tag{3.15}$$

Eqn. (3.15) is consistent with the node connections shown in Fig. 3-6(c); and since the other meshes are subject to the same reasoning, the complete dual graph must have the topology shown in Fig. 3-6(d).

Eqns. (3.14) and (3.15) may be generalised in the forms

$$Z_{k1}I_1 + Z_{k2}I_2 + \cdots + Z_{kk}I_k + \cdots + Z_{kn}I_n = 0 \tag{3.16}$$

and

$$Y_{k1}V_1 + Y_{k2}V_2 + \cdots + Y_{kk}V_k + \cdots + Y_{kn}V_n = 0 \tag{3.17}$$

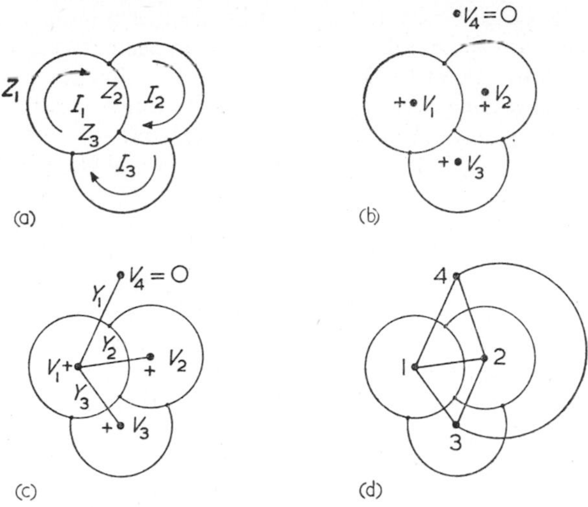

Fig. 3-6. Illustrating the evolution of a dual graph.

in which the sum of impedances Z_{kk} forming the contour of any mesh k has its dual in the sum of admittances Y_{kk} from every node including the datum to the kth. node, while an impedance of the form Z_{ik} representing the mutual branch between the ith. and kth. meshes has its dual in an admittance Y_{ik} linking the ith. and kth. nodes. This generalisation is consistent with the following general rule for constructing the dual of a given planar, and connected, network graph:

(1) Place one dot in each mesh of the given graph and one anywhere outside it to represent the nodes of the dual graph.
(2) Join each pair of dots in adjacent meshes by a line traversing the corresponding mutual branch.
(3) Join the external dot to each dot within every mesh that contributes to the periphery of the graph, by a line traversing the peripheral segment of the corresponding mesh.

This rule gives not only the topology of the dual graph but also the elements of the dual network; for the admittance represented by each line thus drawn is the dual of the impedance represented by the mesh-segment it traverses. Mutual inductance can be included by using the transformation explained in Chapter 2, sect. 5.2.3.

If the given graph is oriented with branch currents, the dual is oriented with branch voltages. The orientations must, however, be governed by conventions giving a term-by-term correspondence in signs between the equations for the dual and given networks (as in eqns. (3.16) and (3.17), for example). While the choice of direction to be taken as positive is arbitrary (a reversal of convention reversing all orientations based on it), the standardisation of node-potentials in the dual graph as positive relative to the datum seems apposite as a convention to correspond to the clockwise convention for positive mesh-currents in the given network. The construction rule may embrace the orientations according to the chosen convention.

A link from a positive node to the datum will be oriented with an arrow in the direction from node to datum, thus identifying fall in potential with orientation away from a node. Since this orientation is to correspond to clockwise flow for mesh-currents reckoned positive in the given network, any branch in the given network whose orientation is coincident with a clockwise mesh-current has its dual oriented away from the node that is the dual of the mesh concerned. This is illustrated by Fig. 3-7, in which (a) shows the orientations of branches cut by the construction lines, and (b) is the resultant oriented dual graph. The graphs in this case illustrate self-duality, for the topologies of the dual and given graphs are basically the same.

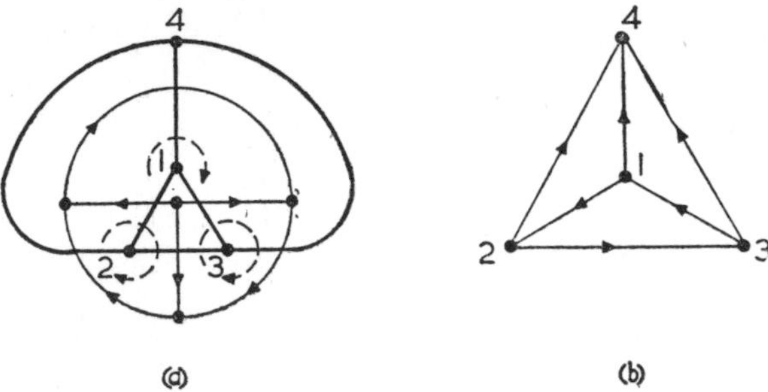

Fig. 3-7. The construction and orientation of a dual graph.

The construction of a dual network is illustrated in Fig. 3-8. The circuit (a) is that of a transistor Colpitts oscillator, in which the transistor is represented by an equivalent circuit incorporating a capacitor (C_3) to simulate in simplest form the complex intrinsic behaviour of the transistor at frequencies somewhat above the audio range (the representation is valid for frequencies of order 10–20 kc/s). The transistor is connected in the common-emitter circuit, and in terms of the common-base parameters,

$$R_1 = r_b,\ R_2 = r_e,\ G_3 = 1/r_c(1 - \alpha_0)$$
$$I_3 = \beta I_1 = \alpha_0 I_1/(1 - \alpha_0)$$
$$C_3 = C_c/(1 - \alpha_0)$$

where α_0 is the low-frequency common-base current-gain factor, and C_c is the total collector capacitance (diffusion capacitance plus collector transition-region capacitance).

In drawing the graph and finding its dual as in Fig. 3-8(b), the current-source I_3 is excluded from the loops since such a source implies an infinite impedance or open-loop condition (whereas an e.m.f. source implies a closed condition). The dual of I_3 is however readily introduced into the final dual network.

The oriented dual graph is shown in Fig. 3-8(c) and the actual dual network in (d). Each element in this is the dual of the element traversed by the relevant construction line in (b), and the e.m.f.-source E_3 introduced in series with R_3 is the dual of the current-source I_3 which appears in parallel with G_3 in (a). In the original network (a), the orientation of I_3 is fixed relative to I_1 by the properties of the transistor circuit. The orientations of E_3 and V_1 are similarly related to one another in the dual network, in which the arrow V_1 implies a fall in potential towards node 2 in accordance with the duality convention used. The arrow E_3 however indicates the direction of potential rise, since E_3 is a source (though a function of V_1).

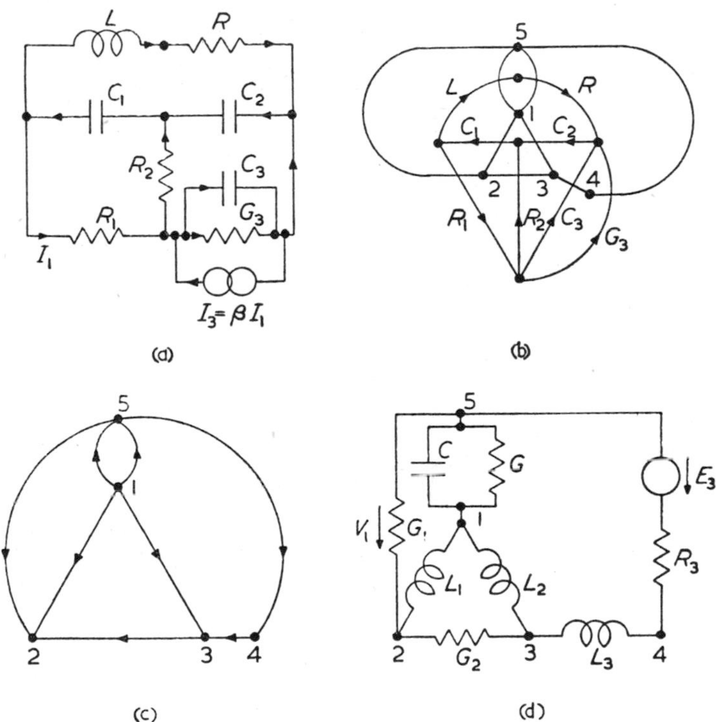

Fig. 3-8. Illustrating the construction of a dual network.

3.2 QUANTITATIVELY RELATED DUAL NETWORKS

Numerical values can be assigned to the elements in the dual network so that its solution is numerically equal to, or in a real ratio to, that for the given network; but in the dual units and under dual conditions. Fig. 3-9 provides a simple illustration.

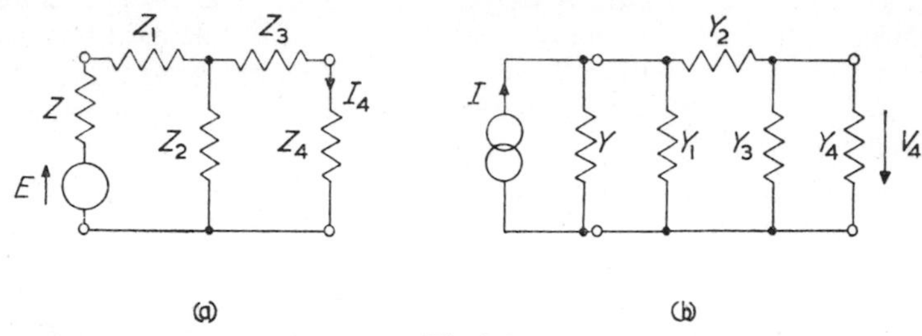

Fig. 3-9.

The networks (a) and (b) are duals, and

$$I_4 = EZ_2/[(Z_3 + Z_4)(Z + Z_1 + Z_2) + Z_2(Z + Z_1)] \tag{3.18}$$

while

$$V_4 = IY_2/[(Y_3 + Y_4)(Y + Y_1 + Y_2) + Y_2(Y + Y_1)] \tag{3.19}$$

The solution of eqn. (3.19) in volts is numerically equal to that for eqn. (3.18) in amps, provided I in amps is numerically the same as E in volts, and each admittance in mhos is numerically the same as its dual impedance in ohms and has the same argument if complex.

The numerical correspondence between dual networks need not, however, be restricted to an arithmetical identity. Each element in the given network is in a wholly real ratio to its dual in the dual network, as exemplified by C_1/L_1 and R_2/G_2 in Figs. 3-8(a) and (d). Moreover, in terms of mass (M) length (L) time (T) and charge (Q), the dimensions of inductance and capacitance are ML^2Q^{-2} and $Q^2M^{-1}L^{-2}T^2$, so that L/C has the dimensions $M^2L^4T^{-2}Q^{-4}$, which corresponds to resistance squared.

Let every pair of dual elements L, C and R, G be in the same ratio,

$$\frac{L}{C} = \frac{R}{G} = R_0^2 \tag{3.20}$$

Let $Z_{ik} = R_{ik} + sL_{ik} + 1/sC_{ik}$ denote any impedance element in $[Z]$ for the given network, and let $Y_{ik} = G'_{ik} + sC'_{ik} + 1/sL'_{ik}$ denote its dual admittance element in $[Y]$ for the dual network. Then, when

$$\frac{L_{ik}}{C'_{ik}} = \frac{R}{G'_{ik}} = \frac{L'_{ik}}{C_{ik}} = R_0^2 \tag{3.21}$$

the ratio Z_{ik}/Y_{ik} reduces to

$$Z_{ik}/Y_{ik} = R_0^2 \tag{3.22}$$

Consider first an arbitrary planar network driven from e.m.f. sources only, and its dual. These are soluble with mesh-current and node-datum equations having the simple compressed forms

$$[Z]\cdot[I] = [E_s] \tag{3.23}$$

and

$$[Y]\cdot[V] = [I_s] \tag{3.24}$$

Let every pair of dual immittances be related in the form $Z_{ik} = Y_{ik}R_0^2$, so that

$$[Z] = [Y]\cdot[R_0^2] \tag{3.25}$$

where

$$[R_0^2] = \begin{bmatrix} R_0^2 & 0 & . & . & 0 \\ 0 & R_0^2 & . & . & 0 \\ . & . & . & . & . \\ . & . & . & . & . \\ 0 & 0 & . & . & R_0^2 \end{bmatrix} \tag{3.26}$$

is a *scalar matrix*, being a diagonal matrix of equal elements and having the property of scaling the elements of the matrix with which it is conformable, as illustrated by

$$\begin{bmatrix} Y_{11} & Y_{12} & Y_{13} \\ Y_{21} & Y_{22} & Y_{23} \\ Y_{31} & Y_{32} & Y_{33} \end{bmatrix}\cdot\begin{bmatrix} R_0^2 & 0 & 0 \\ 0 & R_0^2 & 0 \\ 0 & 0 & R_0^2 \end{bmatrix} = \begin{bmatrix} Y_{11}R_0^2 & Y_{12}R_0^2 & Y_{13}R_0^2 \\ Y_{21}R_0^2 & Y_{22}R_0^2 & Y_{23}R_0^2 \\ Y_{31}R_0^2 & Y_{32}R_0^2 & Y_{33}R_0^2 \end{bmatrix} \tag{3.27}$$

By reversing the multiplication order in eqn. (3.27) it may be verified that

$$[Y]\cdot[R_0^2] = [R_0^2]\cdot[Y] \tag{3.28}$$

The product of a square matrix with a conformable scalar matrix is in general a special case in which the product is commutative, or in general symbols,

$$[\alpha]_n\cdot[X]_n = [X]_n\cdot[\alpha]_n \tag{3.29}$$

where

$$[\alpha]_n = \begin{bmatrix} \alpha_{11} & 0 & \cdot & \cdot & 0 \\ 0 & \alpha_{22} & \cdot & \cdot & 0 \\ \cdot & \cdot & \cdot & \cdot & \cdot \\ \cdot & \cdot & \cdot & \cdot & \cdot \\ 0 & 0 & \cdot & \cdot & \alpha_{nn} \end{bmatrix}, \quad [X]_n = \begin{bmatrix} x_{11} & x_{12} & \cdot & \cdot & x_{1n} \\ x_{21} & x_{22} & \cdot & \cdot & x_{2n} \\ \cdot & \cdot & \cdot & \cdot & \cdot \\ \cdot & \cdot & \cdot & \cdot & \cdot \\ x_{n1} & x_{n2} & \cdot & \cdot & x_{nn} \end{bmatrix} \tag{3.30}$$

Eqn. (3.29) is the particularisation, for $m = n$, of

$$[\alpha]_m\cdot[X]_{mn} = [X]_{mn}\cdot[\alpha]_n \tag{3.31}$$

where $[X]_{mn}$ is a rectangular matrix of m rows and n columns, while $[\alpha]_n$ has n rows and n columns.

Substituting $[Y]\cdot[R_0^2]$ for $[Z]$ in eqn. (3.23) gives

$$[Y]\cdot[R_0^2]\cdot[I] = [E_s] \tag{3.32}$$

Pre-multiplying both sides by a conformable scalar matrix

$$[1/R_0] = [R_0^{-1}] = \begin{bmatrix} R_0^{-1} & . & . & 0 & 0 \\ 0 & R_0^{-1} & . & . & 0 \\ . & . & . & . & . \\ . & . & . & . & . \\ 0 & 0 & . & . & R_0^{-1} \end{bmatrix} \tag{3.33}$$

but writing $[Y]\cdot[R_0^{-1}]$ in place of $[R_0^{-1}]\cdot[Y]$ in accordance with eqn. (3.29), gives

$$[Y]\cdot[R_0^{-1}]\cdot[R_0^2]\cdot[I] = [R_0^{-1}]\cdot[E_s]$$

which reduces to $$[Y]\cdot[R_0]\cdot[I] = [1/R_0]\cdot[E_s] \tag{3.34}$$

This is of the form $$[Y]\cdot[V] = [I_s] \tag{3.35}$$

where the relations between any element V_k in $[V]$ and I_k in $[I]$, and between any element I_{sk} in $[I_s]$ and E_{sk} in $[E_s]$, are

$$V_k = I_k R_0 \tag{3.36}$$

and

$$I_{sk} = E_{sk}/R_0 \tag{3.37}$$

The relations expressed by eqns. (3.36) and (3.37) for a planar network and its dual are readily extended by induction to the general case of a network which is essentially planar* but which contains both e.m.f. and current sources. The comprehensive matrix relations for general loop-current and nodal-voltage analysis are given in eqns. (2.14) and (2.15). Let $[E]$, $[I]$ denote the source matrices for the given network, and $[E]_d$, $[I]_d$ denote those for its dual. Eqns. (2.14) and (2.15), as applied to the given network and its dual respectively, are then

$$[M]\cdot[Z_b]\cdot[M]^t\cdot[I_L] = [M]\{[E]-[Z_b]\cdot[I]\} \tag{3.38}$$

and

$$[Q]\cdot[Y_b]\cdot[Q]^t\cdot[V_n] = [Q]\{[I]_d-[Y_b]\cdot[E]_d\} \tag{3.39}$$

Since each term in eqn. (3.39) must be the dual of the corresponding term in eqn. (3.38), it follows from the forms of eqns. (3.36) and (3.37)

*A non-planar graph, which is not mappable on a sphere, has no dual (C.Kuratowski, Sur le probleme des courbes gauches en topologie, *Fundamenta Mathematicae*, Vol.15, p.271, 1930). But ideal transformers may be introduced to make the network planar.

that the node-pair voltages $[V_n]$ in eqns. (3.39) will be related numerically to the loop-currents $[I_L]$ in eqns. (3.38) in the form

$$[V_n] = [R_0]\cdot[I_L] \tag{3.40}$$

provided

$$\begin{aligned} [Y_b] &= [R_0^2]^{-1}\cdot[Z_b] \\ [I]_d &= [1/R_0]\cdot[E] \\ [E]_d &= [R_0]\cdot[I] \end{aligned} \tag{3.41}$$

4. THE IDEALISED TRANSFORMATION OF VOLTAGE, CURRENT, AND IMMITTANCE

An important theoretical operation in both analysis and synthesis is the transformation of voltage, current, and immittance to new values, without loss of energy. This is commonly achieved with an ideal transformer, an abstract artifice evolved through the idealisation of a practical transformer. From this physical origin, however, transformation in wholly real ratios only is conceivable. In many instances of the sinusoidal steady-state ($s = j\omega$), in which the quantities are vectorial and algebraically of the complex forms $x + jy$, $A\angle\theta$, or $Ae^{j\theta}$, transformation in a complex ratio may be desired in analysis to convert an impedance $Z_1(j\omega)$ into $Z_2(j\omega)$, where $\arg Z_1(j\omega) \neq \arg Z_2(j\omega)$. The realisation of complex transformation ratios is possible with an idealised non-dissipative network, provided it is assumed capable of storing energy. Such a network, comprising purely reactive elements, is shown to have transformation properties resembling those of an ideal transformer; but it has an hypothetical structure that is not bound in origin to the notion of a two-winding physical transformer.

4.1 THE IDEAL TRANSFORMER

Its evolution from the physical transformer is illustrated by reference to Fig. 3-10, in which, as a first step in idealisation, the inductive elements are assumed non-dissipative.

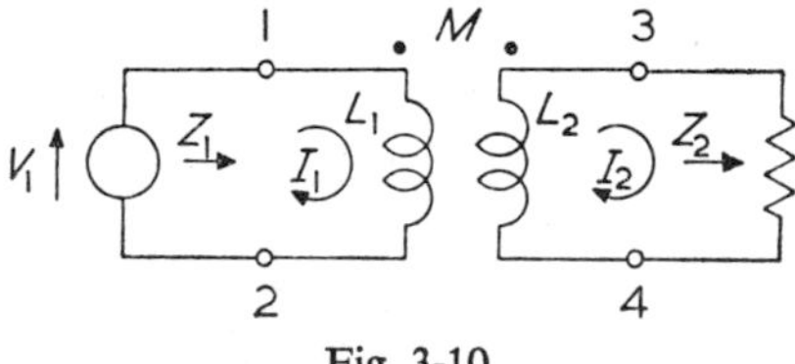

Fig. 3-10.

The excitation voltage V_1 is assumed to be a function of the general complex variable s, so that the impedance concept may be freely used in its most general sense. Let V_2 denote the voltage across Z_2.

It is expedient to eliminate the volt-drop V_2 from the mesh equations by absorbing Z_2 into Z_{22}.
Then,

$$\begin{bmatrix} Z_{11} & Z_{12} \\ Z_{21} & Z_{22} \end{bmatrix} \cdot \begin{bmatrix} I_1 \\ I_2 \end{bmatrix} = \begin{bmatrix} V_1 \\ 0 \end{bmatrix} \tag{3.42}$$

where

$$Z_{11} = sL_1, \quad Z_{22} = sL_2 + Z_2$$

and, for the dot notation shown,

$$Z_{12} = Z_{21} = -sM = -sk\sqrt{(L_1L_2)}$$

where k denotes the coefficient of coupling, $k = M/\sqrt{(L_1 L_2)}$.

Applying Cramer's rule to the determinant of the matrix,

$$I_1 = V_1\Delta_{11}/\Delta, \quad I_2 = V_1\Delta_{12}/\Delta$$

and then the voltage-drop (in the sense of I_2) is

$$V_2 = I_2Z_2 = V_1\Delta_{12}Z_2/\Delta \tag{3.43}$$

The voltage ratio is thus

$$\frac{V_1}{V_2} = \frac{\Delta}{\Delta_{12}} \cdot \frac{1}{Z_2} = \frac{Z_{11}Z_{22} - Z_{21}Z_{12}}{-Z_{21}} \cdot \frac{1}{Z_2}$$

$$= \frac{s^2L_1L_2(1-k^2) + sL_1Z_2}{sk\sqrt{(L_1L_2)}Z_2} \tag{3.44}$$

As $k \to 1$, $(1-k^2) \to 0$ and in the limit eqn. (3.44) becomes

$$\frac{V_1}{V_2} = \sqrt{\frac{L_1}{L_2}} \tag{3.45}$$

Thus, even with finite inductors (but non-dissipative), perfect coupling would result in a wholly real voltage ratio, independent both of the terminating impedance and of the form of excitation.

From eqns. (3.42), the current ratio for $k=1$ is

$$\frac{I_1}{I_2} = \frac{\Delta_{11}}{\Delta_{12}} = \frac{sL_2 + Z_2}{s\sqrt{(L_1L_2)}} = \frac{1 + Z_2/sL_2}{\sqrt{(L_1/L_2)}} \tag{3.46}$$

For s finite, $sL_2 \to \infty$ as $L_2 \to \infty$; and then for Z_2 finite, $Z_2/sL_2 \to 0$, so that

$$\frac{I_1}{I_2} \to \sqrt{\frac{L_2}{L_1}} \tag{3.47}$$

It is now preferable to denote $\sqrt{(L_1/L_2)}$ by a real positive constant λ; indefinitely great values for L_1 and L_2 are incompatible with physical realism, yet mathematical realism remains in their fixed ratio. Then in the limit, as $L_2 \to \infty$ and $L_1 \to \infty$, eqn. (3.47) becomes

$$\frac{I_1}{I_2} = \frac{1}{\lambda} \tag{3.48}$$

while eqn. (3.45) may be re-stated as

$$\frac{V_1}{V_2} = \lambda \tag{3.49}$$

Since s is absent from eqns. (3.48) and (3.49), the current and voltage transformation properties apply to transitory as well as steady-state conditions.

Referring to Fig. 3-10, the input impedance at terminals 1–2 is V_1/I_1, while the terminating impedance Z_2 is V_2/I_2. Then,

$$\frac{Z_1}{Z_2} = \frac{V_1}{I_1} \cdot \frac{I_2}{V_2} = \frac{V_1}{V_2} \cdot \frac{I_2}{I_1}$$

or,

$$\frac{Z_1}{Z_2} = \lambda^2 \tag{3.50}$$

While the ideal transformer does not dissipate energy, it does not store it either. Since λ is a positive real constant, eqns. (3.48) and (3.49) are valid for instantaneous values of currents and voltages varying in an arbitrary way with time. The energy entering at any instant τ is

$$w_1 = \int_0^\tau v_1 i_1 \, dt$$

while the energy leaving is

$$w_2 = \int_0^\tau v_2 i_2 \, dt = \int_0^\tau \frac{v_1}{\lambda} \cdot \lambda \, i_1 \, dt = \int_0^\tau v_1 i_1 \, dt$$

and therefore $w_1 = w_2$.

The ideal transformer can now be defined as 'a hypothetical four-terminal network that neither stores nor dissipates energy, and which embodies the attributes of a perfect but unrealisable two-winding transformer'. These are, a wholly real voltage transformation ratio λ, and current and impedance transformation ratios $1/\lambda$ and λ^2 respectively, all in the direction from one terminal-pair to the other.

4.1.1 *Simple energy considerations*

The voltage current and impedance ratios for the ideal transformer are not unique, but exemplify the forms that are in general consistent with conservation of the instantaneous energy transmitted through any hypothetical four-terminal network that neither dissipates nor stores energy. The ratios could therefore have been deduced easily without reference to the physical transformer at all.

Consider an hypothetical four-terminal network that neither dissipates nor stores energy, and let v_1, i_1 and v_2, i_2 denote respectively the instantaneous values of the input and output voltages and currents when a load is connected to the output terminals. Since energy is neither dissipated nor stored, the input and output energies must be equal at every instant, or

$$\int_0^t v_1 i_1 \, dt = \int_0^t v_2 i_2 \, dt$$

Differentiating both sides then gives

$$v_1 i_1 = v_2 i_2 \qquad (3.51)$$

Let

$$v_1/v_2 = \lambda \qquad (3.52)$$

Then by eqn. (3.51)

$$i_1/i_2 = 1/\lambda \qquad (3.53)$$

Using the notation $Z(p)$ to denote a transient impedance of form v/i,

$$\frac{v_1}{i_1} = Z_1(p) = \lambda v_2 \cdot \frac{\lambda}{i_2}$$
$$= \lambda^2 v_2/i_2$$
$$= \lambda^2 Z_2(p)$$

or

$$Z_1(p)/Z_2(p) = \lambda^2 \qquad (3.54)$$

Eqns. (3.52), (3.53) and (3.54) are identical in form with the relations derived in sect. 4.1 by reference to a physical transformer.

4.2 TRANSFORMATION IN COMPLEX RATIOS

4.2.1 *General considerations*

A complex ratio of the form

$$V_1/V_2 = \lambda = |\lambda| e^{j\psi} \qquad (3.55)$$

is significant for the sinusoidal steady-state and implies a phase-change ψ, or equivalently, a time-delay ψ/ω between the instants at which the voltages reach corresponding values in a cycle, such as maxima. Time-delay or phase-change can arise in a passive network only through the storage of energy; and a suitable non-dissipative transforming network must therefore be assumed to comprise pure inductive and capacitative elements disposed for the storage of energy.

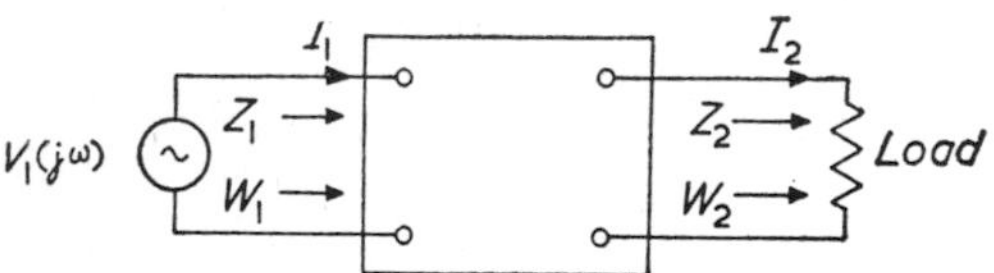

Fig. 3-11. Generalised pure inductor-capacitor storage network.

Referring to the generalised storage network of Fig. 3-11, let the instantaneous voltages and currents be

$$\begin{aligned} v_1 &= \hat{V}_1 \sin \omega t, & i_1 &= \hat{I}_1 \sin(\omega t - \theta_1) \\ v_2 &= \hat{V}_2 \sin(\omega t - \psi), & i_2 &= \hat{I}_2 \sin(\omega t - \psi - \theta_2) \end{aligned} \tag{3.56}$$

where ψ, θ_1 and θ_2 are arbitrary phase-displacements.

The rate of energy supply, or input power, averaged over the period $T = 2\pi/\omega$ for one cycle, is

$$P_1 = \frac{1}{T}\int_0^T w_1\, dt = \frac{\omega}{2\pi}\int_0^{T=2\pi/\omega} v_1 i_1\, dt$$

$$= \tfrac{1}{2}\hat{V}_1\hat{I}_1 \cos\theta_1 \tag{3.57}$$

or

$$P_1 = |V_1|\cdot|I_1| \cos\theta_1 \tag{3.58}$$

where $|V_1|$, $|I_1|$ denote r.m.s. magnitudes.

Similarly, the output power is

$$P_2 = |V_2|\cdot|I_2| \cos\theta_2 \tag{3.59}$$

The energies w_1 and w_2 are in general unequal at any particular instant, for under sinusoidal conditions the energy-flow has a pulsating character.* But under steady sinusoidal conditions, the average energies entering and leaving the network over some period of time must be equal; for only a finite maximum of energy can be stored, governed by the finite maximum values of the currents and voltages within the network. These energies are $\frac{1}{2}L\hat{I}^2$ and $\frac{1}{2}C\hat{V}^2$ joules for each inductor and capacitor. By solving any illustrative pure inductor-capacitor

* A very thorough account of energy relations in an a.c. circuit is given by E. A. Guillemin in his book, *Introductory Circuit Theory* (John Wiley and Sons, Inc., New York; Chapman and Hall Ltd., London, 1953).

network terminated with a dissipative load and energised from a sinusoidal source, as in Fig. 3-11, it can be confirmed that the input and output energies and powers are equal when averaged over a cycle, or

$$|V_1|\cdot|I_1|\cos\theta_1 = |V_2|\cdot|I_2|\cos\theta_2 \tag{3.60}$$

where

$$\theta_1 = \arg I_1 \text{ relative to } V_1$$
$$\theta_2 = \arg I_2 \text{ relative to } V_2$$

Provided the voltages and currents are sinusoidal, eqn. (3.60) is valid in general for networks of pure inductive and capacitative elements, regardless of complexity. Since the impedances of such elements are wholly reactive, it is appropriate to classify the networks as pure-reactance networks.

4.2.2 *The transformation properties of a generalised pure-reactance network*

Referring to Fig. 3-11, let

$$\begin{aligned} V_1 &= |V_1|\, e^{j0} && \text{(reference vector)} \\ V_2 &= |V_2|\, e^{-j\psi} && \\ I_1 &= |I_1|\, e^{-j\theta_1} && \\ I_2 &= |I_2|\, e^{-j\theta_2} && \text{relative to } V_2 \\ &= |I_2|\, e^{-j(\psi+\theta_2)} && \text{relative to } V_1 \end{aligned} \tag{3.61}$$

By eqn. (3.60),

$$|V_1|\cdot|I_1|\cos\theta_1 = |V_2|\cdot|I_2|\cos\theta_2 \tag{3.62}$$

Let the impedance ratio be specified as

$$\frac{Z_1}{Z_2} = \lambda^2 = |\lambda|^2\, e^{j(\theta_1-\theta_2)} \tag{3.63}$$

where

$$Z_1 = \frac{V_1}{I_1} = \frac{|V_1|}{|I_1|}\, e^{j\theta_1}$$

and

$$Z_2 = \frac{V_2}{I_2} = \frac{|V_2|}{|I_2|}\, e^{j\theta_2}$$

Then, substituting $|I_1| = |V_1|/|Z_1|$ and $|I_2| = |V_2|/|Z_2|$ in eqn. (3.62) and transposing,

$$\frac{|V_1|^2}{|V_2|^2} = \frac{|Z_1|}{|Z_2|}\cdot\frac{\cos\theta_2}{\cos\theta_1} \tag{3.64}$$

or

$$\frac{|V_1|}{|V_2|} = |\lambda|\cdot\sqrt{\frac{\cos\theta_2}{\cos\theta_1}} \tag{3.65}$$

Eqn. (3.64) may be put in the form

$$\frac{|V_1|^2}{|V_2|^2} = \frac{|Y_2|\cos\theta_2}{|Y_1|\cos\theta_1} = \frac{G_2}{G_1}$$

or

$$\frac{|V_1|}{|V_2|} = \sqrt{\frac{G_2}{G_1}} \tag{3.66}$$

where G_1 and G_2 are the conductance components of the admittances $Y_1 = 1/Z_1$ and $Y_2 = 1/Z_2$.

Similarly, writing eqn. (3.62) in the form

$$|I_1|^2 \cdot |Z_1|\cos\theta_1 = |I_2|^2 \cdot |Z_2|\cos\theta_2$$

gives

$$\frac{|I_1|^2}{|I_2|^2} = \frac{|Z_2|}{|Z_1|} \cdot \frac{\cos\theta_2}{\cos\theta_1} = \frac{R_2}{R_1} \tag{3.67}$$

or

$$\frac{|I_1|}{|I_2|} = \frac{1}{|\lambda|} \cdot \sqrt{\frac{\cos\theta_2}{\cos\theta_1}} \tag{3.68}$$

and alternatively

$$\frac{|I_1|}{|I_2|} = \sqrt{\frac{R_2}{R_1}} \tag{3.69}$$

where R_1 and R_2 are the resistance components of the impedances Z_1 and Z_2.

In vector form, then,

$$\frac{Z_1}{Z_2} = \lambda^2 = |\lambda|^2 \, e^{j(\theta_1 - \theta_2)} \tag{3.70}$$

$$\frac{V_1}{V_2} = |\lambda| \cdot \sqrt{\left[\frac{\cos\theta_2}{\cos\theta_1}\right]} \cdot e^{j\psi} = \sqrt{\frac{G_2}{G_1}} \, e^{j\psi} \tag{3.71}$$

$$\frac{I_1}{I_2} = \frac{1}{|\lambda|} \cdot \sqrt{\left[\frac{\cos\theta_2}{\cos\theta_1}\right]} \cdot e^{j(\psi + \theta_2 - \theta_1)} = \sqrt{\frac{R_2}{R_1}} \, e^{j(\psi + \theta_2 - \theta_1)} \tag{3.72}$$

For an unspecified network, the argument ψ in eqn. (3.71) is arbitrary.

5. ILLUSTRATIVE EXAMPLES

Example 3.1

The external relations for a linear four-terminal network may be expressed in the form

$$V_1 = AV_2 - BI_2$$
$$I_1 = CV_2 - DI_2$$

where V_1, I_1 and V_2, I_2 denote the input and output voltages and currents, while A, B, C, and D are constants for the network. Show, by means of the reciprocity theorem, that if the network is passive and bilateral, $AD - BC = 1$.

Since A, B, C, and D are constants for the network, they are invariable with external conditions and therefore valid for short-circuit conditions. Let the output terminals be short-circuited. Then $V_2 = 0$, and from the first equation,

$$I_2 = -V_1/B$$

Now let the input terminals be short-circuited while V_2 is applied to the output terminals. Then $V_1 = 0$, and the equations give

$$I_2 = AV_2/B$$
$$I_1 = CV_2 - DI_2 = V_2(C - AD/B)$$

As the network is linear, passive, and bilateral, it conforms to the reciprocity theorem. Thus, if $V_2 = V_1$, where V_1 is the voltage that was applied when the output terminals were short-circuited,

$$I_1 = V_2(C - AD/B) = I_2 = -V_1/B = -V_2/B$$

whence

$$AD - BC = 1.$$

See also Chapter 4, sect. 2.2, and eqn. (4.25).

Example 3.2

An e.m.f. source E, having negligible internal impedance, is connected in series with an impedance Z_1 to the input terminals 1–2 of a linear bilateral four-terminal network. It produces a current I_2 in an impedance Z_2 connected across the output terminals 3–4. The e.m.f. source is now transformed so as to act, in series with Z_2, between terminals 3–4. Z_1 is disconnected and the input terminals 1–2 are short-circuited. The short-circuit current traversing terminals 1–2 is then I_1. Prove that the impedance looking-into terminals 1–2 under the first condition is

$$Z_{1-2} = \beta Z_1/(1 - \beta)$$

where $\beta = I_2/I_1$

Z_{1-2} under the first condition is also the internal impedance of a simple Thévenin equivalent generator replacing the network at terminals 1–2 under the second condition. Let E' denote the e.m.f. of this generator. Then,

$$I_1 = E'/Z_{1-2}$$

If, however, the short-circuit were replaced by Z_1, the current would be

$$I_1' = E'/(Z_1 + Z_{1-2})$$

But by the reciprocity theorem, $I_1' = I_2$. Therefore,

$$\frac{I_2}{I_1} = \beta = \frac{I_1'}{I_1} = \frac{E'}{Z_1 + Z_{1-2}} \cdot \frac{Z_{1-2}}{E'}$$

or

$$\beta = \frac{Z_{1-2}}{Z_1 + Z_{1-2}}$$

whence

$$Z_{1-2} = \frac{\beta Z_1}{1 - \beta}$$

Example 3.3

Two single-phase transformers A and B are connected in parallel to a 2-kV supply. Each transformer has a percentage impedance drop of $0.8 + j4.0$ when its input current is 200 amperes. On no load, with secondary windings independent, the secondary terminal p.d. is 405 volts for transformer A, and 395 volts for transformer B. Determine to a reasonable approximation the input current to transformer A, and the load p.d., when the secondary windings are joined in parallel and together supply 2,500 amperes at unity power factor to a common load.

(*L.U. Part 3, Electrical Power and Machines*)

This problem is typical of many in power engineering to which the parallel-generator theorem is directly applicable, and illustrates additionally the use of Thévenin's theorem for initial simplification.

The percentage impedance volt-drop is assumed to refer to the primary winding of each transformer, and to be the percentage of the primary voltage of 2,000 that is dropped when the primary current I_p is the stated value of 200A. Thus, if the actual voltage-drop is V_{pd},

$$0.8 + j4 = (V_{pd}/2{,}000) \times 100$$

and

$$V_{pd} = 20(0.8 + j4)$$

The corresponding series impedance to be associated with the primary side of an ideal transformer having a voltage-ratio equal to the open-circuit voltage-ratio of the actual transformer is therefore

$$Z = \frac{V_{pd}}{I_p} = \frac{20(0.8 + j4)}{200} = 0.08 + j0.4 \text{ ohms}$$

Then by Thévenin's theorem, the transformer A is replaceable at its secondary terminals by a simple generator of e.m.f.

$$E_A = 405 \text{ V}$$

and internal impedance

$$\begin{aligned} Z_A &= (0.08 + j0.4)(405/2{,}000)^2 \\ &= (3.28 + j16.4)10^{-3} \text{ ohms} \end{aligned}$$

Similarly for transformer B,

$$\begin{aligned} E_B &= 395 \text{ V} \\ Z_B &= (0.08 + j0.4)(395/2{,}000)^2 \\ &= (3.12 + j15.6)10^{-3} \text{ ohms} \end{aligned}$$

The circuit is thus resolved into the two simple generators E_A, Z_A and E_B, Z_B, in parallel with a load Y_L. Then, by the parallel generator theorem, the common voltage V is given by

$$V = \frac{E_A Y_A + E_B Y_B}{Y_A + Y_B + Y_L}$$

where

$$\begin{aligned} Y_A &= 1/Z_A = 11.7 - j58.6 \text{ mhos} \\ Y_B &= 1/Z_B = 12.3 - j61.7 \text{ mhos} \\ Y_L &= I_L/V = 2{,}500/V \text{ mhos} \end{aligned}$$

Substituting these values gives

$$\begin{aligned} V &= \frac{(96.0 - j482)10^2}{24.0 - j120.3 + 2{,}500/V} \\ &= (71 - j482)/(0.24 - j1.203) \\ &= 397\underline{/2°45'} \text{ V} \end{aligned}$$

The secondary currents have magnitudes

$$\begin{aligned} I_{SA} &= (E_A - V)Y_A = 1{,}236 \text{ A} \\ I_{SB} &= (E_B - V)Y_B = 1{,}200 \text{ A} \end{aligned}$$

Then, introducing the current-ratios of the ideal transformers, the primary currents are

$$\begin{aligned} I_{PA} &= I_{SA} \times (405/2{,}000) = 250 \text{ A} \\ I_{PB} &= I_{SB} \times (395/2{,}000) = 237 \text{ A} \end{aligned}$$

Example 3.4

Fig. 3-12(a) is an important form of feedback amplifier circuit, readily solved by the parallel-generator theorem.

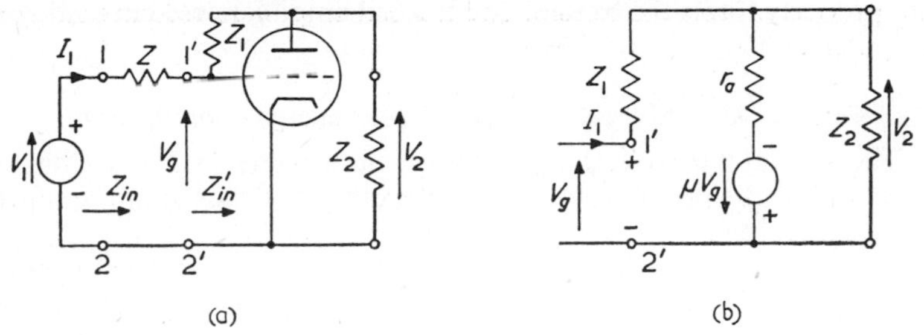

Fig. 3-12.

Fig. 3-12(b) is an equivalent representation with respect to the grid-cathode terminals, 1′, 2′. Let Y_1, Y_2, and G_a denote respectively the reciprocals of Z_1, Z_2, and r_a. Then, by the parallel-generator theorem, noting that V_2 is a voltage drop in the positive sense of μV_g,

$$V_2 = -\frac{V_g(\mu G_a - Y_1)}{Y_1 + Y_2 + G_a}$$

and therefore

$$V_2/V_g = -A$$

where

$$A = (\mu G_a - Y_1)/(Y_1 + Y_2 + G_a)$$

The potential difference across Z_1 in Fig. 3-12(b) is $V_g - V_2$, and therefore

$$I_1 = (V_g - V_2)/Z_1 = V_g(1 + A)/Z_1$$

and

$$Z'_{in} = Z_{1'-2'} = V_g/I_1 = Z_1/(1 + A)$$

Now consider terminals 1–2 in Fig. 3-12(a). Z and Z'_{in} form a potential divider across V_1, so that

$$V_g = V_1 Z'_{in}/(Z + Z'_{in})$$

Thence,

$$\frac{V_g}{V_1} = -\frac{V_2}{A}\cdot\frac{1}{V_1} = 1/(1 + Z/Z'_{in})$$

$$= Z_1/[Z_1 + Z(1 + A)]$$

and therefore,

$$\frac{V_2}{V_1} = -\frac{AZ_1}{Z_1 + Z(1 + A)}$$

As $Z(1 + A)/Z_1 \to \infty$,

$$V_2/V_1 \to -A\,Z_1/Z(1 + A)$$

and as $A \to \infty$,

$$V_2/V_1 \to -Z_1/Z$$

This property forms the basis of operational amplifiers used in analogue computers.

Example 3.5. An analytical example of the superposition theorem.

The general star-mesh transformation has been referred to in Chapter 2, sect. 5.2.1. Its proof provides a good example of the use of the superposition theorem.

Two networks are equivalent if the replacement of one of them by the other in a fixed external system of e.m.f. sources causes no change whatsoever in the currents and potentials external to the networks. Therefore, let the star network of n terminals and n admittances be inserted in an arbitrary system of e.m.fs. as indicated in Fig. 3-13, and let the currents traversing each terminal be calculated: this is readily done with the superposition theorem, provided the network is linear.

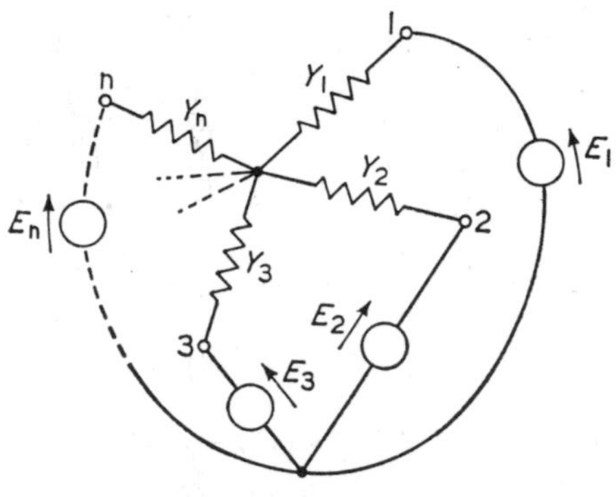

Fig. 3-13.

In Fig. 3-13, all the e.m.fs. have been assumed to act in the same direction from the common point as a matter of convenience. By the superposition theorem, the current traversing terminal 1 is therefore

$$I_1 = I_{1(1)} - I_{1(2)} - \cdots - I_{1(n)}$$

Reducing all e.m.fs. to zero except E_1 gives

$$I_{1(1)} = E_1 Y_1 (Y_2 + Y_3 + \cdots + Y_n)/\sum Y$$

Similarly, the current at terminal 2 due to the independent action of E_2 is

$$I_{2(2)} = E_2 Y_2 (Y_1 + Y_3 + \cdots + Y_n)/\sum Y$$

The proportion of this current that flows through Y_1 and terminal 1 is

$$I_{1(2)} = I_{2(2)} \cdot \frac{Y_1}{Y_1 + Y_3 + \cdots + Y_n}$$
$$= E_2 Y_1 Y_2 / \sum Y$$

The superposed currents due to all other e.m.fs. are given similarly, and therefore in general,

$$I_{i(k)} = E_k Y_i Y_k / \sum Y \qquad (k \neq i)$$

where $I_{i(k)}$ denotes the current at any terminal i due to an e.m.f. E_k acting at any other terminal k.

Thus, the total current traversing terminal 1 is

$$I_1 = E_1 \cdot \frac{Y_1(Y_2 + Y_3 + \cdots + Y_n)}{\sum Y} - E_2 \cdot \frac{Y_1 Y_2}{\sum Y} - \cdots - E_n \cdot \frac{Y_1 Y_n}{\sum Y}$$
$$= (E_1 - E_2) \frac{Y_1 Y_2}{\sum Y} + (E_1 - E_3) \frac{Y_1 Y_3}{\sum Y} + \cdots + (E_1 - E_n) \frac{Y_1 Y_n}{\sum Y}$$

or generalising,

$$I_i = (E_i - E_1) \frac{Y_i Y_1}{\sum Y} + (E_i - E_2) \frac{Y_i Y_2}{\sum Y} + \cdots + (E_i - E_n) \frac{Y_i Y_n}{\sum Y}$$

In this equation, each e.m.f. term represents the difference of potential between one particular pair of terminals, and each corresponding admittance term represents the admittance of a branch joining them. The star arrangement is thus equivalently represented by a completely pair-connected system of admittances of the general form

$$Y_i Y_1 / \sum Y,\ Y_i Y_2 / \sum Y,\ \ldots\ Y_i Y_n / \sum Y$$

connecting each terminal ($i = 1, 2, \ldots n$) to every other one. Fig. 2-18 illustrates the equivalence for $n = 4$.

Example 3.6

The normalised network in Fig. 3-14(a) has the transfer function

$$\frac{I_2(s)}{E_1(s)} = \frac{4 + 3s^2}{8(1 + s) + 10s^2 + 4s^3} = F(s)$$

A network is required for operation instead from a constant-current $I_1(s)$, and to deliver an output voltage $V_2(s)$ so that

$$\frac{V_2(s)}{I_1(s)} = 5F(s)$$

Find a network to meet this specification, and the normalised values of its elements.

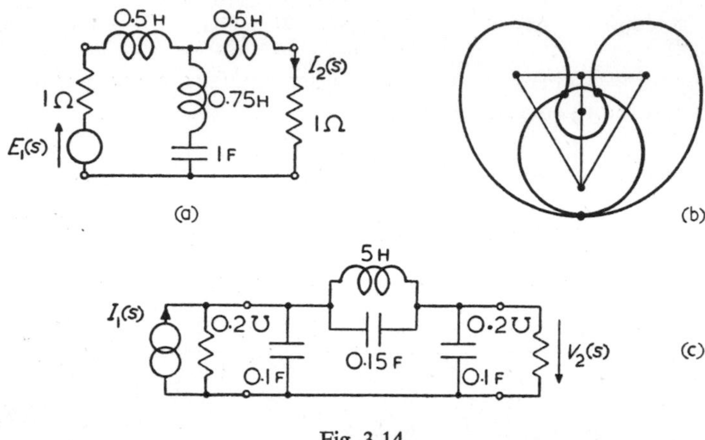

Fig. 3-14.

The required transfer function is the scaled dual of the given one, $F(s)$; and the required network is therefore the numerically-related dual of the given network, Fig. 3-14(a). The construction of the dual graph is indicated in Fig. 3-14(b), while the actual dual network is shown in Fig. 3-14(c).

In terms of eqns. (3.40) and (3.41), $I_2(s)$ and $E_1(s)$ are elements of the loop-current and e.m.f.-source matrices $[I_L]$ and $[E]$ for the given network, while $V_2(s)$ and $I_1(s)$ are elements of the node-pair voltage and current-source matrices $[V_n]$ and $[I]_d$ for the dual network. Therefore, by consideration of eqns. (3.40) and (3.41), if $V_2(s) = R_0 I_2(s)$,

$$\frac{V_2(s)}{I_1(s)} = \frac{R_0 I_2(s)}{E_1(s)/R_0} = \frac{I_2(s)}{E_1(s)} \cdot R_0^2$$

or

$$5F(s) = F(s)R_0^2$$

and therefore

$$R_0^2 = 5$$

According to eqn. (3.41), each admittance in the dual network, Fig. 3-14(c), must be $1/R_0^2$ times its impedance dual in the given network, Fig. 3-14(a). Therefore, in Fig. 3-14(c), each capacitance is 1/5th of its inductance dual, each inductance is 5 times its capacitance dual, and each conductance is 1/5th of its resistance dual.

REFERENCES

1. ROGERS, F. E.: *The Theory of Networks in Electrical Communication and Other Fields* (Macdonald, London; D. Van Nostrand, New York, 1957).
2. FREEMAN, G. F.: A General Superposition Theorem of the Thévenin Type, *Philosophical Mag.*, Sept. 1942 (33, Ser. 7, p. 679).
3. FREEMAN, G. F.: Note on the Helmholtz Make and Break Theorem and an Application to the Wheatstone Net, *Philosophical Mag.*, Aug. 1945 (36, Ser. 7, p. 541).
4. MILLMAN, J.: A Useful Network Theorem, *Proc. I.R.E.*, Sept. 1940 (XXVIII, p. 413).

4

MATRICES APPLIED TO FOUR-TERMINAL NETWORKS AND GROUPS OF NETWORKS

1. INTRODUCTION

Electrical systems are generally composed of groups of networks. This is especially evident in the case of communication and electronic systems, in which individual networks each perform a specific operation, such as amplifying, attenuating, filtering, phase-changing or time delaying, etc. Such operations are mostly sequential, and therefore much of the system can be resolved into a number of networks of the *four-terminal* type (or 2 *terminal-pair* or 2-*port networks*) connected so that the output from one is the input to the next. Some of the system may comprise such networks connected in parallel or in series-parallel (as in a voltage-feedback arrangement), while the networks themselves may sometimes be resolved into sub-networks connected in parallel (as in the case of the four-terminal parallel-T network) or in sequence (as in a ladder structure, such as a multi-section filter).

Matrix algebra is particularly appropriate to problems involving groups: in the case of groups of interconnected networks it affords elegant simplification.

2. THE EQUATIONS AND PARAMETERS FOR FOUR-TERMINAL NETWORKS

While the actual network within the boundaries of the four accessible terminals may have any degree of complexity, it is nevertheless possible to define its external behaviour with two simultaneous equations only. This is easily demonstrated by reference to the determinantal solution for an arbitrary linear network such as that indicated by Fig. 4-1(a).

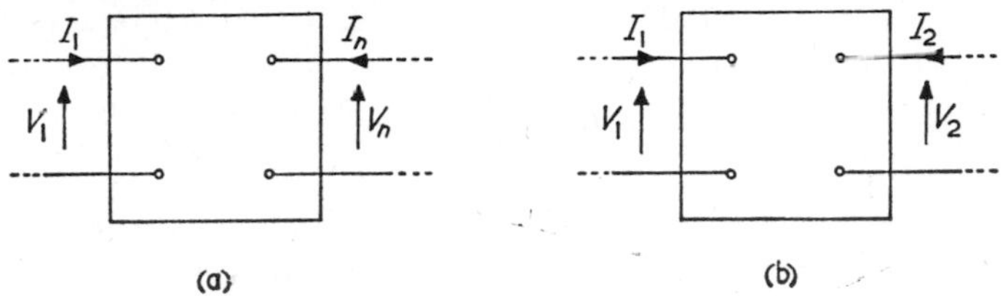

Fig. 4-1. Arbitrary linear networks.

First, let the two currents I_1 and I_n, in the first and last meshes of the network, be treated as sources. Then the nodal-voltage equations for the whole network are of the form

$$\begin{bmatrix} Y_{11} & Y_{12} & \cdots & Y_{1n} \\ Y_{21} & Y_{22} & \cdots & Y_{2n} \\ \cdot & \cdot & \cdots & \cdot \\ Y_{n1} & Y_{n2} & \cdots & Y_{nn} \end{bmatrix} \cdot \begin{bmatrix} V_1 \\ V_2 \\ \vdots \\ V_n \end{bmatrix} = \begin{bmatrix} I_1 \\ 0 \\ \vdots \\ I_n \end{bmatrix} \tag{4.1}$$

By Cramer's rule the first and last node-pair voltages V_1 and V_n are given by

$$\begin{aligned} V_1 &= I_1 \frac{\Delta_{11}}{\Delta} + I_n \frac{\Delta_{n1}}{\Delta} \\ V_n &= I_n \frac{\Delta_{nn}}{\Delta} + I_1 \frac{\Delta_{1n}}{\Delta} \end{aligned} \tag{4.2}$$

where Δ is the determinant of the Y-matrix and $\Delta_{11} \ldots \Delta_{nn}$ are co-factors of Δ.

Similarly, when the two voltages V_1 and V_n are regarded as sources, the mesh equations have the form

$$\begin{bmatrix} Z_{11} & Z_{12} & \cdots & Z_{1n} \\ Z_{21} & Z_{22} & \cdots & Z_{2n} \\ \cdot & \cdot & \cdots & \cdot \\ Z_{n1} & Z_{n2} & \cdots & Z_{nn} \end{bmatrix} \cdot \begin{bmatrix} I_1 \\ I_2 \\ \vdots \\ I_n \end{bmatrix} = \begin{bmatrix} V_1 \\ 0 \\ \vdots \\ V_n \end{bmatrix} \tag{4.3}$$

and the first and last mesh-currents are given by

$$\begin{aligned} I_1 &= V_1 \frac{\Delta_{11}}{\Delta} + V_n \frac{\Delta_{n1}}{\Delta} \\ I_n &= V_n \frac{\Delta_{nn}}{\Delta} + V_1 \frac{\Delta_{1n}}{\Delta} \end{aligned} \tag{4.4}$$

where Δ and $\Delta_{11} \ldots \Delta_{nn}$ are the determinant and cofactors of the Z-matrix.

Thus, the voltages and currents external to a four-terminal network may be related independently of the internal topology, by invoking immittance parameters that are functions of the determinant of the network immittance-matrix and its cofactors. Since the internal topology is not directly involved (though implied in Δ and its cofactors) in eqns. (4.2) and (4.4), it is more appropriate to designate the currents and voltages as in Fig. 4-1(b). The determinantal coefficients are impedances in eqns. (4.2) and admittances in eqns. (4.4), so that the equations can be re-stated in the forms

$$\begin{aligned} Z_{11}I_1 + Z_{12}I_2 &= V_1 \\ Z_{21}I_1 + Z_{22}I_2 &= V_2 \end{aligned} \tag{4.5}$$

and

$$\begin{aligned} Y_{11}V_1 + Y_{12}V_2 &= I_1 \\ Y_{21}V_1 + Y_{22}V_2 &= I_2 \end{aligned} \tag{4.6}$$

An alternative justification for eqns. (4.5) and (4.6) is provided by the fact that any four-terminal network is subject to at least theoretical representation in the form of T or Π-networks, which in turn reduce to the basic star and delta topologies, involving only two meshes and two node-pairs respectively. This is indicated in Fig. 4-2.

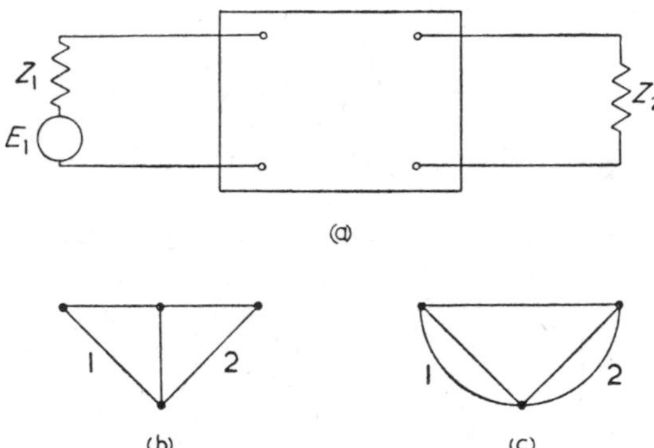

Fig. 4-2. (a) Multi-mesh four-terminal network. (b), (c) Equivalent two mesh and two node-pair graphs.

2.1 A NOTE ON POLARITY CONVENTIONS

In general loop-current and nodal-voltage analysis there are no rigid conventions for orientation of the graph, except in respect of correlation with the polarities of actual sources. In the particularisations of mesh-current and node-datum analysis, the adoption of a standard direction for mesh-currents, and like polarities for node-potentials, are practical conveniences for standardisation of solution procedures (as with determinants, for example).

In the case of four-terminal networks, however, a rigid polarity convention is necessary to ensure standardisation of matrix forms and transformations, which is essential to their ordered application to groups of networks. For example, transformations from one form to another, such as [Z] to [Y], vary in signs according to the convention used: matrix representations lose their value if the forms are not universal and amenable to standard manipulations.

Two representations are indicated in Fig. 4-3. Fig. 4-3(a) is consistent with the convention of general mesh-current analysis, and also with the probable direction of the actual output current I_2 for excitation by a single source of voltage V_1 in the sense indicated; while the output voltage V_2 is portrayed logically as a potential-drop in a load impedance, in the sense of I_2. But the arrangement of Fig. 4-3(a) is a particular (though common) case: for generality it must be assumed that any of the currents or voltages may be an independent source. A representation adaptable to any practical condition, and now almost universally adopted as a convention for the standardisation of four-terminal network equation and matrix forms, is shown in Fig. 4-3(b).

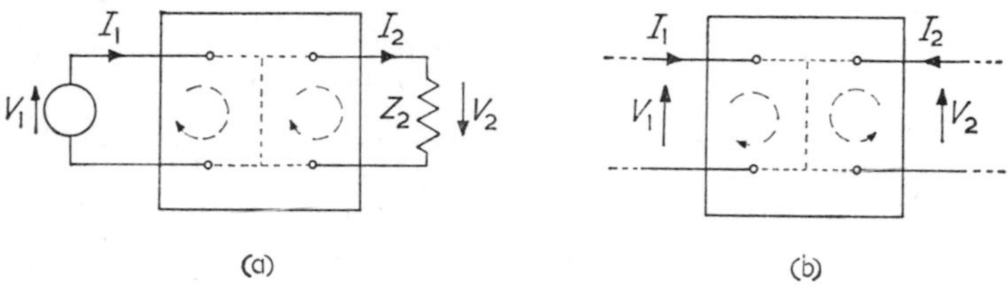

Fig. 4-3. Pertaining to polarity conventions.

For Fig. 4-3(a), the mesh type equations have the forms

$$\begin{aligned} Z_{11}I_1 + Z_{12}I_2 &= V_1 \\ Z_{21}I_1 + Z_{22}I_2 &= -V_2 \end{aligned} \tag{4.7}$$

where V_2 denotes the *fall* in potential I_2Z_2 in the load Z_2.

In Fig. 4-3(b), both V_1 and V_2 are oriented for potential *rise*, and the equations then have the general forms

$$\begin{aligned} Z_{11}I_1 + Z_{12}I_2 &= V_1 \\ Z_{21}I_1 + Z_{22}I_2 &= V_2 \end{aligned} \tag{4.8}$$

in which V_2 is written as $V_2 = -I_2Z_2$ if, in fact, it is not a potential rise but corresponds to a fall in potential due to I_2 traversing an external load Z_2.

In the case of a linear, passive network, conforming to the reciprocity theorem, $Z_{12} = Z_{21}$. For the orientations assumed in Fig. 4-3(a), both these parameters are negative, by virtue of the opposing senses in which the mesh-currents traverse the single equivalent mutual branch indicated on the figure; but in Fig. 4-3(b), the mesh-currents add in the mutual branch, and therefore both Z_{12} and Z_{21} are reckoned positive for this scheme of orientations.

The correct practical interpretation of the convention illustrated by Fig. 4-3(b) is fully illustrated in subsequent sections.

2.2 THE SIX PAIRS OF EQUATIONS FOR A FOUR-TERMINAL NETWORK

If the network is linear, each of the four quantities V_1, I_1, V_2, I_2, that define its external behaviour, may be assumed to be linearly related to each other. Now, the number of ways of selecting r things at a time out of n things is given by

$$ {}_nC_r = \frac{n!}{(n-r)!\,r!} \tag{4.9}$$

Thus, the number of ways in which two quantities out of the four currents and voltages can be selected as functions of the remaining two is given by

$$ {}_nC_r = \frac{4!}{2!\,2!} = 6 \tag{4.10}$$

The six possible pairs of equations, including the direct Kirchhoff-law forms already given in equations (4.5) and (4.6), are as follows:—

$$\begin{aligned} Z_{11}I_1 + Z_{12}I_2 &= V_1 \\ Z_{21}I_1 + Z_{22}I_2 &= V_2 \end{aligned} \tag{4.11}$$

$$\begin{aligned} Y_{11}V_1 + Y_{12}V_2 &= I_1 \\ Y_{21}V_1 + Y_{22}V_2 &= I_2 \end{aligned} \tag{4.12}$$

$$\begin{aligned} a_{11}V_2 - a_{12}I_2 &= V_1 \\ a_{21}V_2 - a_{22}I_2 &= I_1 \end{aligned} \tag{4.13}$$

$$\begin{aligned} b_{11}V_1 - b_{12}I_1 &= V_2 \\ b_{21}V_1 - b_{22}I_1 &= I_2 \end{aligned} \tag{4.14}$$

$$\begin{aligned} h_{11}I_1 + h_{12}V_2 &= V_1 \\ h_{21}I_1 + h_{22}V_2 &= I_2 \end{aligned} \tag{4.15}$$

$$\begin{aligned} g_{11}V_1 + g_{12}I_2 &= I_1 \\ g_{21}V_1 + g_{22}I_2 &= V_2 \end{aligned} \tag{4.16}$$

The signs are consistent with the convention of Fig. 4-3(b), while the symbols in eqns. (4.13) to (4.16) comply with accepted practice (as influenced by extensive American literature in this field).

The parameters are functions of the network only, and, being invarient with external conditions, may be defined in terms of the extremes of an open-circuit or short-circuit at a pair of terminals. These conditions are convenient, for they eliminate from the equations one current or one voltage, respectively. Thus, for example, in the case of eqns. (4.11) and Fig. 4-3(b), imposing open-circuit conditions first on the right and then on the left gives

$$\begin{aligned} Z_{11} &= V_1/I_1 \text{ when } I_2 = 0 \\ Z_{21} &= V_2/I_1 \text{ when } I_2 = 0 \\ Z_{12} &= V_1/I_2 \text{ when } I_1 = 0 \\ Z_{22} &= V_2/I_2 \text{ when } I_1 = 0 \end{aligned} \tag{4.17}$$

The admittances in eqns. (4.12) are determined similarly, but all under short-circuit conditions ($V_2 = 0$, $V_1 = 0$) instead. The *a*, *h*, *b*, and *g* parameters in eqns. (4.13)–(4.16) are defined by imposing either an open-circuit or a short-circuit according to which term it is desired to eliminate from an equation. In eqns. (4.15), for example,

$$\begin{aligned} h_{11} &= V_1/I_1 \text{ when } V_2 = 0 \\ h_{12} &= V_1/V_2 \text{ when } I_1 = 0 \\ h_{21} &= I_2/I_1 \text{ when } V_2 = 0 \\ h_{22} &= I_2/V_2 \text{ when } I_1 = 0 \end{aligned} \tag{4.18}$$

The parameters in this case are mixed, and are commonly called *hybrid parameters*. They are best known in connection with transistors, although they are certainly not special to them. From eqns. (4.18), h_{11} is the input impedance under a short-circuit condition at the output terminals (or simply, the *short-circuit input impedance*); h_{22} is the *open-circuit output admittance*; h_{12} is an *open-circuit voltage ratio*; and h_{21} is a *short-circuit current ratio*.

While, on the premise of linearity, the validity of the forms in eqns. (4.13) to (4.16) might be regarded as self-evident, any of them may be shown to be a transformation of the basic Kirchhoff-law forms, eqns. (4.11) and (4.12). Eqns. (4.15) provide an illustration.

The solutions of eqns. (4.11) are

$$I_1 = V_1 \frac{\Delta_{11}}{\Delta} + V_2 \frac{\Delta_{21}}{\Delta} \tag{4.19}$$

$$I_2 = V_1 \frac{\Delta_{12}}{\Delta} + V_2 \frac{\Delta_{22}}{\Delta} \tag{4.20}$$

where

$$\Delta = \begin{vmatrix} Z_{11} & Z_{12} \\ Z_{21} & Z_{22} \end{vmatrix}$$

Transposing in eqn. (4.19),

$$V_1 = I_1 \frac{\Delta}{\Delta_{11}} - V_2 \frac{\Delta_{21}}{\Delta_{11}} \tag{4.21}$$

Substituting for V_1 in eqn. (4.20),

$$I_2 = I_1 \frac{\Delta_{12}}{\Delta_{11}} + V_2 \left[\frac{\Delta_{22}}{\Delta} - \frac{\Delta_{12}\Delta_{21}}{\Delta\Delta_{11}}\right]$$

$$= I_1 \frac{\Delta_{12}}{\Delta_{11}} + V_2 \frac{1}{\Delta_{11}} \tag{4.22}$$

Eqns. (4.21) and (4.22) may be compressed into the forms of eqns. (4.15), viz.:

$$V_1 = h_{11}I_1 + h_{12}V_2$$
$$I_2 = h_{21}I_1 + h_{22}V_2$$

where

$$\begin{aligned} h_{11} &= \frac{\Delta}{\Delta_{11}} = Z_{11} - Z_{21}Z_{12}/Z_{22} \\ h_{12} &= -\frac{\Delta_{21}}{\Delta_{11}} = \frac{Z_{12}}{Z_{22}} \\ h_{21} &= \frac{\Delta_{12}}{\Delta_{11}} = -\frac{Z_{21}}{Z_{22}} \\ h_{22} &= \frac{1}{\Delta_{11}} = 1/Z_{22} \end{aligned} \tag{4.23}$$

In a similar way it can be shown for eqns. (4.13) that

$$\begin{aligned} a_{11} &= -\frac{\Delta_{22}}{\Delta_{12}} = \frac{Z_{11}}{Z_{21}} \\ a_{12} &= -\frac{\Delta}{\Delta_{12}} = -Z_{12} + \frac{Z_{11}Z_{22}}{Z_{21}} \\ a_{21} &= -\frac{1}{\Delta_{12}} = \frac{1}{Z_{21}} \\ a_{22} &= -\frac{\Delta_{11}}{\Delta_{12}} = \frac{Z_{22}}{Z_{21}} \end{aligned} \tag{4.24}$$

where a_{11} is the open-circuit voltage ratio V_1/V_2, a_{12} the short-circuit transfer impedance $V_1/(-I_2)$, a_{21} the mutual admittance or open-circuit transfer admittance I_1/V_2, and a_{22} is the short-circuit current ratio $I_1/(-I_2)$.

It is an important property of eqn. (4.13) that, in the case of a linear, passive, bilateral network obeying the reciprocity theorem, or *reciprocal network*,

$$\begin{vmatrix} a_{11} & a_{12} \\ a_{21} & a_{22} \end{vmatrix} = a_{11}a_{22} - a_{21}a_{12} = 1 \tag{4.25}$$

This has been proved with the reciprocity theorem in Example 3.1. It is also easily shown by substituting for the a-coefficients, writing $Z_{12} = Z_{21}$:

$$a_{11}a_{22} - a_{21}a_{12} = \frac{\Delta_{22}}{\Delta_{12}} \cdot \frac{\Delta_{11}}{\Delta_{12}} - \frac{\Delta}{\Delta_{12}} \cdot \frac{1}{\Delta_{12}}$$
$$= (Z_{11}Z_{22} - Z_{11}Z_{22} + Z_{12}^2)/Z_{12}^2 = 1$$

The form of eqn. (4.25) also applies to the determinant of eqns. (4.14).

2.2.1 *Practical functions*

While the six equation-pairs (4.11) to (4.16) are equivalent as representations for the equilibrium of a four-terminal network, each is identifiable, though not always manifestly, with a particular set of conditions or data to which it is most adaptable.

The basic forms, eqns. (4.11) and (4.12), are adaptable to any external arrangements and to the calculation of any input or output quantities. The choice between them is that between mesh-current and nodal-voltage analysis. If the matrix of coefficients is available in both $[Z]$ and $[Y]$ forms, the choice is governed mainly by whether the external sources are of the constant-e.m.f. or constant-current type. This is illustrated by Fig. 4-4.

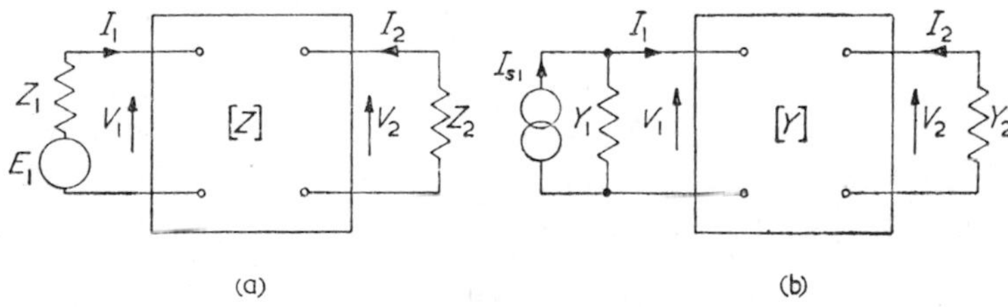

Fig. 4-4.

Let the coefficient matrices for the network be

$$[Z] = \begin{bmatrix} Z_{11} & Z_{12} \\ Z_{21} & Z_{22} \end{bmatrix} \tag{4.26}$$

$$[Y] = \begin{bmatrix} Y_{11} & Y_{12} \\ Y_{21} & Y_{22} \end{bmatrix} \tag{4.27}$$

Then for the arrangement of Fig. 4-4(a),

$$\begin{bmatrix} Z_{11} & Z_{12} \\ Z_{21} & Z_{22} \end{bmatrix} \cdot \begin{bmatrix} I_1 \\ I_2 \end{bmatrix} = \begin{bmatrix} V_1 \\ V_2 \end{bmatrix} = \begin{bmatrix} E_1 - Z_1 I_1 \\ - Z_2 I_2 \end{bmatrix}$$

or, absorbing Z_1 and Z_2 into Z_{11} and Z_{22}, respectively,

$$\begin{bmatrix} Z_{11} + Z_1 & Z_{12} \\ Z_{21} & Z_{22} + Z_2 \end{bmatrix} \cdot \begin{bmatrix} I_1 \\ I_2 \end{bmatrix} = \begin{bmatrix} E_1 \\ 0 \end{bmatrix} \tag{4.28}$$

In the case of Fig. 4-4(b), [Z] is less convenient (unless the source is transformed with Thévenin's theorem into an e.m.f. one). But in terms of [Y],

$$\begin{bmatrix} Y_{11} & Y_{12} \\ Y_{21} & Y_{22} \end{bmatrix} \cdot \begin{bmatrix} V_1 \\ V_2 \end{bmatrix} = \begin{bmatrix} I_1 \\ I_2 \end{bmatrix} = \begin{bmatrix} I_{s1} - Y_1 V_1 \\ - Y_2 V_2 \end{bmatrix}$$

or, (4.29)

$$\begin{bmatrix} Y_{11} + Y_1 & Y_{12} \\ Y_{21} & Y_{22} + Y_2 \end{bmatrix} \cdot \begin{bmatrix} V_1 \\ V_2 \end{bmatrix} = \begin{bmatrix} I_{s1} \\ 0 \end{bmatrix}$$

which is the dual of eqn. (4.28).

If the network configuration is given and a matrix must first be determined for it, the choice of equation is more likely to be decided by which of the matrices is the easier to find. As an example, for a T-network [Z] is much more obvious than [Y]; but for a Π-network the reverse is the case.

Eqns. (4.13) correspond (except for polarity convention) to the $A\ B\ C\ D$ parameter equations

$$\begin{aligned} V_1 &= AV_2 + BI_2 \\ I_1 &= CV_2 + DI_2 \end{aligned} \tag{4.30}$$

This form, in relating the input quantities directly to the output, is natural for transmission calculations. It was originally applied mainly to power transmission problems, in which the specified quantities are usually the load volt-amperes (V_2, I_2) at the receiving end of the system, and the corresponding input quantities (V_1, I_1) are those to be found. It is also noteworthy that the form of eqns. (4.30) corresponds to that of the transmission-line equations,

$$\begin{aligned} V_s &= V_r \cosh \gamma l + I_r Z_o \sinh \gamma l \\ I_s &= I_r \cosh \gamma l + V_r Y_o \sinh \gamma l \end{aligned} \tag{4.31}$$

where

$$I_1 = I_s,\ I_2 = I_r,\ V_1 = V_s,\ V_2 = V_r,\ A = D = \cosh \gamma l,$$

$$B = Z_o \sinh \gamma l,\ C = Y_o \sinh \gamma l.$$

Equations (4.14) are simply reversed forms of (4.13), and may seem more appropriate to the common problem in communication and electronics, which is the calculation of output quantities (*response*) as functions of known input quantities (*excitation*). There is, however, a simple correlation between the two forms. Rewriting eqns. (4.13) with the symbols A, B, C, D, which are poignant in this connection,

$$\begin{aligned} V_1 &= AV_2 - BI_2 \\ I_1 &= CV_2 - DI_2 \end{aligned} \tag{4.32}$$

Substituting for I_2 from the second into the first and transposing,

$$V_2 \cdot \frac{AD - BC}{D} = V_1 - \frac{B}{D} I_1$$

But by reference to eqn. (4.25), in the case of a reciprocal network, $AD - BC = a_{11}a_{22} - a_{21}a_{12} = 1$ and therefore

$$V_2 = DV_1 - BI_1$$

Substituting then for V_2 in the second of eqns. (4.32),

$$I_2 = CV_1 - \frac{1 + CB}{D} I_1$$

or

$$I_2 = CV_1 - AI_1$$

Thus, given

$$\begin{bmatrix} V_1 \\ I_1 \end{bmatrix} = \begin{bmatrix} A & B \\ C & D \end{bmatrix} \cdot \begin{bmatrix} V_2 \\ -I_2 \end{bmatrix} \tag{4.33}$$

then

$$\begin{bmatrix} V_2 \\ I_2 \end{bmatrix} = \begin{bmatrix} D & B \\ C & A \end{bmatrix} \cdot \begin{bmatrix} V_1 \\ -I_1 \end{bmatrix} \tag{4.34}$$

The interchange of input and output quantities in the case of a reciprocal network thus simply changes the order of the matrix elements from $A\,B\,C\,D$ to $D\,B\,C\,A$, which is an exchange of elements on the leading diagonal. In practice, eqns. (4.13), (4.32), or (4.30) are the more commonly encountered forms.

Equations (4.16) are likewise an inversion of (4.15); but as both are flexible hybrid types, there are no obvious applications to a single network in which either has a marked advantage over the other. But each has an especially distinctive role, along with each of the other forms, in relation to interconnected networks.

2.3 DETERMINATION OF THE COEFFICIENT MATRICES

In principle, each coefficient may be found from external measurements of current and voltage, under the open or short-circuit conditions implied in their definitions. This is exemplified by eqns. (4.17) and (4.18). When the network configuration and element values are known, as is often the case, the coefficients may be calculated in any of the six forms, although generally a particular form is likely to be the easiest to find for a given configuration. But any form is readily transformed into another.

2.3.1 *A note on measurement*

In practice the coefficients must be regarded generally as complex or vector quantities, and bridge or potentiometric methods capable of determining complex ratios of voltages or currents, or voltages to currents (i.e., impedances) are required.

A linear passive network, obeying the reciprocity theorem, has transfer coefficients that are equal for both directions of excitation or transmission. Three measurements with an impedance or admittance bridge are then sufficient to determine, for example, the Z- or Y-matrices. Referring to eqns. (4.11), Z_{11} and Z_{22} are given directly by impedance measurements under open-circuit conditions at the respective far-end of the network. Then Z_{12} and Z_{21}, which are equal, can be calculated from a further measurement under short-circuit conditions. For example, putting $V_2 = 0$ in eqns. (4.11) and substituting $I_2 = -Z_{21} I_1/Z_{22}$ into the first one gives

$$\begin{aligned} V_1/I_1 = Z^s &= Z_{11} - Z_{21}Z_{12}/Z_{22} \\ &= Z_{11} - Z_{12}^2/Z_{22} \\ &= Z_{11} - Z_{21}^2/Z_{22} \end{aligned} \qquad (4.35)$$

from which Z_{12} or Z_{21} may be calculated in terms of the measured values of Z_{11}, Z_{22}, and the short circuit impedance Z^s.

In the case of a non-reciprocal network or device, such as a valve or transistor, the transfer coefficients exemplified by Z_{12} and Z_{21} are unequal. Consideration of eqns. (4.11) and (4.35) will show that Z_{12} and Z_{21} cannot be separately found from impedance measurements alone, and a method of the potentiometric type capable of determining also the input-output open-circuit voltage ratio, or short-circuit current ratio, is necessary. When the coefficients are known to be real, as is nearly so for a transistor in the audio-frequency range, all the measurements can be made with sensitive a.c. voltmeters and ammeters.

2.3.2 *Calculation of the matrices for given configurations*

The basic topologies are few, and for each, at least one of the matrix forms can be recognised by inspection, or almost. This is illustrated by reference to Fig. 4-5.

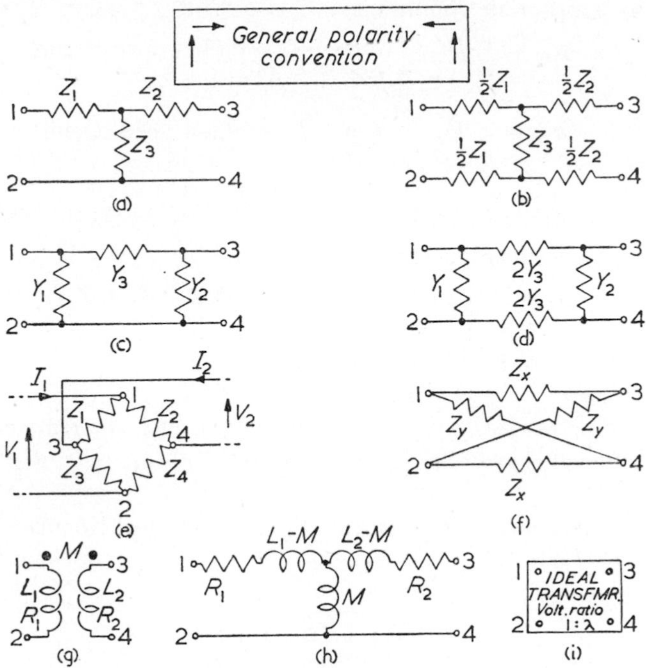

Fig. 4-5. Basic passive, reciprocal 4-terminal networks.

(1) The T-network and corresponding balanced H-network have a self-evident Z-matrix. Referring to the equations

$$Z_{11}I_1 + Z_{12}I_2 = V_1$$
$$Z_{21}I_1 + Z_{22}I_2 = V_2$$

and Figs. 4-5(a) and (b),

$$Z_{11} = V_1/I_{1(I_2=0)} = Z^0_{1-2} = Z_1 + Z_3$$
$$Z_{22} = V_2/I_{2(I_1=0)} = Z^0_{3-4} = Z_2 + Z_3$$
$$Z_{12} = Z_{21} = V_2/I_{1(I_2=0)} = I_1Z_3/I_1 = Z_3$$

Thus,

$$[Z] = \begin{bmatrix} Z_{11} & Z_{12} \\ Z_{21} & Z_{22} \end{bmatrix} = \begin{bmatrix} Z_1 + Z_3 & Z_3 \\ Z_3 & Z_2 + Z_3 \end{bmatrix} \tag{4.36}$$

None of the other matrices is so obvious. For example, consider the matrix of a-coefficients in the equations

$$V_1 = a_{11}V_2 - a_{12}I_2$$
$$I_1 = a_{21}V_2 - a_{22}I_2$$

Imposing appropriate conditions:

$$a_{11} = V_1/V_2 \quad \text{when} \quad I_2 = 0 \text{ (3–4 open-circuit)}$$
$$= V_1/[V_1Z_3/(Z_1+Z_3)] = 1 + Z_1/Z_3$$

$$a_{21} = I_1/V_2 \quad \text{when} \quad I_2 = 0 \text{ (3–4 open-circuit)}$$
$$= I_1/I_1Z_3 = 1/Z_3$$

$$a_{12} = V_1/(-I_2) \quad \text{when} \quad V_2 = 0 \text{ (3–4 short-circuit)}$$

Using Thévenin's theorem,

$$-I_2 = [V_1Z_3/(Z_1+Z_3)]/[Z_2 + Z_1Z_3/(Z_1+Z_3)]$$
$$= V_1/(Z_1 + Z_2 + Z_1Z_2/Z_3)$$

and therefore

$$a_{12} = Z_1 + Z_2 + Z_1Z_2/Z_3$$

As the network is a passive and reciprocal one, the remaining coefficient a_{22} could be found by solving the equation $a_{11}a_{22} - a_{21}a_{12} = 1$. Alternatively,

$$a_{22} = I_1/(-I_2) \quad \text{when} \quad V_2 = 0 \text{ (3–4 short circuit)}$$
$$(-I_2) = I_1Y_2/(Y_2+Y_3),$$

therefore

$$a_{22} = 1 + \frac{Y_3}{Y_2} = 1 + \frac{Z_2}{Z_3}$$

The matrix is therefore

$$[a] = \begin{bmatrix} a_{11} & a_{12} \\ a_{21} & a_{22} \end{bmatrix} = \begin{bmatrix} 1 + Z_1/Z_3 & Z_1 + Z_2 + Z_1Z_2/Z_3 \\ 1/Z_3 & 1 + Z_2/Z_3 \end{bmatrix} \qquad (4.37)$$

It may be noted that the *short-circuit transfer impedance*,

$$Z_{tr} = a_{12} = Z_1 + Z_2 + Z_1Z_2/Z_3 \qquad (4.38)$$

is important outside the context of matrices, as a basis for deriving null conditions for paralleled T-networks. It is also interesting that it represents the series branch of the equivalent Π-network. The result is worth remembering. See Example 4.9.

(2) For the Π-network and its balanced O-equivalent, it is the Y-matrix that is obvious. Applying the equations

$$Y_{11}V_1 + Y_{12}V_2 = I_1$$
$$Y_{21}V_1 + Y_{22}V_2 = I_2$$

to Figs. 4-5(c) and (d),

$$Y_{11} = I_1/V_{1(V_2=0)} = Y^s_{1-2} = Y_1 + Y_3$$
$$Y_{22} = I_2/V_{2(V_1=0)} = Y^s_{3-4} = Y_2 + Y_3$$
$$Y_{12} = Y_{21} = I_2/V_{1(V_2=0)} = -V_1Y_3/V_1 = -Y_3$$

Thus,

$$[Y] = \begin{bmatrix} Y_{11} & Y_{12} \\ Y_{21} & Y_{22} \end{bmatrix} = \begin{bmatrix} Y_1 + Y_3 & -Y_3 \\ -Y_3 & Y_2 + Y_3 \end{bmatrix} \tag{4.39}$$

Y_{12} and Y_{21} are negative because of the polarity convention in use: under short-circuit conditions, I_1 due to V_2 and I_2 due to V_1 are opposite to the directions assumed in the convention. A change in convention to that of Fig. 4-3(a) would make Z_{12} and Z_{21} negative but Y_{12} and Y_{21} positive.

(3) The bridge network has an h-matrix that is surprisingly easy to find. Referring to the equations

$$V_1 = h_{11}I_1 + h_{12}V_2$$
$$I_2 = h_{21}I_1 + h_{22}V_2$$

and Fig. 4-5(e),

$$h_{11} = V_1/I_{1(V_2=0)} = Z^s_{1-2}$$

$$= \frac{Z_1Z_2}{Z_1 + Z_2} + \frac{Z_3Z_4}{Z_3 + Z_4} \tag{4.40}$$

$$h_{12} = V_1/V_{2(I_1=0)} \qquad \text{(1–2 open circuit)}$$

Observing that $Z_1 + Z_2$ and $Z_3 + Z_4$ form potential-dividers across V_2,

$$V_1 = V_2\left[\frac{Z_2}{Z_1 + Z_2} - \frac{Z_4}{Z_3 + Z_4}\right]$$

and

$$h_{12} = V_1/V_2 = \frac{Z_2}{Z_1 + Z_2} - \frac{Z_4}{Z_3 + Z_4} \tag{4.41}$$

h_{21}, however, is not so easily found. But for a passive reciprocal network, eqns. (4.23) show that

$$h_{21} = -h_{12} \tag{4.42}$$

so that separate calculation is unnecessary.

$$h_{22} = I_2/V_{2(I_1=0)} = Y^0_{3-4}$$

$$= \frac{Y_1Y_2}{Y_1 + Y_2} + \frac{Y_3Y_4}{Y_3 + Y_4} \tag{4.43}$$

Eqn. (4.43) is the dual of eqn. (4.40).

The Z-matrix is also easily found. Its elements are

$$Z_{11} = Z^0_{1-2} = (Z_1 + Z_3)(Z_2 + Z_4)/\Sigma Z \tag{4.44}$$

$$Z_{22} = Z^0_{3-4} = (Z_3 + Z_4)(Z_1 + Z_2)/\Sigma Z \quad (4.45)$$

$$Z_{12} = Z_{21} = V_2/I_{1(I_2=0)} \quad \text{(3–4 open circuit)}$$

$$= (Z_2Z_3 - Z_1Z_4)/\Sigma Z \quad (4.46)$$

(4) The lattice network of Fig. 4-5(f) may be regarded as a symmetrical non-planar version of the bridge, Fig. 4-5(e). However, it is interesting to obtain its Z-matrix independently and easily with the aid of *Bartlett's bisection theorem.*

Let a T-network equivalent to the lattice have series branches Z_p and a shunt branch Z_q. Then, according to the theorem, as explained in Chapter 2, sect. 5.2.3,

$$Z_x = Z_p, \quad Z_y = Z_p + 2Z_q$$

Transposing,

$$Z_p = Z_x, \quad \text{and} \quad Z_q = (Z_y - Z_x)/2$$

The matrix for the lattice network must equal that for its equivalent network. Therefore,

$$[Z] = \begin{bmatrix} Z_p + Z_q & Z_q \\ Z_q & Z_p + Z_q \end{bmatrix}$$

$$= \begin{bmatrix} \frac{1}{2}(Z_y + Z_x) & \frac{1}{2}(Z_y - Z_x) \\ \frac{1}{2}(Z_y - Z_x) & \frac{1}{2}(Z_y + Z_x) \end{bmatrix} \quad (4.47)$$

(5) The mutual inductor or transformer shown in Fig. 4-5(g) has a Z-matrix that is obvious, except for the sign of Z_{12} or Z_{21}.

For the winding senses indicated by the dot notation (Chapter 2, sect. 2.4.1), a current I_1 traversing L_1 produces self and mutually induced voltages V_1 and V_2 such that terminals 1 and 3 are instantaneously of like polarity. Thus, for I_1 in the conventional (clockwise) sense, both V_1 and V_2 are also in the conventional (upward) sense, and V_2 is reckoned positive with respect to I_1. The matrix elements are therefore

$$Z_{11} = Z^0_{1-2} = R_1 + sL_1$$

$$Z_{22} = Z^0_{3-4} = R_2 + sL_2$$

$$Z_{12} = Z_{21} = V_2/I_{1(I_2=0)} = sMI_1/I_1 = sM$$

and

$$[Z] = \begin{bmatrix} R_1 + sL_1 & sM \\ sM & R_2 + sL_2 \end{bmatrix} \quad (4.48)$$

The equivalent T-network for the particular winding-senses (Fig. 2-22(b) and eqns. 2.98) is shown for comparison in Fig. 4-5(h). Its Z-matrix is obviously consistent with eqn. (4.48).

(6) The ideal transformer, Fig. 4-5(i), having a voltage-ratio $V_2/V_1 = \lambda$, has a current ratio $(-I_2)/I_1 = 1/\lambda$. Since these ratios are (for this ideal concept), entirely independent of external conditions, the equations

$$\begin{aligned} V_1 &= a_{11}V_2 - a_{12}I_2 \\ I_1 &= a_{21}V_2 - a_{22}I_2 \end{aligned}$$

become

$$\begin{aligned} V_1 &= (1/\lambda)V_2 = a_{11}V_2 - a_{12}I_2 \\ I_1 &= \lambda(-I_2) \;\; = a_{21}V_2 - a_{22}I_2 \end{aligned}$$

whence,

$$\begin{aligned} a_{11} &= 1/\lambda, \qquad & a_{12} &= 0 \\ a_{21} &= 0, \qquad & a_{22} &= \lambda \end{aligned}$$

or,

$$[a] = \begin{bmatrix} a_{11} & a_{12} \\ a_{21} & a_{22} \end{bmatrix} = \begin{bmatrix} 1/\lambda & 0 \\ 0 & \lambda \end{bmatrix} \tag{4.49}$$

Neither the Z- nor Y-matrices are finite, but

$$[h] = \begin{bmatrix} 0 & 1/\lambda \\ -1/\lambda & 0 \end{bmatrix} \tag{4.50}$$

(7) The derivation of matrices for non-reciprocal active networks is illustrated by Fig. 4-6. Linearity is assumed.

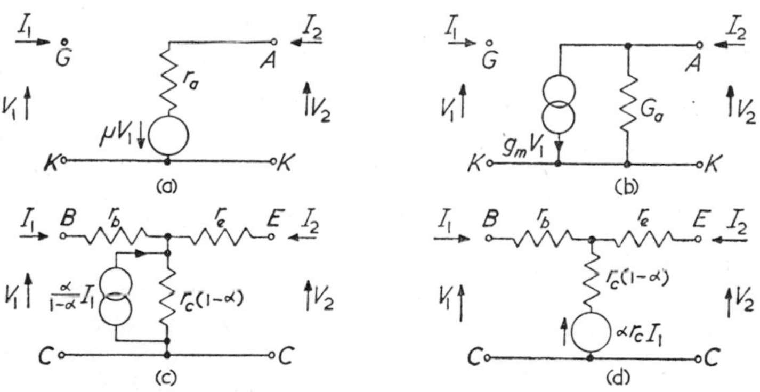

Fig. 4-6. Examples of active networks: (a), (b), low-frequency equivalences for a valve in the common-cathode circuit; (c), (d), representations for a transistor at audio frequencies in the common-collector circuit.

Assuming class-A linear operating conditions, under which there is no grid-current ($I_1 = 0$), and excluding inter-electrode capacitances, the valve behaves as a purely unilateral device: there is no "network" coupling between input and output circuits. For Fig. 4-6(a), eqns. (4.16) are appropriate; but as $I_1 = 0$, only the second applies:

$$g_{21}V_1 + g_{22}I_2 = V_2$$

in which

$$\begin{aligned} g_{21} &= V_2/V_{1(I_2=0)} = -\mu V_1/V_1 = -\mu \\ g_{22} &= V_2/I_{2(V_1=0)} = V_2/(V_2/r_a) = r_a \end{aligned} \tag{4.51}$$

For Fig. 4-6(b), the second of eqns. (4.12),

$$Y_{21}V_1 + Y_{22}V_2 = I_2$$

gives

$$\begin{aligned} Y_{21} &= I_2/V_{1(V_2=0)} = g_m V_1/V_1 = g_m \\ Y_{22} &= I_2/V_{2(V_1=0)} = G_a = 1/r_a \end{aligned} \tag{4.52}$$

For illustration, consider the voltage gain V_2/V_1 of a valve with a load impedance, Z. The formal matrix equation

$$\begin{bmatrix} g_{11} & g_{12} \\ g_{21} & g_{22} \end{bmatrix} \cdot \begin{bmatrix} V_1 \\ I_2 \end{bmatrix} = \begin{bmatrix} I_1 \\ V_2 \end{bmatrix}$$

becomes

$$\begin{bmatrix} 0 & 0 \\ -\mu & r_a \end{bmatrix} \cdot \begin{bmatrix} V_1 \\ I_2 \end{bmatrix} = \begin{bmatrix} 0 \\ V_2 \end{bmatrix}$$

whence

$$-\mu V_1 + r_a I_2 = V_2$$

or

$$-\mu V_1 - r_a V_2/Z = V_2$$

which gives

$$V_2/V_1 = \frac{-\mu Z}{r_a + Z}$$

Of course, this is a pretentious approach to what has reduced to a simple one-mesh problem. Nevertheless, it is important for illustrating the generality of the matrix concept, and identifying it with parameters often thought of as peculiar to a thermionic valve.

Fig. 4-6(c) is the customary representation for a transistor in the common-collector circuit, in which r_b, r_e and r_c are the resistance values in the common-base low-frequency equivalent circuit, and α is the common-base short-circuit current amplification factor, $\alpha = I_c/I_e$. To calculate the Z-matrix, it is an advantage to replace the constant-current source $\alpha I_1/(1-\alpha)$ by an equivalent e.m.f. source, as in Fig. 4-6(d).*

* While it is conventional to show transistor equivalent circuits incorporating constant-current sources (because it is the current relationships that approximate linearity), the setting-up of equations for such circuits for practical problems is often simplified by using the equivalent e.m.f. form.

Consider Fig. 4-6(d) and the equations

$$Z_{11}I_1 + Z_{12}I_2 = V_1$$
$$Z_{21}I_1 + Z_{22}I_2 = V_2$$

When $I_2 = 0$ (E-C open-circuit),

$$I_1 = (V_1 - \alpha r_c I_1)/[r_b + r_c(1 - \alpha)]$$

whence

$$V_1/I_{1(I_2=0)} = Z_{11} = r_b + r_c$$

Also

$$V_2 = I_1 r_c(1 - \alpha) + \alpha r_c I_1 = I_1 r_c$$

and therefore

$$V_2/I_{1(I_2=0)} = Z_{21} = r_c$$

When $I_1 = 0$ (B-C open-circuit), the e.m.f. $\alpha r_c I_1$ vanishes. Then,

$$V_2/I_{2(I_1=0)} = Z_{22} = r_e + r_c(1 - \alpha)$$

Also,

$$V_1 = I_2 r_c(1 - \alpha)$$

and

$$V_1/I_{2(I_1=0)} = Z_{12} = r_c(1 - \alpha)$$

Thus,

$$[Z] = \begin{bmatrix} Z_{11} & Z_{12} \\ Z_{21} & Z_{22} \end{bmatrix} = \begin{bmatrix} r_b + r_c & r_c(1 - \alpha) \\ r_c & r_e + r_c(1 - \alpha) \end{bmatrix} \tag{4.53}$$

2.3.3 *Matrix conversions*

The form in which a matrix is available or in which it is expedient to calculate or measure it, may not be appropriate to a particular problem. For example, Z- or Y-matrices may be available, but a-matrices are required if the problem is concerned with a sequential arrangement of networks.

The convertibility of equations and their coefficient matrices has been illustrated in sect. 2.2. For example, referring to eqns. (4.11), (4.15) and (4.23),

$$\begin{bmatrix} h_{11} & h_{12} \\ h_{21} & h_{22} \end{bmatrix} = \begin{bmatrix} \dfrac{\Delta}{\Delta_{11}} & -\dfrac{\Delta_{21}}{\Delta_{11}} \\ \dfrac{\Delta_{12}}{\Delta_{11}} & \dfrac{1}{\Delta_{11}} \end{bmatrix} = \begin{bmatrix} \dfrac{\Delta}{Z_{22}} & \dfrac{Z_{12}}{Z_{22}} \\ -\dfrac{Z_{21}}{Z_{22}} & \dfrac{1}{Z_{22}} \end{bmatrix} \tag{4.54}$$

where $\Delta = \text{det.}[Z] = Z_{11}Z_{22} - Z_{21}Z_{12}$.

Other conversions such as $[a]$ to $[Z]$, eqns. (4.24), or $[a]$ to $[Y]$, etc., follow similarly.

Equations (4.11), (4.12) and (4.15), (4.16) are inverse pairs. For example, given eqns. (4.11), $[Z]\cdot[I] = [V]$, then the form of eqns. (4.12), $[Y]\cdot[V]=[I]$, is equivalent to $[Z]^{-1}\cdot[V]=[I]$, and

$$[Y] = [Z]^{-1} \tag{4.55}$$

Similarly, by reference to eqns. (4.15) and (4.16),

$$[g] = [h]^{-1} \tag{4.56}$$

Equations (4.13) and (4.14), however, are mutually transposed forms. From eqns. (4.13), for a reciprocal network,*

$$\begin{bmatrix} V_2 \\ -I_2 \end{bmatrix} = [a]^{-1} \cdot \begin{bmatrix} V_1 \\ I_1 \end{bmatrix} = \begin{bmatrix} a_{22} & -a_{12} \\ -a_{21} & a_{11} \end{bmatrix} \cdot \begin{bmatrix} V_1 \\ I_1 \end{bmatrix}$$

This transforms into the form of eqns. (4.14) on pre-multiplying by a diagonal sign-changing matrix:

$$\begin{bmatrix} V_2 \\ I_2 \end{bmatrix} = \begin{bmatrix} 1 & 0 \\ 0 & -1 \end{bmatrix} \cdot \begin{bmatrix} a_{22} & -a_{12} \\ -a_{21} & a_{11} \end{bmatrix} \cdot \begin{bmatrix} V_1 \\ I_1 \end{bmatrix}$$

$$= \begin{bmatrix} a_{22} & a_{12} \\ a_{21} & a_{11} \end{bmatrix} \cdot \begin{bmatrix} V_1 \\ -I_1 \end{bmatrix} = [\mathrm{b}] \cdot \begin{bmatrix} V_1 \\ -I_1 \end{bmatrix} \tag{4.57}$$

$[b]$ is not $[a]^{-1}$, but corresponds to transformation from $A\ B\ C\ D$ to $D\ B\ C\ A$ form, illustrated for a reciprocal network in section 2.2.1.

Inversion is simple, for the matrices are of order 2×2 only. For example, let the given matrix be

$$[Z] = \begin{bmatrix} Z_{11} & Z_{12} \\ Z_{21} & Z_{22} \end{bmatrix} \tag{4.58}$$

Inverting as explained in Chapter 2, sect. 2.5.3, the transpose matrix is

$$[Z]^t = \begin{bmatrix} Z_{11} & Z_{21} \\ Z_{12} & Z_{22} \end{bmatrix}$$

and replacing each element by its cofactor,

$$[Z]^t_c = \begin{bmatrix} Z_{22} & -Z_{12} \\ -Z_{21} & Z_{11} \end{bmatrix}$$

Then,

$$[Y] = [Z]^{-1} = \frac{[Z]^t_c}{\Delta} = \begin{bmatrix} \dfrac{Z_{22}}{\Delta} & -\dfrac{Z_{12}}{\Delta} \\ -\dfrac{Z_{21}}{\Delta} & \dfrac{Z_{11}}{\Delta} \end{bmatrix} \tag{4.59}$$

As the conversions are standard for the customary polarity convention and notation, it is more efficient in practice to refer to a conversion chart such as that given in Table 4-1.

* In the case of a non-reciprocal network the determinant of the matrix is not unity, as implied here.

It is interesting to note that transformation from $[Z]$ to $[Y]$ corresponds to transforming a T-network equivalent to the given network into an equivalent Π-network: $[Y]$ as given by eqn. (4.59) may be identified with a Π-network equivalent to a T-network when the Z-matrix is eqn. (4.58).

To \ From	$[Z]$	$[Y]$	$[h]$	$[g]$	$[a]$	$[b]$
$[Z]$	$\begin{matrix} Z_{11} & Z_{12} \\ Z_{21} & Z_{22} \end{matrix}$	$\begin{matrix} \frac{Y_{22}}{\Delta} & \frac{-Y_{12}}{\Delta} \\ \frac{-Y_{21}}{\Delta} & \frac{Y_{11}}{\Delta} \end{matrix}$	$\begin{matrix} \frac{\Delta}{h_{22}} & \frac{h_{12}}{h_{22}} \\ \frac{-h_{21}}{h_{22}} & \frac{1}{h_{22}} \end{matrix}$	$\begin{matrix} \frac{1}{g_{11}} & \frac{-g_{12}}{g_{11}} \\ \frac{g_{21}}{g_{11}} & \frac{\Delta}{g_{11}} \end{matrix}$	$\begin{matrix} \frac{a_{11}}{a_{21}} & \frac{\Delta}{a_{21}} \\ \frac{1}{a_{21}} & \frac{a_{22}}{a_{21}} \end{matrix}$	$\begin{matrix} \frac{b_{22}}{b_{21}} & \frac{1}{b_{21}} \\ \frac{\Delta}{b_{21}} & \frac{b_{11}}{b_{21}} \end{matrix}$
$[Y]$	$\begin{matrix} \frac{Z_{22}}{\Delta} & \frac{-Z_{12}}{\Delta} \\ \frac{-Z_{21}}{\Delta} & \frac{Z_{11}}{\Delta} \end{matrix}$	$\begin{matrix} Y_{11} & Y_{12} \\ Y_{21} & Y_{22} \end{matrix}$	$\begin{matrix} \frac{1}{h_{11}} & \frac{-h_{12}}{h_{11}} \\ \frac{h_{21}}{h_{11}} & \frac{\Delta}{h_{11}} \end{matrix}$	$\begin{matrix} \frac{\Delta}{g_{22}} & \frac{g_{12}}{g_{22}} \\ \frac{-g_{21}}{g_{22}} & \frac{1}{g_{22}} \end{matrix}$	$\begin{matrix} \frac{a_{22}}{a_{12}} & \frac{-\Delta}{a_{12}} \\ \frac{-1}{a_{12}} & \frac{a_{11}}{a_{12}} \end{matrix}$	$\begin{matrix} \frac{b_{11}}{b_{12}} & \frac{-1}{b_{12}} \\ \frac{-\Delta}{b_{12}} & \frac{b_{22}}{b_{12}} \end{matrix}$
$[h]$	$\begin{matrix} \frac{\Delta}{Z_{22}} & \frac{Z_{12}}{Z_{22}} \\ \frac{-Z_{21}}{Z_{22}} & \frac{1}{Z_{22}} \end{matrix}$	$\begin{matrix} \frac{1}{Y_{11}} & \frac{-Y_{12}}{Y_{11}} \\ \frac{Y_{21}}{Y_{11}} & \frac{\Delta}{Y_{11}} \end{matrix}$	$\begin{matrix} h_{11} & h_{12} \\ h_{21} & h_{22} \end{matrix}$	$\begin{matrix} \frac{g_{22}}{\Delta} & \frac{-g_{12}}{\Delta} \\ \frac{-g_{21}}{\Delta} & \frac{g_{11}}{\Delta} \end{matrix}$	$\begin{matrix} \frac{a_{12}}{a_{22}} & \frac{\Delta}{a_{22}} \\ \frac{-1}{a_{22}} & \frac{a_{21}}{a_{22}} \end{matrix}$	$\begin{matrix} \frac{b_{12}}{b_{11}} & \frac{1}{b_{11}} \\ \frac{-\Delta}{b_{11}} & \frac{b_{21}}{b_{11}} \end{matrix}$
$[g]$	$\begin{matrix} \frac{1}{Z_{11}} & \frac{-Z_{12}}{Z_{11}} \\ \frac{Z_{21}}{Z_{11}} & \frac{\Delta}{Z_{11}} \end{matrix}$	$\begin{matrix} \frac{\Delta}{Y_{22}} & \frac{Y_{12}}{Y_{22}} \\ \frac{-Y_{21}}{Y_{22}} & \frac{1}{Y_{22}} \end{matrix}$	$\begin{matrix} \frac{h_{22}}{\Delta} & \frac{-h_{12}}{\Delta} \\ \frac{-h_{21}}{\Delta} & \frac{h_{11}}{\Delta} \end{matrix}$	$\begin{matrix} g_{11} & g_{12} \\ g_{21} & g_{22} \end{matrix}$	$\begin{matrix} \frac{a_{21}}{a_{11}} & \frac{-\Delta}{a_{11}} \\ \frac{1}{a_{11}} & \frac{a_{12}}{a_{11}} \end{matrix}$	$\begin{matrix} \frac{b_{21}}{b_{22}} & \frac{-1}{b_{22}} \\ \frac{\Delta}{b_{22}} & \frac{b_{12}}{b_{22}} \end{matrix}$
$[a]$	$\begin{matrix} \frac{Z_{11}}{Z_{21}} & \frac{\Delta}{Z_{21}} \\ \frac{1}{Z_{21}} & \frac{Z_{22}}{Z_{21}} \end{matrix}$	$\begin{matrix} \frac{-Y_{22}}{Y_{21}} & \frac{-1}{Y_{21}} \\ \frac{-\Delta}{Y_{21}} & \frac{-Y_{11}}{Y_{21}} \end{matrix}$	$\begin{matrix} \frac{-\Delta}{h_{21}} & \frac{-h_{11}}{h_{21}} \\ \frac{-h_{22}}{h_{21}} & \frac{-1}{h_{21}} \end{matrix}$	$\begin{matrix} \frac{1}{g_{21}} & \frac{g_{22}}{g_{21}} \\ \frac{g_{11}}{g_{21}} & \frac{\Delta}{g_{21}} \end{matrix}$	$\begin{matrix} a_{11} & a_{12} \\ a_{21} & a_{22} \end{matrix}$	$\begin{matrix} \frac{b_{22}}{\Delta} & \frac{b_{12}}{\Delta} \\ \frac{b_{21}}{\Delta} & \frac{b_{11}}{\Delta} \end{matrix}$
$[b]$	$\begin{matrix} \frac{Z_{22}}{Z_{12}} & \frac{\Delta}{Z_{12}} \\ \frac{1}{Z_{12}} & \frac{Z_{11}}{Z_{12}} \end{matrix}$	$\begin{matrix} \frac{-Y_{11}}{Y_{12}} & \frac{-1}{Y_{12}} \\ \frac{-\Delta}{Y_{12}} & \frac{-Y_{22}}{Y_{12}} \end{matrix}$	$\begin{matrix} \frac{1}{h_{12}} & \frac{h_{11}}{h_{12}} \\ \frac{h_{22}}{h_{12}} & \frac{\Delta}{h_{12}} \end{matrix}$	$\begin{matrix} \frac{-\Delta}{g_{12}} & \frac{-g_{22}}{g_{12}} \\ \frac{-g_{11}}{g_{12}} & \frac{-1}{g_{12}} \end{matrix}$	$\begin{matrix} \frac{a_{22}}{\Delta} & \frac{a_{12}}{\Delta} \\ \frac{a_{21}}{\Delta} & \frac{a_{11}}{\Delta} \end{matrix}$	$\begin{matrix} b_{11} & b_{12} \\ b_{21} & b_{22} \end{matrix}$

Table 4-1. Conversion chart for four-terminal network matrices. Δ denotes the determinant of the relevant matrix.

2.4 THE SYNTHESIS OF MATRICES FOR COMPOSITE NETWORKS

It is for a group of interconnected networks forming a composite network or system, that the value of the matrix method is fully realised. While the equations for a problem involving a single four-terminal network may be formulated in the matrix style, this is largely for consistency or compactness: there is but trivial use of the algebraic properties of the matrix.

The power of the matrix method for solving composite four or three-terminal networks arises from the fact, subject to certain restrictions, that a matrix governing the external volt-amperes of an agglomeration of such networks may be synthesised directly from suitably chosen matrices for its constituents.

The basic forms of interconnection are indicated in Figs. 4-7(a), (b), and (c), while Fig. 4-7(d) exemplifies the three combined in a complex arrangement, recognisable in fact as a feedback system.

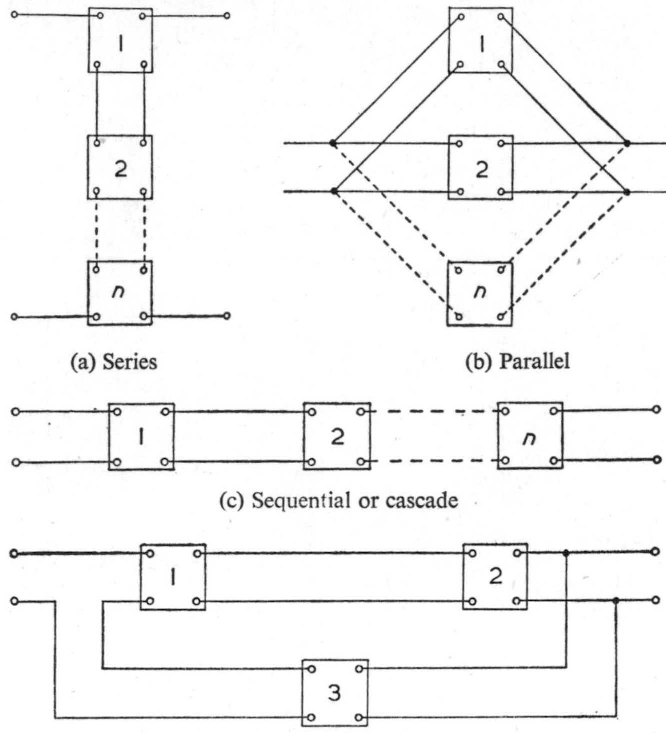

(a) Series

(b) Parallel

(c) Sequential or cascade

(d) Example of a hybrid arrangement.

Fig. 4-7. Network interconnections.

2.4.1 *The composite matrices for series, parallel, and hybrid connections*

In contrast to its role in the solution of a single network, each type of matrix has a unique role in the solution of a composite network. The series, parallel and series-parallel or hybrid arrangements considered here are uniquely and simply served by respectively the Z, Y, and h or g matrices. An interpretation of the solution for a composite network in simple terms of such matrices for its constituents depends, however, on the satisfaction of certain criteria, first pointed out by O. Brune.[1,2] These imply operation of the superposition principle, and independence of the matrices.

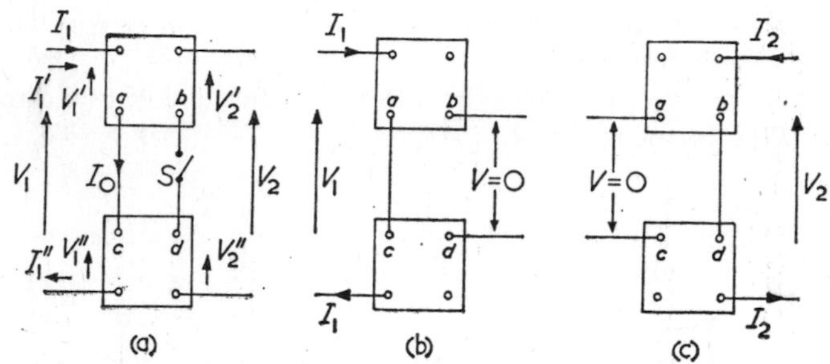

Fig. 4-8. Pertaining to criteria for networks in series.

Referring to Fig. 4-8(a), let both networks be open-circuit on the right, and let I_1 be constant. When S is open, $I_0 = I_1 = I_1' = I_1''$, and

$$\begin{aligned} V_1'/I_1' &= Z_{11}' = V_1'/I_1 \\ V_1''/I_1'' &= Z_{11}'' = V_1''/I_1 \\ V_2'/I_1' &= Z_{21}' = V_2'/I_1 \\ V_2''/I_1'' &= Z_{21}'' = V_2''/I_1 \end{aligned}$$

Therefore, since $V_1 = V_1' + V_1''$ and $V_2 = V_2' + V_2''$,

$$\begin{aligned} V_1/I_1 &= Z_{11} = Z_{11}' + Z_{11}'' \\ V_2/I_1 &= Z_{21} = Z_{21}' + Z_{21}'' \end{aligned} \tag{4.60}$$

But if when S is closed current circulates in the loop *abdc*, $I_0 \neq I_1$ and all currents within and traversing each network are disturbed. Then,

$$V_1'/I_1 \neq Z_{11}', \qquad V_1''/I_1 \neq Z_{11}''$$
$$V_2'/I_1 \neq Z_{21}', \qquad V_2''/I_1 \neq Z_{21}''$$

Eqns. (4.60) are valid when b and d are linked, provided the condition is as shown in Fig. 4-8(b); for then closure of the link *bd* cannot result in the circulation of current in the loop *abdc*. Similar reasoning applies for excitation by I_2 under open-circuit conditions on the left, leading to Fig. 4-8(c) as the criterion for the equations.

$$\begin{aligned} V_2/I_2 = Z_{22} = Z'_{22} + Z''_{22} \\ V_1/I_2 = Z_{12} = Z'_{12} + Z''_{12} \end{aligned} \qquad (4.61)$$

to be satisfied when the link *ac* is closed.

Thus, provided the conditions shown in Figs. 4-8(b) and (c) are simultaneously fulfilled,

$$[Z] = \begin{bmatrix} Z_{11} & Z_{12} \\ Z_{21} & Z_{22} \end{bmatrix} = \begin{bmatrix} Z'_{11} + Z''_{11} & Z'_{12} + Z''_{12} \\ Z'_{21} + Z''_{21} & Z'_{22} + Z''_{22} \end{bmatrix} \qquad (4.62)$$

This extends to any number of networks as in Fig. 4-7(a), for which the Z-matrices are independent.

A simple example in which the criterion is fulfilled in one direction, but not in the other, is shown in Fig. 4-9.

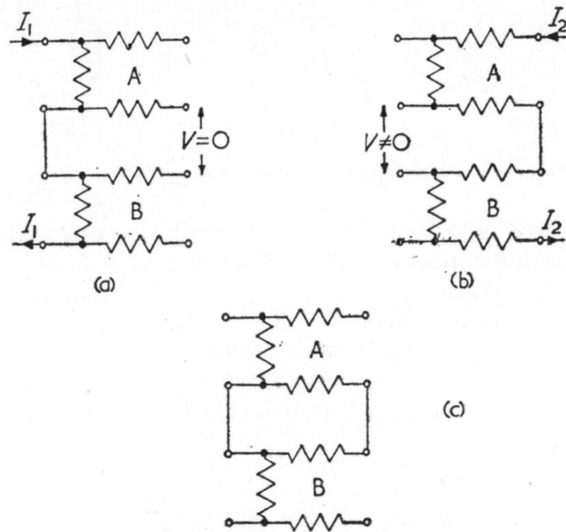

Fig. 4-9. Example violating eqn. (4.62).

The reader may easily verify for Fig. 4-9(c), that

$$\begin{aligned} Z_{11} &= Z_{11(A)} + Z_{11(B)} \\ Z_{12} &= Z_{12(A)} + Z_{12(B)} = Z_{21} = Z_{21(A)} + Z_{21(B)} \end{aligned}$$

but that

$$Z_{22} \neq Z_{22(A)} + Z_{22(B)}$$

so that

$$[Z] \neq [Z_A] + [Z_B]$$

The independence criterion for paralleled networks, illustrated in Fig. 4-10(a), can be reasoned as the dual case. Assuming the criterion to be satisfied in both directions for Fig. 4-10(b), it follows by duality, or by expanding the volt-ampere relationships under short circuit conditions (e.g., for $V_2 = 0$, $I_1/V_1 = (I_1' + I_1'')/V_1 = Y_{11}' + Y_{11}''$, etc.), that

$$[Y] = \begin{bmatrix} Y_{11} & Y_{12} \\ Y_{21} & Y_{22} \end{bmatrix} = \begin{bmatrix} Y_{11}' + Y_{11}'' & Y_{12}' + Y_{12}'' \\ Y_{21}' + Y_{21}'' & Y_{22}' + Y_{22}'' \end{bmatrix} \tag{4.63}$$

This equation similarly extends to any number of paralleled networks for which the connections are valid.

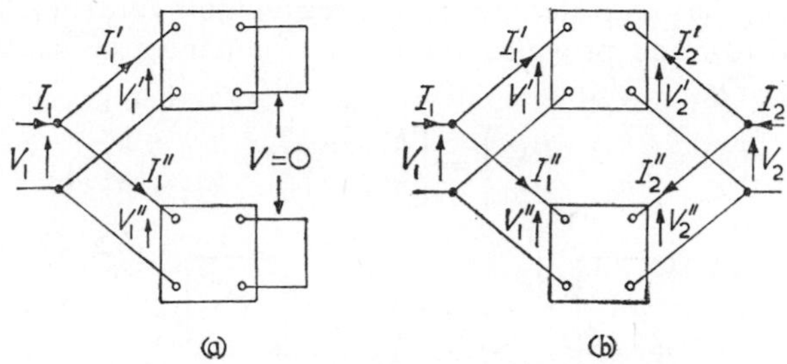

Fig. 4-10. Pertaining to paralleled networks.

It is interesting that Y-matrix independence requires the system to form a balanced-bridge when each network is short-circuited as in Fig. 4-10(a). This is illustrated by Fig. 4-11, in which (a) represents the networks to be paralleled at terminals 3-3 and 4-4, while (b) shows the short-circuited condition after removal of redundant branches. From this Wheatstone-type bridge, $V = 0$ when

$$\frac{Z_1'}{Z_2'} = \frac{Z_1''}{Z_2''}$$

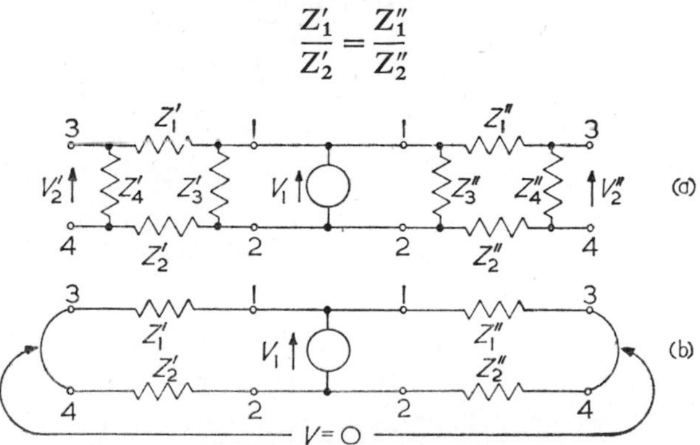

Fig. 4-11. (a) Networks to be paralleled at 3-3, 4-4.
(b) Bridge representation of matrix independence condition.

For the series-parallel arrangement shown in Fig. 4-12(a), an appropriate matrix is one whose elements include a driving-point or input impedance for the series side, and an output admittance for the parallel. This specification is met by the h-matrix, in which

$$h_{11} = V_1/I_{1(V_2=0)} = \text{s.c. input impedance}$$
$$h_{22} = I_2/V_{2(I_1=0)} = \text{o.c. output admittance}$$
$$h_{12} = V_1/V_{2(I_1=0)} \quad \text{and} \quad h_{21} = I_2/I_{1(V_2=0)}$$

The conditions under which these parameters are defined are moreover coincident with the conditions of short-circuit and open-circuit under which the $V = 0$ criterion must apply respectively to parallel and series connections. The parameter independence conditions are shown in Figs. 4-12(c) and (d), and provided these are simultaneously satisfied, the h-matrix for Fig. 4-12(a) is

$$[h] = \begin{bmatrix} h_{11} & h_{12} \\ h_{21} & h_{22} \end{bmatrix} = \begin{bmatrix} h'_{11} + h''_{11} & h'_{12} + h''_{12} \\ h'_{21} + h''_{21} & h'_{22} + h''_{22} \end{bmatrix} \tag{4.64}$$

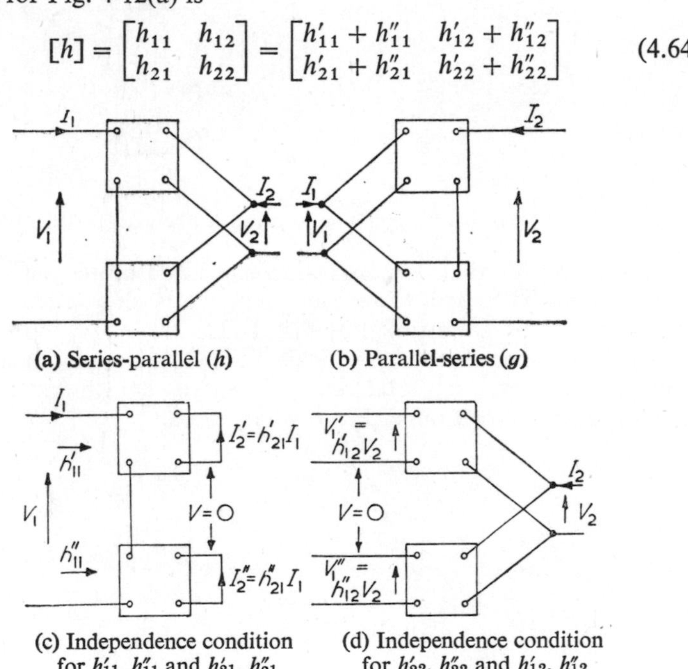

(a) Series-parallel (h) (b) Parallel-series (g)

(c) Independence condition for h'_{11}, h''_{11} and h'_{21}, h''_{21} (d) Independence condition for h'_{22}, h''_{22} and h'_{12}, h''_{12}

Fig. 4-12. Pertaining to hybrid connections.

Since $[g] = [h]^{-1}$, it follows that the reversed or parallel-series arrangement of Fig. 4-12(b) will be served by the g-matrix, and, subject to similar independence criteria,

$$[g] = \begin{bmatrix} g_{11} & g_{12} \\ g_{21} & g_{22} \end{bmatrix} = \begin{bmatrix} g'_{11} + g''_{11} & g'_{12} + g''_{12} \\ g'_{21} + g''_{21} & g'_{22} + g''_{22} \end{bmatrix} \tag{4.65}$$

In practice, given networks may violate the independence criteria in composite arrangements, and isolation with transformers is necessary to comply with the criteria, to avoid the production of a degenerate structure (exemplified by T and lattice networks in parallel), and to realise a composite response that is truly aggregate. Figs. 4-13(a) and (b) demonstrate the use of a transformer to validate series-connection of the networks shown in Fig. 4-9. Figs. 4-13(c) and (d) illustrate the violation of both hybrid criteria in the case of a transistor and voltage-feedback network, and Fig. 4-13(e) shows compliance with both criteria through the incorporation of one isolating transformer.

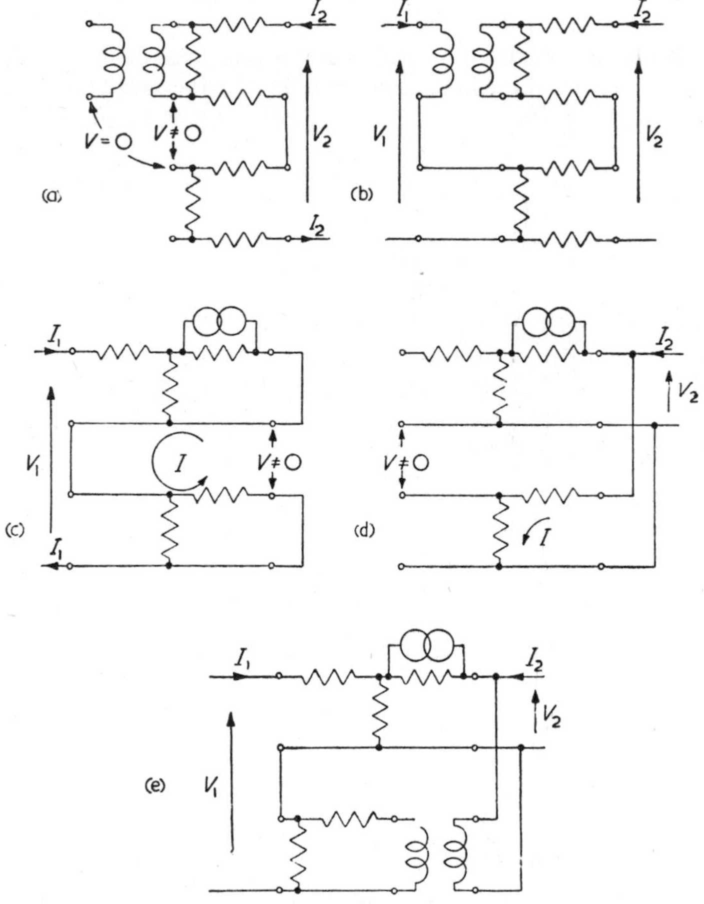

Fig. 4-13. Illustrating the use of isolating transformers.

2.4.2 *Sequential or cascade connection*

When four-terminal networks follow one another, the output voltage and current from one become the input voltage and current for the next. A pertinent equation-form is thus one in which these quantities are related explicitly, as in the *ABCD* (a-matrix) or *DBCA* (b-matrix) forms, eqns. (4.13) and (4.14).

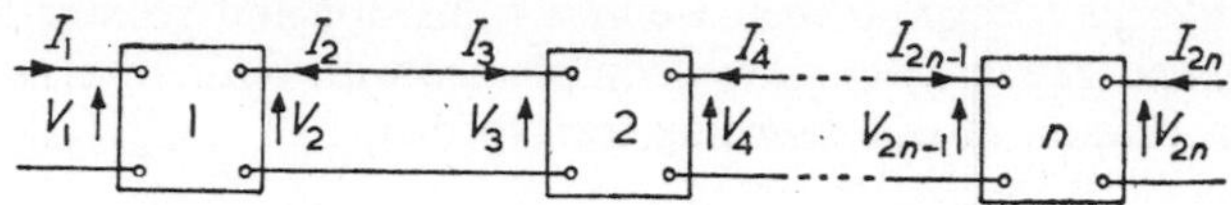

Fig. 4-14. n networks in sequence.

Consider Fig. 4.14. For calculating the quantities at any junction to the right in terms of the input quantities V_1, I_1, the *DBCA* or b-matrix form is apposite. Then,

$$\begin{bmatrix} V_2 \\ I_2 \end{bmatrix} = [b]_1 \cdot \begin{bmatrix} V_1 \\ -I_1 \end{bmatrix}$$

and

$$\begin{bmatrix} V_4 \\ I_4 \end{bmatrix} = [b]_2 \cdot \begin{bmatrix} V_3 \\ -I_3 \end{bmatrix}$$

But $V_3 = V_2$ and $I_3 = -I_2$. Therefore,

$$\begin{bmatrix} V_4 \\ I_4 \end{bmatrix} = [b]_2 \cdot \begin{bmatrix} V_2 \\ I_2 \end{bmatrix} = [b]_2 \cdot [b]_1 \cdot \begin{bmatrix} V_1 \\ -I_1 \end{bmatrix}$$

Extending this result to the n networks,

$$\begin{bmatrix} V_{2n} \\ I_{2n} \end{bmatrix} = [b] \cdot \begin{bmatrix} V_1 \\ -I_1 \end{bmatrix} \tag{4.66}$$

where

$$[b] = [b]_n \cdot [b]_{n-1} \cdots [b]_2 \cdot [b]_1 \tag{4.67}$$

Using the *ABCD* or a-matrix form, which is more common,

$$\begin{bmatrix} V_1 \\ I_1 \end{bmatrix} = [a]_1 \cdot \begin{bmatrix} V_2 \\ -I_2 \end{bmatrix} = [a]_1 \cdot \begin{bmatrix} V_3 \\ I_3 \end{bmatrix} = [a]_1 \cdot [a]_2 \cdot \begin{bmatrix} V_4 \\ -I_4 \end{bmatrix}$$

which leads similarly to

$$\begin{bmatrix} V_1 \\ I_1 \end{bmatrix} = [a] \cdot \begin{bmatrix} V_{2n} \\ -I_{2n} \end{bmatrix} \tag{4.68}$$

where

$$[a] = [a]_1 \cdot [a]_2 \cdots [a]_{n-1} \cdot [a]_n \tag{4.69}$$

When the networks are identical, as for example in a uniform ladder-structure, eqn. (4.69) becomes

$$[A]_n = [a]^n \tag{4.70}$$

where $[a]$ is the matrix per network or section.

The involution of a square matrix as required in eqn. (4.70) can be accomplished by resolving it into the form

$$[a] = X\Lambda X^{-1} \tag{4.71}$$

where Λ is a diagonal matrix and X, X^{-1} are inverse matrices; for then

$$[a]^n = X\Lambda^n X^{-1} \tag{4.72}$$

where Λ^n is given immediately by raising each element in Λ to the nth power, as exemplified by

$$\Lambda^n = \begin{bmatrix} \alpha_{11}^n & 0 & . & . & 0 \\ 0 & \alpha_{22}^n & . & . & 0 \\ . & . & . & . & . \\ . & . & . & . & . \\ 0 & 0 & . & 0 & \alpha_{kk}^n \end{bmatrix} \tag{4.73}$$

where

$$\Lambda = \begin{bmatrix} \alpha_{11} & 0 & . & . & 0 \\ 0 & \alpha_{22} & . & . & 0 \\ . & . & . & . & . \\ . & . & . & . & . \\ 0 & 0 & . & 0 & \alpha_{kk} \end{bmatrix} \tag{4.74}$$

Eqn. (4.73) is easily justified from (4.74) by the laws of matrix multiplication, while eqn. (4.72) is justified by resolving $(X\Lambda X^{-1})$ into n factors. This gives

$$\begin{aligned}(X\Lambda X^{-1})^n &= (X\Lambda X^{-1})(X\Lambda X^{-1}) \ldots (X\Lambda X^{-1}) \\ &= X\Lambda(X^{-1}X)\Lambda(X^{-1}X) \ldots \Lambda(X^{-1}X)\Lambda X^{-1} \\ &= X\Lambda 1\Lambda 1\Lambda \ldots \Lambda 1\Lambda X^{-1} \\ &= X\Lambda^n X^{-1}\end{aligned}$$

Various procedures[3] exist for finding the diagonal matrix Λ and X, X^{-1}. The formal method[4,5] is that in which Λ is derived from $[a]$ by finding the *latent roots* or *eigenvalues* of the *characteristic equation* for the matrix, while X is formed from the corresponding *eigenvectors*. X^{-1} is then obtained from X by the usual process of inversion.

For the 2×2 matrix of interest here, an alternative approach for numerical evaluation is proposed. It has the advantage of leading quite simply to explicit formulae for the elements of Λ and X. The principle, illustrated in Fig. 4-15, lies in simulation of each of the matrices X, Λ and X^{-1}, by corresponding matrices defining each part of a three-part equivalent network.

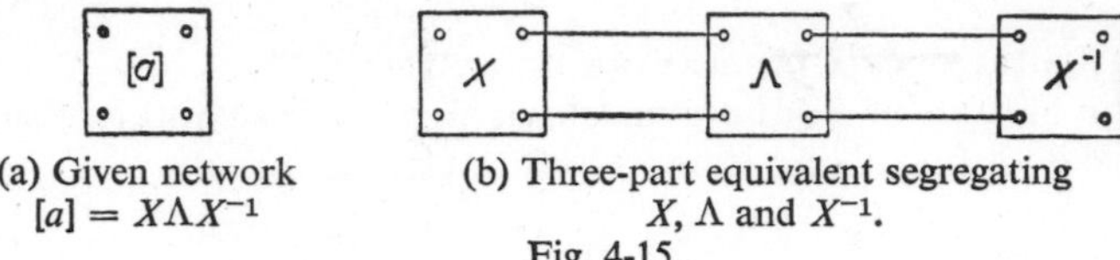

(a) Given network $[a] = X\Lambda X^{-1}$

(b) Three-part equivalent segregating X, Λ and X^{-1}.

Fig. 4-15.

In Fig. 4-15(b), the central unit is a network having by choice an a-matrix of diagonal form, while the end units are canonic (i.e. simplest) forms having inverse a-matrices. Since a physical realisation is not required, network conceptions for the parts of Fig. 4-15(b) are of interest only as a basis for assigning the simplest valid forms to the matrices. There is thus no objection to forms that might be identified with networks having negative or otherwise unrealisable elements.

A 2-element diagonal matrix is identifiable with an ideal transformer. Strictly, this is a network realisation for wholly real voltage and current ratios only; but the form of its matrix is suggestive of a general form that might be assumed for the central unit (Λ). Therefore, let

$$\Lambda = \begin{bmatrix} \lambda & 0 \\ 0 & 1/\lambda \end{bmatrix} \tag{4.75}$$

where λ and $1/\lambda$ denote the voltage and current transformation ratios, V_1/V_2 and I_1/I_2.

Let

$$X = \begin{bmatrix} A & B \\ C & D \end{bmatrix} \tag{4.76}$$

Then

$$X^{-1} = \begin{bmatrix} D & -B \\ -C & A \end{bmatrix} \tag{4.77}$$

These matrices are to have the simplest forms consistent with theoretical equivalence between Figs. 4-15(a) and (b). Since all elements $a_{11} \ldots a_{22}$ in the given matrix $[a]$ must in general be assumed finite, this precludes any form for X that contains an element which is zero; for when Λ, X and X^{-1} are defined by eqns. (4.75), (4.76) and (4.77), one condition for all elements in the product $X\Lambda X^{-1}$ to be non-zero is that each of the elements A, B, C, D should be non-zero:

$$\begin{aligned} X\Lambda X^{-1} &= \begin{bmatrix} A & B \\ C & D \end{bmatrix} \cdot \begin{bmatrix} \lambda & 0 \\ 0 & 1/\lambda \end{bmatrix} \cdot \begin{bmatrix} D & -B \\ -C & A \end{bmatrix} \\ &= \begin{bmatrix} AD\lambda - BC/\lambda & -AB(\lambda - 1/\lambda) \\ CD(\lambda - 1/\lambda) & -BC\lambda + AD/\lambda \end{bmatrix} \end{aligned} \tag{4.78}$$

Canonic networks representing X and X^{-1}, consistent with non-zero elements in eqn. (4.78), are shown in Fig. 4-16.

Fig. 4-16.

The matrix for (a) is

$$\begin{bmatrix} 1+YZ & Z \\ Y & 1 \end{bmatrix} = \begin{bmatrix} A & B \\ C & D \end{bmatrix} \tag{4.79}$$

and for (b),

$$\begin{bmatrix} 1 & -Z \\ -Y & 1+YZ \end{bmatrix} = \begin{bmatrix} D & -B \\ -C & A \end{bmatrix} \tag{4.80}$$

Figs. 4-16 are canonic, in the sense that they are simplest forms for which the matrices are inverse, and also in respect of the number of immitances which, together with λ, are sufficient for formulating the minimum of three independent equations necessary to establish a four-terminal network equivalence. While Z and Y are not explicitly required, eqns. (4.79) and (4.80) confirm that a matrix for X having $D = 1$ may be assumed.

Referring to eqn. (4.78), let each element in the product $X\Lambda X^{-1}$ be equated to the corresponding element in $[a]$. Then,

$$\begin{aligned} AD\lambda^2 - BC &= \lambda a_{11} \\ AB(1-\lambda^2) &= \lambda a_{12} \\ CD(\lambda^2 - 1) &= \lambda a_{21} \\ AD - BC\lambda^2 &= \lambda a_{22} \end{aligned} \tag{4.81}$$

Noting that $AD - BC = 1$ in the case of a reciprocal network, and assuming $D = 1$, eliminating between three of eqns. (4.81) yields

$$\begin{aligned} \lambda &= \frac{a_{22}+a_{11}}{2} \pm \sqrt{\frac{(a_{22}+a_{11})^2}{4} - 1} \\ A &= (\lambda a_{11} - 1)/(\lambda^2 - 1) \\ B &= (1 - \lambda a_{22})/\lambda a_{21} \\ C &= \lambda a_{21}/(\lambda^2 - 1) \\ D &= 1 \end{aligned} \tag{4.82}$$

Referring to eqn. (4.72), a general form for $[a]^n$ is thus

$$[a]^n = \begin{bmatrix} A & B \\ C & 1 \end{bmatrix} \cdot \begin{bmatrix} \lambda^n & 0 \\ 0 & 1/\lambda^n \end{bmatrix} \cdot \begin{bmatrix} 1 & -B \\ -C & A \end{bmatrix}$$

$$= \begin{bmatrix} A\lambda^n - BC\lambda^{-n} & AB(\lambda^{-n} - \lambda^n) \\ C(\lambda^n - \lambda^{-n}) & A\lambda^{-n} - BC\lambda^n \end{bmatrix} \tag{4.83}$$

where ABC and λ are defined by eqns. (4.82).

In the case of a chain of symmetrical identical networks, one simple approach to involution is afforded by defining each network in terms of its propagation coefficient γ and characteristic impedance Z_o. These are expressed by

$$Z_o = \sqrt{Z_{sc}Z_{oc}} \tag{4.84}$$

$$\gamma = \tanh^{-1}\sqrt{(Z_{sc}/Z_{oc})} \tag{4.85}$$

where Z_{sc} and Z_{oc} denote the impedances looking into either pair of terminals under respectively short and open-circuit conditions at the other. For a symmetrical network $a_{11} = a_{22}$, and imposing the conditions $V_2 = 0, I_2 = 0$, on the equations $V_1 = a_{11}V_2 - a_{12}I_2, I_1 = a_{21}V_2 - a_{22}I_2$, gives

$$Z_o = \sqrt{(a_{12}/a_{21})} \tag{4.86}$$

and

$$\gamma = \tan^{-1}\sqrt{\left[\frac{a_{12}a_{21}}{a_{11}a_{22}}\right]} \tag{4.87}$$

$$= \cosh^{-1}\sqrt{(a_{11}a_{22})} \tag{4.88}$$

For a uniform transmission line of length l, propagation coefficient γ per unit length and characteristic impedance Z_o, the input and output voltages and currents are related by the well-known transmission-line equations,

$$\begin{aligned} V_1 &= V_2 \cosh \gamma l + I_2 Z_o \sinh \gamma l \\ I_1 &= V_2 Y_o \sinh \gamma l + I_2 \cosh \gamma l \end{aligned} \tag{4.89}$$

(in which I_1 and I_2 are in the same sense). Then, adapting eqns. (4.89) by writing $n\gamma$ in place of γl as the total propagation coefficient, and reversing I_2 to conform with the network convention, the matrix equation for the chain of n symmetrical identical networks becomes

$$\begin{bmatrix} V_1 \\ I_1 \end{bmatrix} = \begin{bmatrix} \cosh n\gamma & Z_0 \sinh n\gamma \\ Y_0 \sinh n\gamma & \cosh n\gamma \end{bmatrix} \cdot \begin{bmatrix} V_2 \\ -I_2 \end{bmatrix} \tag{4.90}$$

and

$$[A]_n = [a]^n = \begin{bmatrix} \cosh n\gamma & Z_0 \sinh n\gamma \\ Y_0 \sinh n\gamma & \cosh n\gamma \end{bmatrix} \tag{4.91}$$

It is also easy by this adaption to find the transmission matrix for an asymmetrical network having image impedances Z_{i1} and Z_{i2} and an image-transfer coefficient Γ.

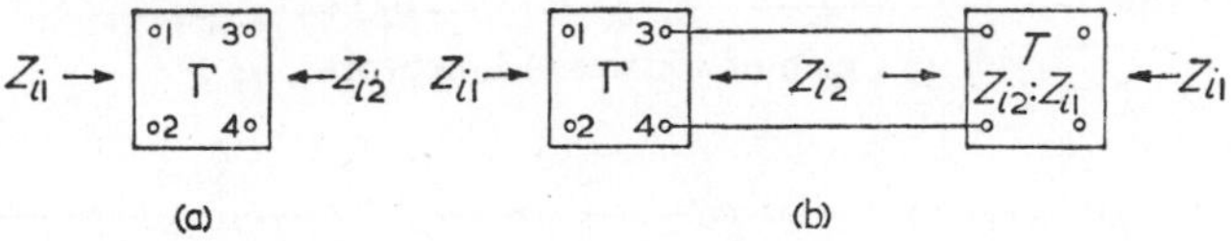

Fig. 4-17.

In Fig. 4-17, the given network (a) is made externally symmetrical by adding an ideal transformer T, which changes the impedance-level at terminals 3-4 in the ratio $Z_{i1}/Z_{i2} = \lambda^2$, so that the image impedances, being then equal on both sides, correspond to a characteristic impedance of value Z_{i1}.

Let $[a]$ be the matrix for the network (a), and $[a]_T$ that for the ideal transformer T. Then, noting that the image transfer coefficient Γ is synonymous with the propagation coefficient γ in the case of a symmetrical network, the matrix for the symmetrical system of Fig. 4-17(b) is

$$[A] = [a]\cdot[a]_T = \begin{bmatrix} \cosh\Gamma & Z_{i1}\sinh\Gamma \\ Y_{i1}\sinh\Gamma & \cosh\Gamma \end{bmatrix}$$

where

$$[a]_T = \begin{bmatrix} 1/\lambda & 0 \\ 0 & \lambda \end{bmatrix}$$

Then, removing the ideal transformer,

$$\begin{aligned}[a] &= [A]\cdot[a]_T^{-1} = [a]\cdot[a]_T\cdot[a]_T^{-1} \\ &= \begin{bmatrix} \cosh\Gamma & Z_{i1}\sinh\Gamma \\ Y_{i1}\sinh\Gamma & \cosh\Gamma \end{bmatrix}\cdot\begin{bmatrix} \lambda & 0 \\ 0 & 1/\lambda \end{bmatrix} \\ &= \begin{bmatrix} \lambda\cosh\Gamma & (1/\lambda)Z_{i1}\sinh\Gamma \\ \lambda Y_{i1}\sinh\Gamma & (1/\lambda)\cosh\Gamma \end{bmatrix} \qquad (4.92) \\ &= \begin{bmatrix} \sqrt{Z_{i1}/Z_{i2}}\cosh\Gamma & \sqrt{Z_{i1}Z_{i2}}\sinh\Gamma \\ (1/\sqrt{Z_{i1}Z_{i2}})\sinh\Gamma & (\sqrt{Z_{i2}/Z_{i1}})\cosh\Gamma \end{bmatrix}\end{aligned}$$

A chain of n identical L-networks having the form of Fig. 4-18(a) is also adaptable to the transmission line equations when re-cast as in Fig. 4-18(b). This resolves it into $n - 1$ symmetrical T-networks, with residues having simple a-matrices, at each end.

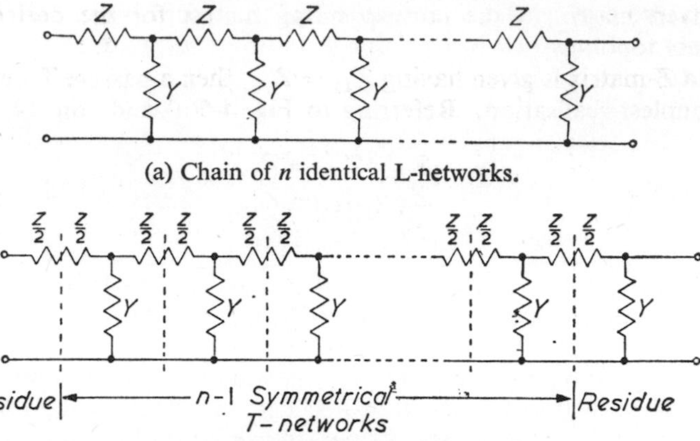

(a) Chain of n identical L-networks.

(b) Rearrangement of (a)

Fig. 4-18. Alternative representations for a ladder network.

For each T-network in Fig. 4-18(b),

$$\gamma = \cosh^{-1}(1 + \tfrac{1}{2}ZY) \tag{4.93}$$

$$Z_0 = \sqrt{\left[\frac{Z}{Y} + \frac{Z^2}{4}\right]} \tag{4.94}$$

Then, including the matrices for the residues,

$$[A]_n = \begin{bmatrix} 1 & \tfrac{1}{2}Z \\ 0 & 1 \end{bmatrix} \cdot \begin{bmatrix} \cosh(n-1)\gamma & Z_0 \sinh(n-1)\gamma \\ Y_0 \sinh(n-1)\gamma & \cosh(n-1)\gamma \end{bmatrix} \cdot \begin{bmatrix} 1 + \tfrac{1}{2}YZ & \tfrac{1}{2}Z \\ Y & 1 \end{bmatrix} \tag{4.95}$$

S. R. Deards[6] has derived the following expression for this case:

$$[A]_n = \begin{bmatrix} \sum\limits_{r=0}^{n} \begin{bmatrix} n+r \\ 2r \end{bmatrix} Z^r Y^r & \sum\limits_{r=0}^{n-1} \begin{bmatrix} n+r \\ 2r+1 \end{bmatrix} Z^{r+1} Y^r \\ \sum\limits_{r=0}^{n-1} \begin{bmatrix} n+r \\ 2r+1 \end{bmatrix} Z^r Y^{r+1} & \sum\limits_{r=0}^{n-1} \begin{bmatrix} n+r-1 \\ 2r \end{bmatrix} Z^r Y^r \end{bmatrix} \tag{4.96}$$

Each element is in polynomial form, and the polynomial coefficients have been computed and tabulated for n from 1 to 12. Polynomial forms are of special interest in network synthesis.

2.5 NETWORK REALISATIONS FOR GIVEN MATRICES

These are important in respect of equivalences, circuit representations for non-reciprocal or unilateral devices such as transistors, and network synthesis. In general, the realisation is obtained by equating the given matrix to the corresponding matrix for the desired four-terminal topology.

If a Z-matrix is given having $Z_{21} = Z_{12}$, then a passive T-network is the simplest realisation. Referring to Fig. 4-5(a) and eqn. (4.36),

$$\begin{aligned} Z_3 &= Z_{12} = Z_{21} \\ Z_1 &= Z_{11} - Z_{12} \\ Z_2 &= Z_{22} - Z_{12} \end{aligned} \tag{4.97}$$

Similarly, for a Y-matrix having $Y_{21} = Y_{12}$ the Π-network is the simplest realisation, and Fig. 4-5(c) and eqn. (4.39) give

$$\begin{aligned} Y_3 &= -Y_{12} = -Y_{21} \\ Y_1 &= Y_{11} + Y_{12} \\ Y_2 &= Y_{22} + Y_{12} \end{aligned} \tag{4.98}$$

When the given matrix refers to a device that violates the reciprocity theorem, such as a transistor, the transfer immittances Z_{12} and Z_{21} or Y_{12} and Y_{21} are unequal. This inequality is readily shown to contribute an active element or source to the equivalent network. Consider, for example, the equations

$$\begin{aligned} Z_{11}I_1 + Z_{12}I_2 &= V_1 \\ Z_{21}I_1 + Z_{22}I_2 &= V_2 \end{aligned}$$

If $Z_{12} \neq Z_{21}$, these equations may be re-arranged in the forms

$$\begin{aligned} Z_{11}I_1 + Z_{12}I_2 &= V_1 \\ Z_{12}I_1 + Z_{22}I_2 &= V_2 - (Z_{21} - Z_{12})I_1 \end{aligned}$$

or

$$\begin{bmatrix} Z_{11} & Z_{12} \\ Z_{12} & Z_{22} \end{bmatrix} \cdot \begin{bmatrix} I_1 \\ I_2 \end{bmatrix} = \begin{bmatrix} V_1 \\ V_2 - (Z_{21} - Z_{12})I_1 \end{bmatrix}$$

The modified immittance matrix is now reciprocal, and realisable with a passive T-network as before; but the voltage matrix includes the term $(Z_{21} - Z_{12})I_1$, which is equivalent to an e.m.f. source. The complete realisation is therefore as shown in Fig. 4-19(a).

The active network realisations for Y, h and g matrices may be approached similarly. In forming the matrix corresponding to the passive part of the network it should be noted that for a passive reciprocal network, $Y_{12} = Y_{21}, h_{12} = -h_{21}$, and $g_{12} = -g_{21}$. For example, in the case of the h-matrix for a non-reciprocal device, the equations

$$\begin{bmatrix} h_{11} & h_{12} \\ h_{21} & h_{22} \end{bmatrix} \cdot \begin{bmatrix} I_1 \\ V_2 \end{bmatrix} = \begin{bmatrix} V_1 \\ I_2 \end{bmatrix}$$

can be re-arranged in the form

$$\begin{bmatrix} h_{11} & h_{12} \\ -h_{12} & h_{22} \end{bmatrix} \cdot \begin{bmatrix} I_1 \\ V_2 \end{bmatrix} = \begin{bmatrix} V_1 \\ I_2 - (h_{21} + h_{12})I_1 \end{bmatrix}$$

in which the new h-matrix is identifiable with a passive network, while the term $-(h_{21} + h_{12})I_1$ represents a current source in parallel with the output terminals. A Π-representation is shown in Fig. 4-19(b).

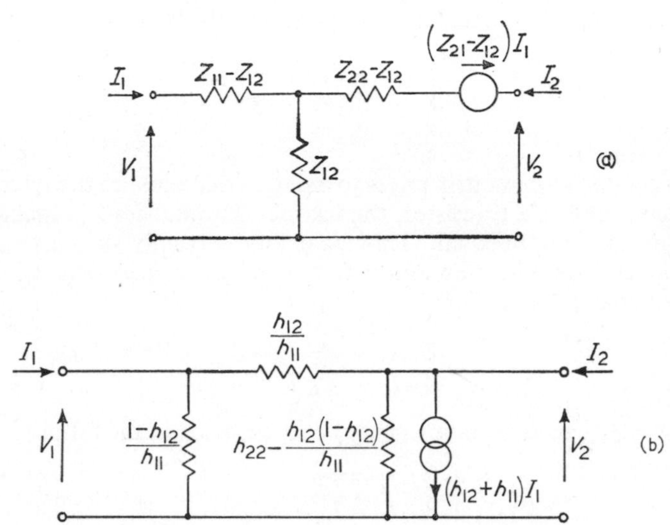

Fig. 4-19. Examples of network realisations for (a) non-reciprocal Z-matrix ($Z_{21} \neq Z_{12}$) and (b) non-reciprocal h-matrix ($h_{21} \neq -h_{12}$).

3. ILLUSTRATIVE EXAMPLES

In most of the numerical examples, the immittances and matrices are assigned wholly real values for arithmetic simplicity. The complex immittances (involving L, C, and R) likely to be encountered in practice complicate the arithmetic, but do not contribute further to the basic matrix principles involved.

In the case of transistor calculations, a high order of accuracy is not generally justified in practice; for only nominal values are likely to be available for the parameters. In the following illustrations, however, three or four significant figures are sometimes shown in order to preserve the details of procedure.

Example 4.1. Calculations for basic arrangements

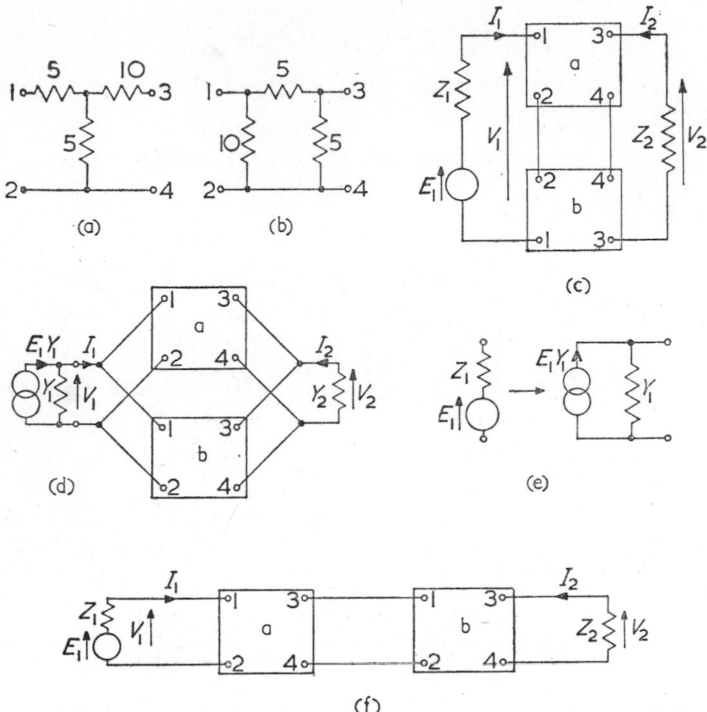

Fig. 4-20. Example 1. All impedances are in ohms, pure resistance and $E_1 = 1$ V, $Z_1 = 5\Omega$, $Z_2 = 10\Omega$.

By inspection (see sect. 2.3.2), the immittance matrices for Figs. 4-20(a) and (b) are respectively

$$[Z]_a = \begin{bmatrix} Z_{11} & Z_{12} \\ Z_{21} & Z_{22} \end{bmatrix} = \begin{bmatrix} 5+5 & 5 \\ 5 & 10+5 \end{bmatrix} = \begin{bmatrix} 10 & 5 \\ 5 & 15 \end{bmatrix} \quad (4.99)$$

and

$$[Y]_b = \begin{bmatrix} Y_{11} & Y_{12} \\ Y_{21} & Y_{22} \end{bmatrix} = \begin{bmatrix} \frac{1}{5}+\frac{1}{10} & -\frac{1}{5} \\ -\frac{1}{5} & \frac{1}{5}+\frac{1}{5} \end{bmatrix} = \begin{bmatrix} 0.3 & -0.2 \\ -0.2 & 0.4 \end{bmatrix} \quad (4.100)$$

The connections in Figs. 4-20(c) and (d) satisfy the Brune criteria for series and parallel connections, respectively.

Series connection, Fig. 4-20(*c*).

Excluding the source and load,

$$[Z] = [Z]_a + [Z]_b = [Z]_a + [Y]_b^{-1} \tag{4.101}$$

$[Y]_b$ may be inverted with the aid of Table 4-1. From eqn. (4.100), the determinant of $[Y]_b$ is

$$\Delta = 0.3 \times 0.4 - (-0.2 \times -0.2) = 0.08$$

Then, from Table 4-1,

$$[Z]_b = [Y]_b^{-1} = \begin{bmatrix} \dfrac{Y_{22}}{\Delta} & -\dfrac{Y_{12}}{\Delta} \\[2ex] -\dfrac{Y_{21}}{\Delta} & \dfrac{Y_{11}}{\Delta} \end{bmatrix} = \begin{bmatrix} \dfrac{0.4}{0.08} & -\dfrac{(-0.2)}{0.08} \\[2ex] -\dfrac{(-0.2)}{0.08} & \dfrac{0.3}{0.08} \end{bmatrix}$$

$$= \begin{bmatrix} 5 & 2.5 \\ 2.5 & 3.75 \end{bmatrix} \tag{4.102}$$

Alternatively, since the matrix is second-order only, it is easily inverted by the procedure of sect. 2.5.3, Chapter 2. Exchanging rows with columns in eqn. (4.100),

$$[Y]_b^t = \begin{bmatrix} Y_{11} & Y_{21} \\ Y_{12} & Y_{22} \end{bmatrix} = \begin{bmatrix} 0.3 & -0.2 \\ -0.2 & 0.4 \end{bmatrix}$$

Numerically there is no change, since $Y_{12} = Y_{21}$. Then, replacing each element with its cofactor,

$$[Y]_{b_c}^t = \begin{bmatrix} 0.4 & 0.2 \\ 0.2 & 0.3 \end{bmatrix}$$

from which

$$[Z]_b = [Y]_b^{-1} = \frac{[Y]_{b_c}^t}{\Delta} = \begin{bmatrix} 5 & 2.5 \\ 2.5 & 3.75 \end{bmatrix}$$

By eqn. (4.101), the total matrix is therefore

$$[Z] = \begin{bmatrix} Z_{11} & Z_{12} \\ Z_{21} & Z_{22} \end{bmatrix} = \begin{bmatrix} 10+5 & 5+2.5 \\ 5+2.5 & 15+3.75 \end{bmatrix} = \begin{bmatrix} 15 & 7.5 \\ 7.5 & 18.75 \end{bmatrix} \tag{4.103}$$

The loop-current matrix equation for the combined networks with source and load is

$$\begin{bmatrix} Z_{11} & Z_{12} \\ Z_{21} & Z_{22} \end{bmatrix} \cdot \begin{bmatrix} I_1 \\ I_2 \end{bmatrix} = \begin{bmatrix} V_1 \\ V_2 \end{bmatrix} = \begin{bmatrix} E_1 - Z_1 I_1 \\ -Z_2 I_2 \end{bmatrix} \tag{4.104}$$

Substituting numerical values from eqn. (4.103) and Fig. 4-20,

$$\begin{bmatrix} 15 & 7.5 \\ 7.5 & 18.75 \end{bmatrix} \cdot \begin{bmatrix} I_1 \\ I_2 \end{bmatrix} = \begin{bmatrix} 1 - 5I_1 \\ -10I_2 \end{bmatrix}$$

which gives the equations

$$\begin{aligned} 20I_1 + 7.5I_2 &= 1 \\ 7.5I_1 + 28.75I_2 &= 0 \end{aligned} \tag{4.105}$$

from which

$$I_1 = 0.0554 \text{ A}; \quad I_2 = -0.0145 \text{ A};$$
$$V_1 = E_1 - I_1 Z_1 = 0.723 \text{ V}; \quad V_2 = -Z_2 I_2 = 0.145 \text{ V}$$

Parallel connection Fig. 4-20(*d*)

Excluding the source and load,

$$[Y] = [Y]_a + [Y]_b = [Z]_a^{-1} + [Y]_b \tag{4.106}$$

Using either of the methods just illustrated,

$$[Y]_a = [Z]_a^{-1} = \begin{bmatrix} \frac{15}{125} & -\frac{5}{125} \\ -\frac{5}{125} & \frac{10}{125} \end{bmatrix} = \begin{bmatrix} 0.12 & -0.04 \\ -0.04 & 0.08 \end{bmatrix}$$

$[Y]_b$ is given by eqn. (4.100), and by eqn. (4.106) the total matrix is therefore

$$[Y] = \begin{bmatrix} 0.12 + 0.3 & -0.04 - 0.2 \\ -0.04 - 0.2 & 0.08 + 0.4 \end{bmatrix} = \begin{bmatrix} 0.42 & -0.24 \\ -0.24 & 0.48 \end{bmatrix} \tag{4.107}$$

To write the nodal-voltage equations for the combined networks with source and load, it has been expedient to replace the original e.m.f. source E_1, Z_1 by a constant-current equivalent $E_1 Y_1$, Y_1, where $Y_1 = 1/Z_1$, as indicated in Fig. 4-20(e). Then,

$$\begin{bmatrix} Y_{11} & Y_{12} \\ Y_{21} & Y_{22} \end{bmatrix} \cdot \begin{bmatrix} V_1 \\ V_2 \end{bmatrix} = \begin{bmatrix} I_1 \\ I_2 \end{bmatrix} = \begin{bmatrix} E_1 Y_1 - Y_1 V_1 \\ -Y_2 V_2 \end{bmatrix} \tag{4.108}$$

where $Y_2 = 1/Z_2$.

Substituting numerical values and manipulating into equation-form gives

$$\begin{aligned} 0.42\, V_1 - 0.24\, V_2 &= 0.2 - 0.2\, V_1 \\ -0.24\, V_1 + 0.48\, V_2 &= -0.1\, V_2 \end{aligned}$$

or

$$\begin{aligned} 0.62\, V_1 - 0.24\, V_2 &= 0.2 \\ -0.24\, V_1 + 0.58\, V_2 &= 0 \end{aligned} \tag{4.109}$$

which gives

$$V_1 = 0.384 \text{ V}; \quad V_2 = 0.159 \text{ V}$$
$$I_1 = E_1 Y_1 - Y_1 V_1 = 0.123 \text{ A}; \quad \text{and} \quad I_2 = -Y_2 V_2 = -0.0159 \text{ A}$$

Sequential connection, Fig. 4.20(*f*)

The required a-matrices are not obvious for the given T and Π networks (a) and (b), but are readily found with the aid of Table 4-1. This gives, in conjunction with eqns. (4.99) and (4.100),

$$[a]_a = \begin{bmatrix} \dfrac{Z_{11}}{Z_{21}} & \dfrac{\Delta}{Z_{21}} \\ \dfrac{1}{Z_{21}} & \dfrac{Z_{22}}{Z_{21}} \end{bmatrix} = \begin{bmatrix} \dfrac{10}{5} & \dfrac{125}{5} \\ \dfrac{1}{5} & \dfrac{15}{5} \end{bmatrix} = \begin{bmatrix} 2 & 25 \\ 0.2 & 3 \end{bmatrix} \tag{4.110}$$

$$[a]_b = \begin{bmatrix} \dfrac{-Y_{22}}{Y_{21}} & \dfrac{-1}{Y_{21}} \\ \dfrac{-\Delta}{Y_{21}} & \dfrac{-Y_{11}}{Y_{21}} \end{bmatrix} = \begin{bmatrix} \dfrac{0.4}{0.2} & \dfrac{1}{0.2} \\ \dfrac{0.08}{0.2} & \dfrac{0.3}{0.2} \end{bmatrix} = \begin{bmatrix} 2 & 5 \\ 0.4 & 1.5 \end{bmatrix} \tag{4.111}$$

The matrix for the combined networks is therefore

$$[a] = [a]_a \cdot [a]_b = \begin{bmatrix} 2 & 25 \\ 0.2 & 3 \end{bmatrix} \cdot \begin{bmatrix} 2 & 5 \\ 0.4 & 1.5 \end{bmatrix} = \begin{bmatrix} 14 & 47.5 \\ 1.6 & 5.5 \end{bmatrix} \tag{4.112}$$

and the matrix equation is

$$\begin{bmatrix} V_1 \\ I_1 \end{bmatrix} = [a] \cdot \begin{bmatrix} V_2 \\ -I_2 \end{bmatrix} = \begin{bmatrix} 14 & 47.5 \\ 1.6 & 5.5 \end{bmatrix} \cdot \begin{bmatrix} V_2 \\ -I_2 \end{bmatrix} \tag{4.113}$$

Incorporating the source and load,

$$V_1 = E_1 - Z_1 I_1 = 1 - 5I_1 \quad \text{and} \quad V_2 = -Z_2 I_2 = -10I_2.$$

Thus,

$$\begin{bmatrix} 1 - 5\,I_1 \\ I_1 \end{bmatrix} = \begin{bmatrix} 14 & 47.5 \\ 1.6 & 5.5 \end{bmatrix} \cdot \begin{bmatrix} -10\,I_2 \\ -I_2 \end{bmatrix}$$

or

$$\begin{aligned} -140\,I_2 - 47.5\,I_2 &= 1 - 5I_1 \\ -16\,I_2 - 5.5\,I_2 &= I_1 \end{aligned} \tag{4.114}$$

whence

$$I_2 = -I_1/21.5; \quad I_1 = 0.0729 \text{ A}; \quad I_2 = -0.00339 \text{ A}$$
$$V_1 = 0.636 \text{ V}; \quad V_2 = 0.0339 \text{ V}$$

Comments

(1) The negative numerical value for I_2 in each case implies that its actual direction is opposite to the direction assumed, but in the positive sense of E_1 and I_1. Likewise, the positive values for V_1 and V_2 imply polarities in common with E_1 at corresponding terminals.

(2) For Figs. 4-20(c) and (d), the source and load immittances could have been absorbed into the total matrices. Thus in the case of (d), for example, if Y_1 and Y_2 are absorbed into Y_{11} and Y_{22}, the source-current $E_1 Y_1$ replaces I_1 and the matrix equation becomes

$$\begin{bmatrix} Y_{11} + Y_1 & Y_{12} \\ Y_{21} & Y_{22} + Y_2 \end{bmatrix} \cdot \begin{bmatrix} V_1 \\ V_2 \end{bmatrix} = \begin{bmatrix} E_1 Y_1 \\ 0 \end{bmatrix}$$

See also example 4.3.

Example 4.2. Synthesis of *a*-matrices

The *a*-matrix for a ladder-type structure can be synthesised from the *a*-matrices for its constituent series and shunt immittances. This is illustrated by reference to Figs. 4-21(a) to (f).

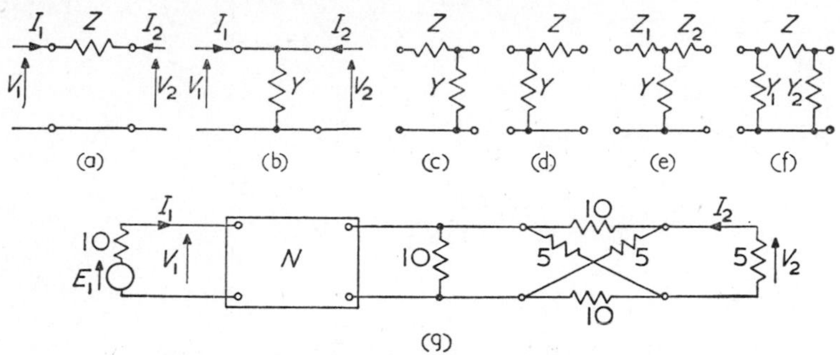

FIG. 4-21. Examples 2 and 3. All impedances in (g) are shown in ohms, pure resistance.

For the single series impedance Z in Fig. 4-21(a),

$$\begin{aligned} V_1 &= V_2 - ZI_2 \\ I_1 &= 0 \quad - I_2 \end{aligned} \quad \text{or} \quad \begin{bmatrix} V_1 \\ I_1 \end{bmatrix} = \begin{bmatrix} 1 & Z \\ 0 & 1 \end{bmatrix} \cdot \begin{bmatrix} V_2 \\ -I_2 \end{bmatrix}$$

Therefore,

$$[a]_z = \begin{bmatrix} 1 & Z \\ 0 & 1 \end{bmatrix} \tag{4.115}$$

Similarly for the single shunt admittance Y in (b),

$$\begin{aligned} V_1 &= V_2 - 0 \\ I_1 &= YV_2 - I_2 \end{aligned} \quad \text{or} \quad \begin{bmatrix} V_1 \\ I_1 \end{bmatrix} = \begin{bmatrix} 1 & 0 \\ Y & 1 \end{bmatrix} \cdot \begin{bmatrix} V_2 \\ -I_2 \end{bmatrix}$$

and therefore

$$[a]_Y = \begin{bmatrix} 1 & 0 \\ Y & 1 \end{bmatrix} \tag{4.116}$$

The a-matrices for (c), (d), (e) and (f) follow as products based on these canonic forms:

For (c),

$$[a]_{ZY} = \begin{bmatrix} 1 & Z \\ 0 & 1 \end{bmatrix} \cdot \begin{bmatrix} 1 & 0 \\ Y & 1 \end{bmatrix} = \begin{bmatrix} 1 + YZ & Z \\ Y & 1 \end{bmatrix} \tag{4.117}$$

For (d),

$$[a]_{YZ} = \begin{bmatrix} 1 & 0 \\ Y & 1 \end{bmatrix} \cdot \begin{bmatrix} 1 & Z \\ 0 & 1 \end{bmatrix} = \begin{bmatrix} 1 & Z \\ Y & 1 + YZ \end{bmatrix} \tag{4.118}$$

For (e),

$$[a]_{\mathrm{T}} = \begin{bmatrix} 1 + YZ_1 & Z_1 \\ Y & 1 \end{bmatrix} \cdot \begin{bmatrix} 1 & Z_2 \\ 0 & 1 \end{bmatrix}$$

$$= \begin{bmatrix} 1 + YZ_1 & Z_1 + Z_2 + YZ_1Z_2 \\ Y & 1 + YZ_2 \end{bmatrix} \tag{4.119}$$

For (f),

$$[a]_{\Pi} = \begin{bmatrix} 1 & Z \\ Y_1 & 1 + Y_1Z \end{bmatrix} \cdot \begin{bmatrix} 1 & 0 \\ Y_2 & 1 \end{bmatrix}$$

$$= \begin{bmatrix} 1 + Y_2Z & Z \\ Y_1 + Y_2 + ZY_1Y_2 & 1 + Y_1Z \end{bmatrix} \tag{4.120}$$

Example 4.3

In Fig. 4-21(g), the network N is specified by the Z-matrix,

$$[Z]_N = \begin{bmatrix} 20 & 10 \\ 10 & 15 \end{bmatrix}$$

(1) The source resistance may be incorporated into $[Z]_N$, giving

$$[Z]_1 = \begin{bmatrix} 20 + 10 & 10 \\ 10 & 15 \end{bmatrix} = \begin{bmatrix} 30 & 10 \\ 10 & 15 \end{bmatrix}$$

In the final equations, E_1 will then take the place of V_1.

(2) $[Z]_1$ is transformed into an a-matrix by means of Table 4-1, giving

$$[a]_1 = \begin{bmatrix} 3 & 35 \\ 0.1 & 1.5 \end{bmatrix}$$

(3) The a-matrix for the 10-ohm shunt is

$$[a]_2 = \begin{bmatrix} 1 & 0 \\ Y & 1 \end{bmatrix} = \begin{bmatrix} 1 & 0 \\ 0.1 & 1 \end{bmatrix}$$

(4) The easiest matrix to state for the lattice is the Z-matrix (see sect. 2.3.2). This is

$$[Z]_L = \begin{bmatrix} \frac{1}{2}(Z_x + Z_y) & \frac{1}{2}(Z_y - Z_x) \\ \frac{1}{2}(Z_y - Z_x) & \frac{1}{2}(Z_x + Z_y) \end{bmatrix} = \begin{bmatrix} 7.5 & -2.5 \\ -2.5 & 7.5 \end{bmatrix}$$

(5) By Table 4-1, the a-matrix for the lattice is

$$[a]_3 = \begin{bmatrix} -3 & -20 \\ -0.4 & -3 \end{bmatrix}$$

(6) The matrix for the system of networks, including the source resistance but not the load, is

$$\begin{aligned} [a] &= [a]_1 \cdot [a]_2 \cdot [a]_3 \\ &= \begin{bmatrix} 3 & 35 \\ 0.1 & 1.5 \end{bmatrix} \cdot \begin{bmatrix} 1 & 0 \\ 0.1 & 1 \end{bmatrix} \cdot \begin{bmatrix} -3 & -20 \\ -0.4 & -3 \end{bmatrix} \\ &= \begin{bmatrix} 6.5 & 35 \\ 0.25 & 1.5 \end{bmatrix} \cdot \begin{bmatrix} -3 & -20 \\ -0.4 & -3 \end{bmatrix} \\ &= \begin{bmatrix} -33.5 & -235 \\ -1.35 & -9.5 \end{bmatrix} \end{aligned}$$

(7) Writing E_1 in place of V_1, since the 10-ohm source resistance has been absorbed in step (1), the matrix equation for the system of networks is

$$\begin{bmatrix} E_1 \\ I_1 \end{bmatrix} = [a] \cdot \begin{bmatrix} V_2 \\ -I_2 \end{bmatrix} = \begin{bmatrix} -33.5 & -235 \\ -1.35 & -9.5 \end{bmatrix} \cdot \begin{bmatrix} V_2 \\ -I_2 \end{bmatrix}$$

(8) Finally, incorporating the load by writing $I_2 = -V_2/5 = -0.2\ V_2$ and manipulating into normal equation-form,

$$E_1 = -33.5\ V_2 - 47\ V_2$$

$$I_1 = -1.35\ V_2 - 1.9\ V_2$$

whence

$$V_2 = -E_1/80.5 \text{ and } I_2 = -V_2/5 = E_1/402.5$$

Example 4.4

In Fig. 4-22(a), T is a transformer, which is assumed ideal, having a voltage ratio $\lambda = 2$ in the sense indicated.

The network may be resolved into the parallel connection of Figs. 4-22(b) and (c). It is unnecessary to deal with (b) as a system of subnetworks in sequence, however, for the Z-matrix is easily stated directly.

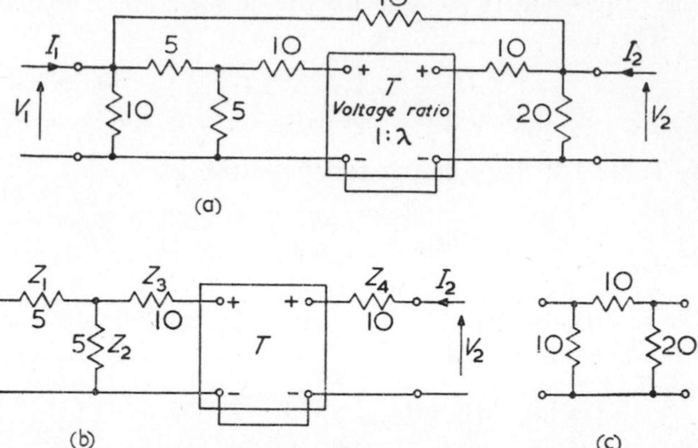

Fig. 4-22. Example 4.4. All impedances are in ohms, pure resistance, and $\lambda = 2$.

Referring to Fig. 4-22 (b) and noting that for a voltage-ratio $1:\lambda$ the ideal transformer T has a current ratio $\lambda:1$ and an impedance ratio $1:\lambda^2$,

$$
\begin{aligned}
Z_{11} &= V_1/I_{1(I_2=0)} = Z_1 + Z_2 &&= 10\\
Z_{22} &= V_2/I_{2(I_1=0)} = Z_4 + (Z_2 + Z_3)\lambda^2 &&= 70\\
Z_{12} &= V_1/I_{2(I_1=0)} = Z_2\lambda I_2/I_2 = \lambda Z_2 &&= 10\\
Z_{21} &= V_2/I_{1(I_2=0)} = Z_2 I_1 \lambda/I_1 = \lambda Z_2 &&= 10
\end{aligned}
$$

Thus,

$$
[Z]_b = \begin{bmatrix} 10 & 10 \\ 10 & 70 \end{bmatrix}
$$

and, by inspection,

$$
[Y]_c = \begin{bmatrix} 0.2 & -0.1 \\ -0.1 & 0.15 \end{bmatrix}
$$

Transforming $[Z]_b$ into $[Y]_b$ and combining with $[Y]_c$,

$$
[Y] = \begin{bmatrix} \frac{7}{60} & -\frac{1}{60} \\ -\frac{1}{60} & \frac{1}{60} \end{bmatrix} + \begin{bmatrix} 0.2 & -0.1 \\ -0.1 & 0.15 \end{bmatrix}
$$

$$
= \begin{bmatrix} \frac{19}{60} & -\frac{7}{60} \\ -\frac{7}{60} & \frac{10}{60} \end{bmatrix}
$$

The nodal-voltage equations are therefore

$$\frac{19}{60}V_1 - \frac{7}{60}V_2 = I_1$$

$$-\frac{7}{60}V_1 + \frac{10}{60}V_2 = I_2$$

If Fig. 4-22(a) is under open-circuit conditions at the output terminals, $I_2 = 0$ and then

$$-\frac{7}{60}V_1 + \frac{10}{60}V_2 = 0$$

or

$$\frac{V_2}{V_1} = \frac{7}{10}$$

Example 4.5

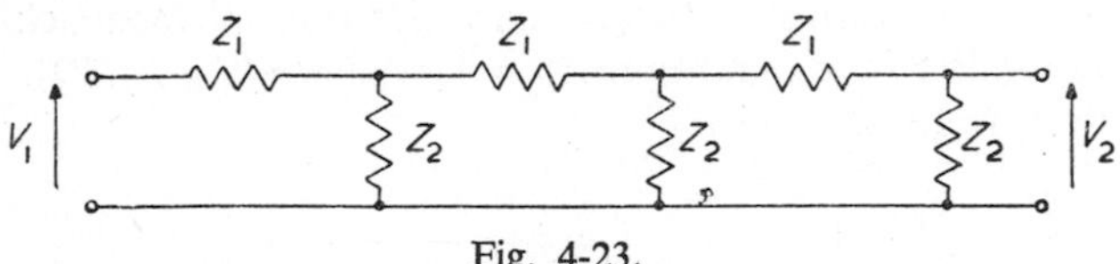

Fig. 4-23.

A sinusoidal voltage V_1 is applied to the input of the network shown in Fig. 4-23. Show that

$$V_2/V_1 = 1/(1 + 6K + 5K^2 + K^3)$$

where $K = Z_1/Z_2$.

A network of this type is used in a phase-shift oscillator. Draw a suitable circuit and use the equation above to find the condition for oscillation and the oscillation frequency. State clearly any assumptions made.

(*I.E.R.E., Section B*)

From the equation

$$\begin{bmatrix} V_1 \\ I_1 \end{bmatrix} = \begin{bmatrix} a_{11} & a_{12} \\ a_{21} & a_{22} \end{bmatrix} . \begin{bmatrix} V_2 \\ -I_2 \end{bmatrix}$$

it is apparent that if the network is operated under open-circuit conditions and $I_2 = 0$,

$$V_1/V_2 = a_{11}$$

By eqn. (4.117) the matrix per section comprising Z_1 and Z_2 is

$$\begin{bmatrix} 1 + Z_1/Z_2 & Z_1 \\ 1/Z_2 & 1 \end{bmatrix} = \begin{bmatrix} 1 + K & Z_1 \\ 1/Z_2 & 1 \end{bmatrix}$$

Multiplying the matrix by itself three times, with strict regard to order but disregarding products not contributing to a_{11},

$$\begin{bmatrix} a_{11} & - \\ - & - \end{bmatrix} = \begin{bmatrix} 1+K & Z_1 \\ - & - \end{bmatrix} \cdot \begin{bmatrix} 1+K & Z_1 \\ 1/Z_2 & 1 \end{bmatrix} \cdot \begin{bmatrix} 1+K & - \\ 1/Z_2 & - \end{bmatrix}$$

$$= \begin{bmatrix} (1+K)^3 + 2K(1+K) + K & - \\ - & - \end{bmatrix}$$

whence

$$1/a_{11} = V_2/V_1 = 1/(1 + 6K + 5K^2 + K^3)$$

In an oscillator incorporating Fig. 4-23, Z_1 is a capacitor C and Z_2 a resistor R. The network is interposed as a feedback path between the anode-cathode (output) and grid-cathode (input) terminals of a pentode valve amplifier with a pure-resistance anode load. In this common-cathode circuit, the amplifier gain A is a negative real number, so that the threshold of oscillation exists when V_1/V_2 is real and negative and equalled by A (in terms of the *Nyquist criterion* of feedback theory, this corresponds to the condition $A\beta = 1\angle 0$ where $\beta = V_2/V_1$).

Substituting for Z_1 and Z_2,

$$\frac{V_1}{V_2} = 1 - \frac{5}{(\omega CR)^2} + j\left[\frac{1}{(\omega CR)^3} - \frac{6}{\omega CR}\right]$$

This is real when

$$\frac{1}{(\omega CR)^3} - \frac{6}{\omega CR} = 0$$

or

$$\frac{1}{(\omega CR)^2} = 6$$

whence

$$\omega = 1/\sqrt{6}CR$$

Substituting then for $(\omega CR)^2$ in the real part gives

$$\frac{V_1}{V_2} = 1 - \frac{5}{(\omega CR)^2} = 1 - 30 = -29$$

The required amplifier gain is therefore -29.

The above analysis assumes that the valve input impedance is infinite so that the feedback network is effectively open-circuit on the output side.

When the loading on the feedback network is significant, as in the case of transistor oscillators, the full matrix is involved. Let $[a]_A$ and

$[a]_F$ denote the matrices for the amplifier and feedback network respectively. Then the loop-matrix is

$$[a] = [a]_A \cdot [a]_F = \begin{bmatrix} a_{11} & a_{12} \\ a_{21} & a_{22} \end{bmatrix}$$

The threshold of oscillation exists when supposed inputs V_1 and I_1 to the amplifier are just reproduced at the output of the feedback network, so that when this is connected to the amplifier input, V_1 and I_1 are just sustained.

If, for the loop,

$$V_1 = a_{11} V_2 - a_{12} I_2$$
$$I_1 = a_{21} V_2 - a_{22} I_2$$

then the threshold of oscillation exists when $V_2 = V_1$ and $-I_2 = I_1$. Imposing these conditions gives

$$\begin{bmatrix} a_{11}-1 & a_{12} \\ a_{21} & a_{22}-1 \end{bmatrix} \cdot \begin{bmatrix} V_1 \\ I_1 \end{bmatrix} = 0$$

The solutions for V_1 and I_1 are non-trivial provided

$$\Delta_a = \begin{vmatrix} a_{11}-1 & a_{12} \\ a_{21} & a_{22}-1 \end{vmatrix} = 0 \qquad (4.121)$$

which is therefore the criterion for oscillation.

This approach has been admirably exploited in relation to a variety of oscillator circuits in reference 7.

Example 4.6

Explain the meaning of the complex constants A, B, C, D, as applied to a four-terminal network such as a transmission line.

A 132 kV transmission line, having constants A, B, C, D, is preceded and terminated by 132/33 kV transformers. The short-circuit impedances of the transformers measured on their 33 kV sides are Z_1 for the input transformer and Z_2 for the output transformer. Neglecting the magnetising current of the transformers, calculate the values of the constants A_1, B_1, C_1, D_1, representing the complete system.

(*I.E.E., Part 3, Advanced Electrical Engineering*)

From left to right, the input transformer may be represented by a series impedance Z_1 followed by an ideal transformer of voltage ratio 33:132 or 1:4, and the output transformer may be represented by an ideal transformer of ratio 132: 33 or 4: 1, followed by a series impedance Z_2. The *a*-matrices for these transformers are therefore

$$\begin{bmatrix} 1 & Z_1 \\ 0 & 1 \end{bmatrix} \cdot \begin{bmatrix} \frac{1}{4} & 0 \\ 0 & 4 \end{bmatrix} = \begin{bmatrix} \frac{1}{4} & 4Z_1 \\ 0 & 4 \end{bmatrix}$$

and

$$\begin{bmatrix} 4 & 0 \\ 0 & \frac{1}{4} \end{bmatrix} \cdot \begin{bmatrix} 1 & Z_2 \\ 0 & 1 \end{bmatrix} = \begin{bmatrix} 4 & 4Z_2 \\ 0 & \frac{1}{4} \end{bmatrix}$$

The system matrix is therefore

$$\begin{bmatrix} A_1 & B_1 \\ C_1 & D_1 \end{bmatrix} = \begin{bmatrix} \frac{1}{4} & 4Z_1 \\ 0 & 4 \end{bmatrix} \cdot \begin{bmatrix} A & B \\ C & D \end{bmatrix} \cdot \begin{bmatrix} 4 & 4Z_2 \\ 0 & \frac{1}{4} \end{bmatrix}$$

$$= \begin{bmatrix} A + 16CZ_1 & (A + 16CZ_1)Z_2 + DZ_1 + B/16 \\ 16C & D + 16CZ_2 \end{bmatrix}$$

Example 4.7

Derive an expression for the ratio V_{out}/V_{in} for the network of Fig. 4-24(a), and show that at a certain frequency the output voltage is zero. Determine this frequency if $C = 0.05$ μF and the inductance of the coil is 150 mH.

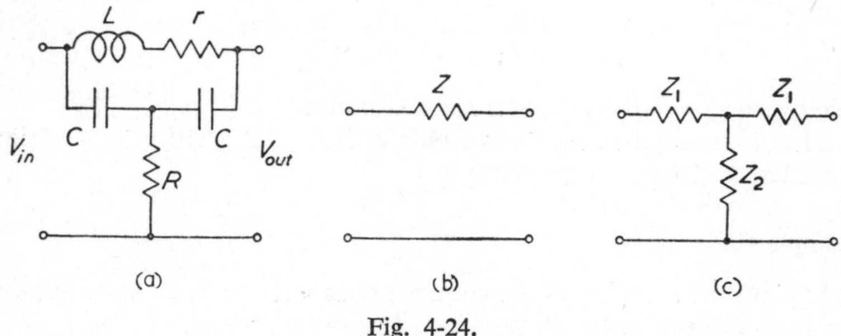

Fig. 4-24.

(*I.E.E., Part 3, Advanced Electrical Engineering*)

The voltage-ratio for the network of Fig. 4-24(a) is given directly from one of the nodal-voltage equations

$$Y_{11} V_1 + Y_{12} V_2 = I_1$$
$$Y_{21} V_1 + Y_{22} V_2 = I_2$$

Putting $I_2 = 0$ in the second,

$$\frac{V_{out}}{V_{in}} = \frac{V_2}{V_1} = -\frac{Y_{21}}{Y_{22}}$$

Note that if a load Y_L were included, it could be absorbed into Y_{22}, giving

$$\frac{V_2}{V_1} = -\frac{Y_{21}}{Y_{22} + Y_L}$$

The network comprises Figs. 4-24(b) and (c) in parallel, where $Z = r + sL$, $Z_1 = 1/sC$ and $Z_2 = R$. By inspection,

$$[Y]_b = \begin{bmatrix} 1/Z & -1/Z \\ -1/Z & 1/Z \end{bmatrix} \quad \text{and} \quad [Z]_c = \begin{bmatrix} Z_1 + Z_2 & Z_2 \\ Z_2 & Z_1 + Z_2 \end{bmatrix}$$

$[Z]_c$ is easily inverted, giving

$$[Y]_c = [Z]_c^{-1} = \begin{bmatrix} \dfrac{Z_1 + Z_2}{\Delta} & \dfrac{-Z_2}{\Delta} \\ \dfrac{-Z_2}{\Delta} & \dfrac{Z_1 + Z_2}{\Delta} \end{bmatrix}$$

where $\Delta = Z_1^2 + 2Z_1Z_2$

Then, adding the matrix elements corresponding to Y_{21} and Y_{22},

$$\frac{V_{\text{out}}}{V_{\text{in}}} = \frac{V_2}{V_1} = -\frac{Y_{21}}{Y_{22}} = \frac{(1/Z) + Z_2/\Delta}{(1/Z) + (Z_1 + Z_2)/\Delta}$$

$$= \frac{\Delta + Z_2Z}{\Delta + Z(Z_1 + Z_2)}$$

$$= \frac{Z_1^2 + Z_2(Z + 2Z_1)}{Z_1^2 + Z(Z_1 + Z_2) + 2Z_1Z_2}$$

$$= \frac{s^2C^2R(r + sL) + 2sCR + 1}{sC(r + sL)(1 + sCR) + 2sCR + 1}$$

$V_{\text{out}} = 0$ when the numerator is zero. For $s = j\omega$, this requires

$$1 - \omega^2C^2Rr + j\omega CR(2 - \omega^2LC) = 0$$

From the imaginary part, $\omega^2LC = 2$, or

$$\omega = \sqrt{2/LC}, \text{ and } f = \frac{\omega}{2\pi} = 2598 \text{ c/s}$$

From the real part,

$$R = 1/\omega^2C^2r = L/2Cr$$

Example 4.8

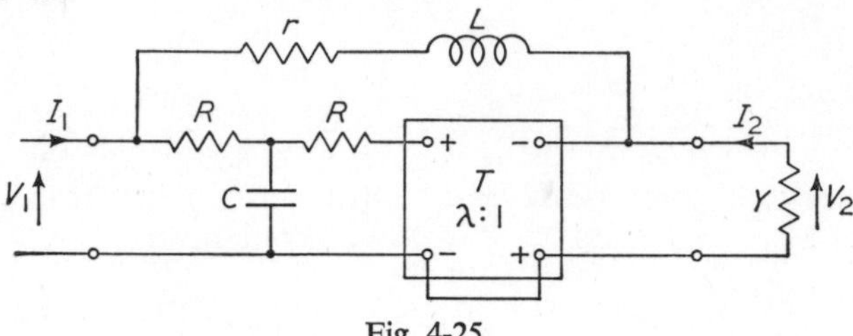

Fig. 4-25.

In Fig. 4-25, T is a transformer that may be regarded as ideal, having a voltage-ratio $\lambda : 1$ in the sense indicated. Show that V_2/V_1 may be zero provided λ is negative, as implied by the polarities marked and that for $\lambda = -\phi$, where ϕ denotes a real positive number, V_2/V_1 is zero when $r = 2R/\phi$ and $L = CR^2/\phi$.

The network is assigned the normalised values $R = 2\Omega$, $C = 1\text{F}$, $r = 1\Omega$, $L = 1\text{H}$, and $\lambda = -2$.

(1) Show that the output admittance, under a short-circuit condition at the input terminals, is independent of the complex-frequency variable s.

(2) Obtain expressions for V_2/V_1 when the load Y is (a) a 1Ω resistor, and (b) a 1F capacitor, and adapt the expressions to give magnitudes and phases for the case $s = j\omega$.

For the complete network loaded with an admittance Y,

$$Y_{21}V_1 + Y_{22}V_2 = I_2 = -YV_2$$

and therefore

$$\frac{V_2}{V_1} = -\frac{Y_{21}}{Y_{22} + Y}$$

Let Y'_{12}, Y'_{22} refer to the four-terminal network formed from the bridging impedance $r + sL$, as in Fig. 4-24(b). Then,

$$Y'_{12} = -1/(r + sL)$$

$$Y'_{22} = 1/(r + sL)$$

For the paralleled network comprising R, R, C, and T, the procedure illustrated in Example 4.4 gives

$$[Z] = \begin{bmatrix} R + \dfrac{1}{sC} & \dfrac{1}{\lambda sC} \\[2ex] \dfrac{1}{\lambda sC} & \dfrac{1}{\lambda^2}\left(R + \dfrac{1}{sC}\right) \end{bmatrix}$$

and

$$\Delta = \text{det.}[Z] = (R^2 + 2R/sC)/\lambda^2$$

Then, denoting the admittance parameters by Y''_{12} and Y''_{22},

$$Y''_{21} = -Z_{21}/\Delta = -\lambda/(2R + sCR^2)$$

$$Y''_{22} = Z_{11}/\Delta \quad = \lambda^2(1 + sCR)/(2R + sCR^2)$$

The null condition

$$V_2/V_1 \text{ is zero when}$$

$$Y_{21} = Y'_{21} + Y''_{21} = 0$$

or,

$$-\frac{\lambda}{2R + sCR^2} - \frac{1}{r + sL} = 0$$

For λ real, this may be satisfied when λ is negative. Let $\lambda = -\phi$, where ϕ is real and positive. Then,

$$2R + sCR^2 = r\phi + sL\phi$$

and therefore, by equating corresponding terms,

$$r = 2R/\phi \quad \text{and} \quad L = CR^2/\phi$$

The output admittance

Under a short-circuit condition at the input terminals,

$$Y_{\text{out}} = Y_{22} = Y'_{22} + Y''_{22}$$

$$= \frac{\lambda^2(1 + sCR)}{2R + sCR^2} + \frac{1}{r + sL}$$

$$= \frac{\lambda^2(1 + 2s) + 4}{4(1 + s)}$$

Imposing then the condition $\lambda = -2$, this reduces to

$$Y_{\text{out}} = \frac{2(1 + s)}{1 + s} = 2 \text{ mhos}$$

The voltage ratio

For $\lambda = -2$ and the given normalised values,

$$Y_{21} = Y'_{21} + Y''_{21} = -\frac{1}{2(1 + s)}$$

$$Y_{22} = Y'_{22} + Y''_{22} = 2$$

(a) For the 1Ω load, $Y_{22} + Y = 3$. Therefore,

$$\frac{V_2}{V_1} = -\frac{Y_{21}}{Y_{22} + Y} = \frac{1}{6(1 + s)}$$

When $s = j\omega$,

$$\left|\frac{V_2}{V_1}\right| = \frac{1}{6\sqrt{1 + \omega^2}} \quad \text{and} \quad \arg\frac{V_2}{V_1} = -\tan^{-1}\omega$$

This is a *Butterworth response* of order $n = 1$: the general form for this type of response is

$$|T(j\omega)| = \frac{1}{\sqrt{1 + \omega^{2n}}} \qquad (n = 1, 2, 3 \ldots)$$

where $T(j\omega)$ denotes a general transfer function.
(b) For the 1F capacitor load, $Y = sC = s$, and $Y_{22} + Y = 2 + s$. Then,

$$\frac{V_2}{V_1} = \frac{1}{2(1 + s)(2 + s)} = \frac{1}{2(2 + 3s + s^2)}$$

When $s = j\omega$,

$$\left|\frac{V_2}{V_1}\right| = \frac{1}{2\sqrt{4 + 5\omega^2 + \omega^4}}$$

and

$$\arg\frac{V_2}{V_1} = -\tan^{-1}\left[\frac{3\omega}{2 - \omega^2}\right]$$

Example 4.9

A "twin-T" or "parallel-T" circuit has input terminals A and B, and output terminals C and D. B and D are common. Between A and C are two parallel circuits, one consisting of two 5,000 ohm resistors in series, and the other of two 0.05 microfarad capacitors in series. A 0.1-microfarad capacitor is connected between B and the junction of the two resistors, and a 2,500-ohm resistor is connected between B and the junction of the two capacitors. Calculate the frequency at which the output is zero with finite input voltage.

(*L.U. Int., Telecommunications*)

For null conditions only, the total transfer admittance ΣY_{21} alone is sufficient. In general, the output from any number of paralleled networks is zero when $\Sigma Y_{21} = 0$; but in the common case of two networks, the condition $\Sigma Y_{21} = 0$ coincides with the condition $\Sigma Z_{tr} = 0$, where Z_{tr} denotes a short-circuit transfer impedance, defined by V_1/I_2 when

$V_2 = 0$. It is the reciprocal of Y_{21} and corresponds to the coefficient a_{12} of the a-matrix (see sects. 2.2 and 2.3.2).

Let $Z_{tr(1)}$ and $Z_{tr(2)}$ denote the respective transfer impedances of two paralleled networks. Then a null exists when

$$\sum Y_{21} = \frac{1}{Z_{tr(1)}} + \frac{1}{Z_{tr(2)}} = \frac{Z_{tr(2)} + Z_{tr(1)}}{Z_{tr(1)} \cdot Z_{tr(2)}} = 0$$

Therefore, provided $Z_{tr(1)} \cdot Z_{tr(2)}$ is finite, the null condition is equivalently defined by

$$Z_{tr(1)} + Z_{tr(2)} = 0$$

The T-network is the structure usually of interest in this connection, and for branches Z_1 (left) Z_2 (right) and Z_3, it is shown in sect. 2.3.2 that

$$Z_{tr} = Z_1 + Z_2 + Z_1 Z_2 / Z_3$$

In the given problem, one T-network comprises series arms R_1, R_1 and shunt-arm C_1, and the other series arms C_2, C_2 and shunt-arm R_2, where $R_1 = 5{,}000$ ohms, $C_1 = 0.1$ μF, $R_2 = 2{,}500$ ohms, and $C_2 = 0.05$ μF. The null condition exists when the sum of the transfer impedances is zero; that is, when

$$(2R_1 + j\omega C_1 R_1^2) + \left[-j\frac{2}{\omega C_2} - \frac{1}{\omega^2 C_2^2 R_2}\right] = 0$$

Equating like terms,

$$2R_1 = 1/\omega^2 C_2^2 R_2 \quad \text{and} \quad \omega C_1 R_1^2 = 2/\omega C_2$$

whence

$$\omega = \frac{1}{C_2\sqrt{(2R_1R_2)}} = \frac{1}{R_1} \cdot \sqrt{\frac{2}{C_1 C_2}}$$

$$= 4{,}000 \text{ rad/s}$$

or

$$f = \omega/2\pi = 636 \text{ c/s}$$

Example 4.10

Identical transistors in the common-emitter connection are used in a two-stage low-frequency amplifier.

Deduce the overall voltage gain, power gain, and input resistance of the amplifier for small signals, if $r_e = 20\Omega$, $r_b = 500\Omega$, $\alpha = 0.98$, and $r_c = 1$ MΩ. Both collector load resistances are 5 kΩ, the input signal-source has zero output impedance, and the effect of coupling and bias networks may be neglected.

(*I.E.R.E., Section B*)

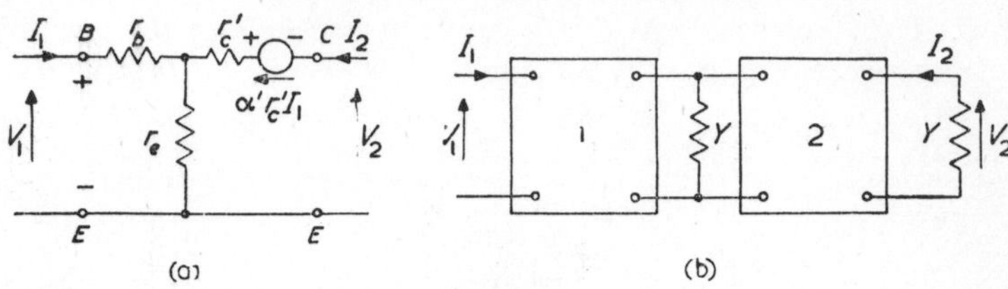

Fig. 4-26.

The adaption of the given common-base parameters to an active representation for the transistor in the common-emitter circuit is shown in Fig. 4-26(a). In this, $r_c' = r_c(1 - \alpha)$ and $\alpha' = \alpha/(1 - \alpha)$.

An elegant approach to the problem is with a-matrices, and for either transistor the a-matrix is easily found from the almost obvious Z-matrix. Referring to Fig. 4-26(a),

$$
\begin{aligned}
Z_{11} I_1 + Z_{12} I_2 &= V_1 \\
Z_{21} I_1 + Z_{22} I_2 &= V_2
\end{aligned}
$$

whence

$$
\begin{aligned}
Z_{11} &= V_1/I_{1(I_2=0)} = r_b + r_e && = 520 \\
Z_{12} &= V_1/I_{2(I_1=0)} = r_e && = 20 \\
Z_{21} &= V_2/I_{1(I_2=0)} = (I_1 r_e - \alpha' r_c' I_1)/I_1 && \\
&= r_e - \alpha' r_c' && \\
&= r_e - \alpha r_c && = -98 \times 10^4 \\
Z_{22} &= V_2/I_{2(I_1=0)} = r_e + r_c' && \\
&= r_e + r_c(1 - \alpha) && = 2 \times 10^4
\end{aligned}
$$

(note r_e is insignificant in Z_{21} and Z_{22}). Thus,

$$
[Z] = \begin{bmatrix} 520 & 20 \\ -98 \times 10^4 & 2 \times 10^4 \end{bmatrix}
$$

and then by Table 4-1, with $\Delta = 3 \times 10^7$,

$$
[a] = \begin{bmatrix} \dfrac{Z_{11}}{Z_{21}} & \dfrac{\Delta}{Z_{21}} \\[2ex] \dfrac{1}{Z_{21}} & \dfrac{Z_{22}}{Z_{21}} \end{bmatrix} = \begin{bmatrix} -5.3 \times 10^{-4} & -30.6 \\[2ex] -1.02 \times 10^{-6} & -2.04 \times 10^{-2} \end{bmatrix}
$$

Referring now to Fig. 4-26(b), the a-matrix for the whole amplifier, including the matrix for the admittance Y of the 5,000 ohm load on the first stage, but excluding the load on the second, is

$$\lfloor a \rfloor = \begin{bmatrix} -5.3 \times 10^{-4} & -30.6 \\ -1.02 \times 10^{-6} & -2.04 \times 10^{-2} \end{bmatrix} \cdot \begin{bmatrix} 1 & 0 \\ 2 \times 10^{-4} & 1 \end{bmatrix} \cdot \begin{bmatrix} -5.3 \times 10^{-4} & -30.6 \\ -1.02 \times 10^{-6} & -2.04 \times 10^{-2} \end{bmatrix}$$

$$= \begin{bmatrix} -66.5 \times 10^{-4} & -30.6 \\ -5.1 \times 10^{-6} & -2.04 \times 10^{-2} \end{bmatrix} \cdot \begin{bmatrix} -5.3 \times 10^{-4} & -30.6 \\ -1.02 \times 10^{-6} & -2.04 \times 10^{-2} \end{bmatrix}$$

$$= \begin{bmatrix} 34.73 \times 10^{-6} & 82.5 \times 10^{-2} \\ 2.35 \times 10^{-8} & 5.72 \times 10^{-4} \end{bmatrix}$$

The a-type equations are therefore

$$V_1 = 34.7 \times 10^{-6}\, V_2 - 82.5 \times 10^{-2}\, I_2$$

$$I_1 = 2.35 \times 10^{-8}\, V_2 - 5.72 \times 10^{-4}\, I_2$$

The output load is incorporated by substituting $I_2 = -V_2 Y = -2 \times 10^{-4}\, V_2$, giving

$$V_1 = (34.7 + 165)10^{-6}\, V_2 = 1.997 \times 10^{-4}\, V_2$$

$$I_1 = (2.35 + 11.44)10^{-8}\, V_2 = 13.79 \times 10^{-8}\, V_2$$

The overall amplification is therefore

$$V_2/V_1 = 10^4/1.997 = 5{,}000$$

and the input resistance is

$$R_{in} = V_1/I_1 = V_1/13.79 \times 10^{-8} \times 5 \times 10^3 V_1 = 1{,}450 \text{ ohms.}$$

The power-gain is

$$\frac{P_{out}}{P_{in}} = \frac{V_2^2}{R} \cdot \frac{R_{in}}{V_1^2} = 25 \times 10^6 \times 1{,}450/5{,}000$$
$$= 7.25 \times 10^6$$

or in decibels,

$$\text{Power gain} = 10 \log_{10} 7.25 \times 10^6 = 68.6 \text{ db.}$$

Example 4.11

In Fig. 4-27(a), $R_1 = 2{,}000$ ohms, $R_2 = 10{,}000$ ohms, and A is an amplifier whose h-matrix is

$$[h]_A = \begin{bmatrix} 1.1 \times 10^3 & 3 \times 10^{-4} \\ 35 & 23 \times 10^{-6} \end{bmatrix}$$

Fig. 4-27(b) shows the same amplifier in a feedback system, in which T is an isolating and polarity-reversing transformer having a voltage-ratio $-1:2$ as indicated, while B is a feedback network having an a-matrix

$$[a]_B = \begin{bmatrix} 2 & 21 \times 10^3 \\ 10^{-3} & 11 \end{bmatrix}$$

Calculate for the amplifier alone, as in Fig. 4-27(a), and for the feedback system, as in Fig. 4-27(b),

(1) The ratio V_2/V_1
(2) The input impedance at terminals 1–2 while the output terminals 3–4 are closed by R_2
(3) The ratio V_2/E_1
(4) The output impedance at terminals 3–4 when R_2 is disconnected but terminals 1–2 are closed by the internal resistance R_1 of the source.

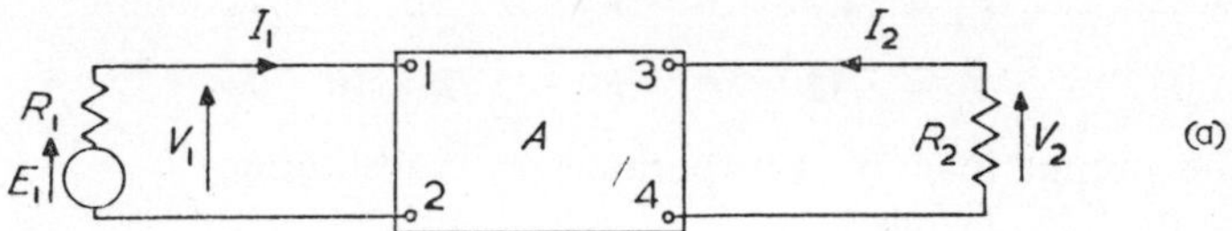

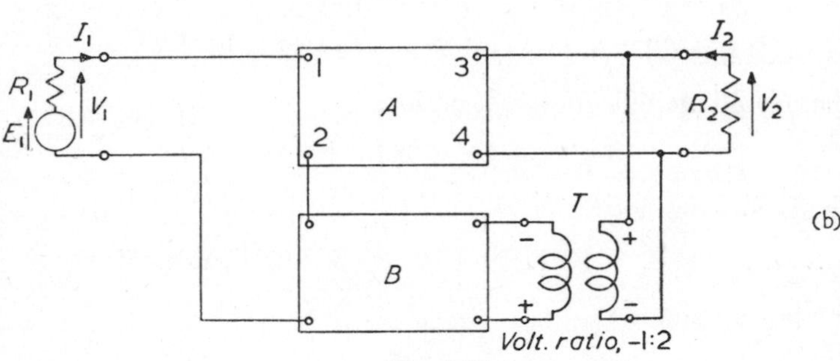

Fig. 4-27.

Including the load, the h-matrix equation for either arrangement has the form

$$\begin{bmatrix} h_{11} & h_{12} \\ h_{21} & h_{22} \end{bmatrix} \cdot \begin{bmatrix} I_1 \\ V_2 \end{bmatrix} = \begin{bmatrix} V_1 \\ I_2 \end{bmatrix} = \begin{bmatrix} V_1 \\ -V_2/R_2 \end{bmatrix} \tag{4.122}$$

whence

$$V_2/V_1 = h_{21}/[h_{12}h_{21} - h_{11}(h_{22} + 1/R_2)] \tag{4.123}$$

$$Z_{\text{in}} = Z_{1-2} = V_1/I_1 = h_{11} - [h_{12}h_{21}/(h_{22} + 1/R_2)] \tag{4.124}$$

Then, since $V_1 = E_1 Z_{\text{in}}/(R_1 + Z_{\text{in}})$,

$$\frac{V_2}{E_1} = \frac{Z_{\text{in}}}{R_1 + Z_{\text{in}}} \cdot \left[\frac{V_2}{V_1}\right] \tag{4.125}$$

The output impedance is calculated by visualising V_2 as an external voltage applied to the output terminals, producing the current I_2. Then, with the input terminals closed by R_1 (but with E_1 reduced to zero),

$$\begin{bmatrix} h_{11} & h_{12} \\ h_{21} & h_{22} \end{bmatrix} \cdot \begin{bmatrix} I_1 \\ V_2 \end{bmatrix} = \begin{bmatrix} V_1 \\ I_2 \end{bmatrix} = \begin{bmatrix} -I_1 R_1 \\ I_2 \end{bmatrix} \tag{4.126}$$

whence

$$I_2 = V_2\{h_{22} - [h_{21}h_{12}/(h_{11} + R_1)]\}$$

and

$$Z_{out} = Z_{3-4} = V_2/I_2 = 1/\{h_{22} - [h_{12}\, h_{21}/(h_{11} + R_1)]\} \tag{4.127}$$

In the case of Fig. 4-27(b), the h-matrix must be calculated from the matrices for its constituents. By reference to the equations $V_1 = a_{11}V_2 - a_{12}I_2$ and $I_1 = a_{21}V_2 - a_{22}I_2$, the a-matrix for the transformer T with the polarities shown is

$$\begin{bmatrix} a_{11} & a_{12} \\ a_{21} & a_{22} \end{bmatrix}_T = \begin{bmatrix} -\frac{1}{2} & 0 \\ 0 & -2 \end{bmatrix}$$

and the a-matrix for the network B followed by T is therefore

$$\begin{bmatrix} a_{11} & a_{12} \\ a_{21} & a_{22} \end{bmatrix}_{BT} = \begin{bmatrix} 2 & 21 \times 10^3 \\ 10^{-3} & 11 \end{bmatrix} \cdot \begin{bmatrix} -\frac{1}{2} & 0 \\ 0 & -2 \end{bmatrix}$$

$$= \begin{bmatrix} -1 & -42 \times 10^3 \\ -\frac{1}{2} & -22 \end{bmatrix}$$

Then by Table 4-1,

$$[h]_{BT} = \begin{bmatrix} \dfrac{a_{12}}{a_{22}} & \dfrac{\Delta}{a_{22}} \\[2ex] -\dfrac{1}{a_{22}} & \dfrac{a_{21}}{a_{22}} \end{bmatrix}_{BT} = \begin{bmatrix} \dfrac{21}{11} \times 10^3 & -\dfrac{1}{22} \\[2ex] \dfrac{1}{22} & \dfrac{1}{44} \times 10^{-3} \end{bmatrix}$$

The total matrix for Fig. 4-27(b), excluding the generator and load, is therefore

$$[h]_F = [h]_A + [h]_{BT} = \begin{bmatrix} 3.01 \times 10^3 & -4.52 \times 10^{-2} \\ 35.05 & 45.7 \times 10^{-6} \end{bmatrix}$$

Substituting the elements of $[h]_F$ and $[h]_A$ respectively in eqns. (4.123) to (4.125) and (4.127) gives the following results for the amplifier with and without the feedback network:

Parameter	*With feedback*	*Without feedback*
V_2/V_1	−17.4	−280
Z_{in}	13,880 ohms	1,015 ohms
V_2/E_1	−15.2	−94.4
Z_{out}	2,765 ohms	51,000 ohms

These results are consistent with a negative feedback condition. It is interesting to compare the gain V_2/V_1 with that predicted by the general feedback relation,

$$A' = A/(1 - A\beta) \tag{4.128}$$

where A denotes the voltage-gain without feedback, and β denotes the fraction of the output voltage V_2 fed-back and applied in series with the input voltage V_1 to the actual input of the amplifier. In this case, $A = -280$ and for the feedback network connected as in Fig. 4-27(b), $\beta = -(h_{12})_{BT} = 1/22$. Thus,

$$A' = A/(1 - A\beta) = -280/(1 + 12.7) = -20.4$$

This is somewhat higher than the result obtained by the matrix method, because it ignores the loading of the amplifier by the feedback network. The matrix approach on the other hand takes everything into account simultaneously, though further investigation would be necessary to establish a criterion of stability equivalent to the condition $A\beta = 1\angle 0$ that is self-evident in the feedback formula, eqn. (4.128). See also Example 4.5.

Example 4.12

Parallel feedback is applied to the amplifier of Fig. 4-27(a) by means of a resistor $R_f = 20{,}000$ ohms bridged across terminals 1 and 3. Calculate V_2/V_1 and the input impedance for this arrangement.

By Table 4-1, the Y-matrix for the amplifier, with the admittance of the 10,000 ohm load absorbed into Y_{22}, is

$$[Y]_A = \begin{bmatrix} \dfrac{1}{h_{11}} & -\dfrac{h_{12}}{h_{11}} \\[2ex] \dfrac{h_{21}}{h_{11}} & \dfrac{\Delta}{h_{11}} + \dfrac{1}{R_2} \end{bmatrix} = \begin{bmatrix} 9.09 \times 10^{-4} & -2.73 \times 10^{-7} \\[2ex] 3.18 \times 10^{-2} & 11.35 \times 10^{-5} \end{bmatrix}$$

The Y-matrix for the bridging resistor R_f (viewed as a four-terminal network as in Fig. 4-21(a)) is

$$[Y]_f = \begin{bmatrix} 1/R_f & -1/R_f \\ -1/R_f & 1/R_f \end{bmatrix} = \begin{bmatrix} 5 \times 10^{-5} & -5 \times 10^{-5} \\ -5 \times 10^{-5} & 5 \times 10^{-5} \end{bmatrix}$$

The total matrix, excluding the source, is therefore

$$[Y] = [Y]_A + [Y]_f = \begin{bmatrix} 9.59 \times 10^{-4} & -5.027 \times 10^{-5} \\ 3.175 \times 10^{-2} & 16.35 \times 10^{-5} \end{bmatrix}$$

In this case the source resistance and e.m.f. are irrelevant, as V_2/V_1 and $Z_{in} = V_1/I_1$ only are required, and I_2 must be regarded as zero since the load has been absorbed into the matrix. The nodal-voltage equations are thus

$$95.9\ V_1 - 5.027\ V_2 = 10^5\ I_1$$

$$317.5\ V_1 + 1.635\ V_2 = 0$$

From the second,

$$V_2/V_1 = -194$$

and then from the first,

$$Z_{\text{in}} = \frac{V_1}{I_1} = 93.5 \text{ ohms.}$$

While the gain is changed by only 30.5% from its non-feedback value of −280, the input resistance is divided by 10.9.

Example 4.13. Quasi-matrix analysis.

When a four-terminal network specified by an immittance-matrix is associated with an extraneous network, it is not always practicable or even efficient to resolve the system into an equivalent group of interconnected four-terminal networks, as in previous examples. It is possible, however, to formulate loop-current or nodal-voltage equations for such a system directly in terms of the network immittance-matrix and the external immittances: a knowledge of the internal topology of the network is unnecessary when the Z or Y-matrix governing its external behaviour is known. This will be illustrated by formulating the nodal-voltage equations for the arrangements shown in Fig. 4-28. The networks are of the unbalanced four-terminal type, having a connection common to one input and one output terminal, but are shown in three-terminal form in order to eliminate one superfluous node.

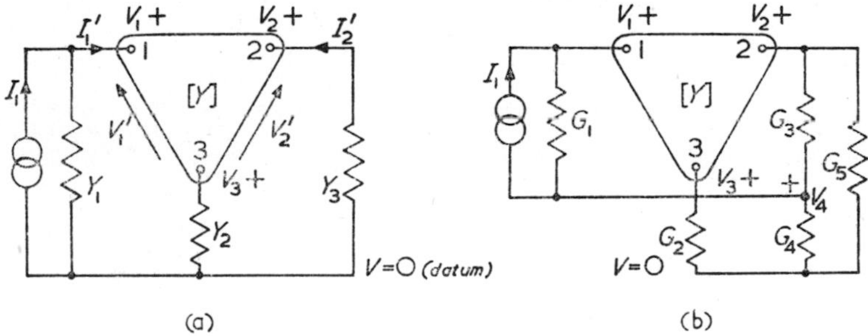

Fig. 4-28.

Referring first to the simpler case of Fig. 4-28(a), the nodal-voltage equations for the whole network must incorporate the four-terminal type equations for the network specified by the matrix $[Y]$. Thus, at terminals 1 and 2,

$$Y_{11}V_1' + Y_{12}V_2' = I_1'$$

$$Y_{21}V_1' + Y_{22}V_2' = I_2'$$

where

$$V_1' = V_1 - V_3 \quad \text{and} \quad V_2' = V_2 - V_3$$

At terminal 3, the current leaving is $I_1' + I_2'$. Therefore,

$$Y_2V_3 - (I_1' + I_2') = 0$$

or,

$$Y_2V_3 - (Y_{11}V_1' + Y_{12}V_2') - (Y_{21}V_1' + Y_{22}V_2') = 0$$

or,

$$Y_{11}(V_3 - V_1) + Y_{12}(V_3 - V_2) + Y_{21}(V_3 - V_1) + Y_{22}(V_3 - V_2) + Y_2V_3 = 0$$

The family of node-datum equations for Fig. 4-28(a) is therefore

$$\begin{aligned} &Y_{11}(V_1 - V_3) + Y_{12}(V_2 - V_3) + Y_1V_1 &&= I_1 \\ &Y_{21}(V_1 - V_3) + Y_{22}(V_2 - V_3) + Y_3V_2 &&= 0 \\ &Y_{11}(V_3 - V_1) + Y_{12}(V_3 - V_2) + Y_{21}(V_3 - V_1) + Y_{22}(V_3 - V_2) + Y_2V_3 &&= 0 \end{aligned} \tag{4.129}$$

These may be put in the matrix form

$$\begin{bmatrix} y_{11} & y_{12} & y_{13} \\ y_{21} & y_{22} & y_{23} \\ y_{31} & y_{32} & y_{33} \end{bmatrix} \cdot \begin{bmatrix} V_1 \\ V_2 \\ V_3 \end{bmatrix} = \begin{bmatrix} I_1 \\ 0 \\ 0 \end{bmatrix} \tag{4.130}$$

where

$$y_{11} = Y_{11} + Y_1, \qquad y_{12} = Y_{12}, \qquad Y_{13} = -(Y_{11} + Y_{12})$$

$$y_{21} = Y_{21}, \qquad y_{22} = (Y_{22} + Y_3), \qquad y_{23} = -(Y_{22} + Y_{21})$$

$$y_{31} = -(Y_{11} + Y_{21}), y_{32} = -(Y_{22} + Y_{12}), y_{33} = Y_{11} + Y_{12} + Y_{21} + Y_{22} + Y_2$$

Fig. 4-28(b) is a more complex case and corresponds to Example 2.7, in which the immittances are wholly real. Using the procedure illustrated by Fig. 4-28(a), but noting that the current source I_1 (which replaces E_1, R_1 in Fig. 2-31, Example 2.7) is now between two high-potential nodes, the following equations may be formulated:

$$
\begin{aligned}
&G_{11}(V_1 - V_3) + G_{12}(V_2 - V_3) + G_1(V_1 - V_4) &&= I_1 \\
&G_{22}(V_2 - V_3) + G_{21}(V_1 - V_3) + G_3(V_2 - V_4) + G_5V_2 &&= 0 \\
&G_{11}(V_3 - V_1) + G_{12}(V_3 - V_2) + G_{22}(V_3 - V_2) + G_{21}(V_3 - V_1) + G_2V_3 &&= 0 \\
&(G_1 + G_3 + G_4)V_4 - G_3V_2 - G_1V_1 &&= -I_1
\end{aligned}
\tag{4.131}
$$

These may be put into the form

$$
\begin{bmatrix} g_{11} & g_{12} & g_{13} & g_{14} \\ g_{21} & g_{22} & g_{23} & g_{24} \\ g_{31} & g_{32} & g_{33} & 0 \\ g_{41} & g_{42} & 0 & g_{44} \end{bmatrix} \cdot \begin{bmatrix} V_1 \\ V_2 \\ V_3 \\ V_4 \end{bmatrix} = \begin{bmatrix} I_1 \\ 0 \\ 0 \\ -I_1 \end{bmatrix} \tag{4.132}
$$

where, for example

$$g_{13} = -(G_{11} + G_{12}), \qquad g_{22} = G_{22} + G_3 + G_5, \qquad \text{and}$$

$$g_{33} = G_{11} + G_{12} + G_{22} + G_{21} + G_2$$

Example 4.14. An alternative solution for the transistor feedback amplifier of Example 2.7

The nodal-voltage approach explained in Example 4.13 is not actually the most economical one for the particular arrangements shown in Fig. 4-28(b) and Fig. 2-31. If the transistor is specified instead by its Z-matrix, mesh analysis is directly applicable, and only 3 equations are required. They are easily formulated, and yield more explicitly the

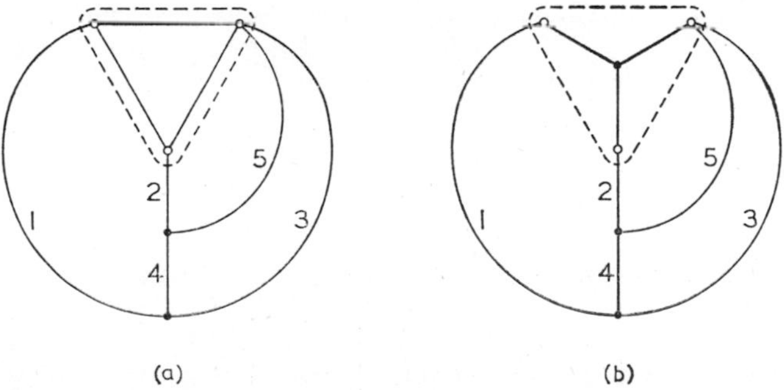

Fig. 4-29.

amplifier gain and impedance values, which are the parameters of ultimate interest.

In this instance, the requirement of 4 nodal-voltage or 3 mesh-current equations is obvious. But in a more complicated case (such as Example 1.1) a graph may be important as an aid to planar representation and to the clear discernment of loops or meshes. For topological purposes, an unbalanced four-terminal network, reduced to its basic three-terminal form as in Fig. 4-28, is representable by a triangle or a star. These graphs are consistent, respectively, with the pairs of nodal-voltage and mesh-current equations that are sufficient to define the external equilibrium of the network, as indicated in sect. 2. Thus, a planar graph to represent an arrangement like Fig. 4-28(b) may have either the form of Fig. 4-29(a) which is appropriate to the Y-matrix for the three-terminal network, or that of Fig. 4-29(b), which is appropriate to its Z-matrix.

The transistor amplifier is shown in more convenient planar form in Fig. 4-30. This is equivalent to Figs. 2-31 and 4-28(b), but the transistor is specified alternatively by the wholly real Z-matrix,

$$[Z] = [R] = \begin{bmatrix} 520 & 20 \\ -98 \times 10^4 & 2 \times 10^4 \end{bmatrix} \tag{4.133}$$

From Example 2.7: $R_1 = 1{,}000\Omega$, $R_2 = 100\Omega$, $R_3 = 10{,}000\Omega$, $R_4 = 500\Omega$, and $R_5 = 10{,}000\Omega$.

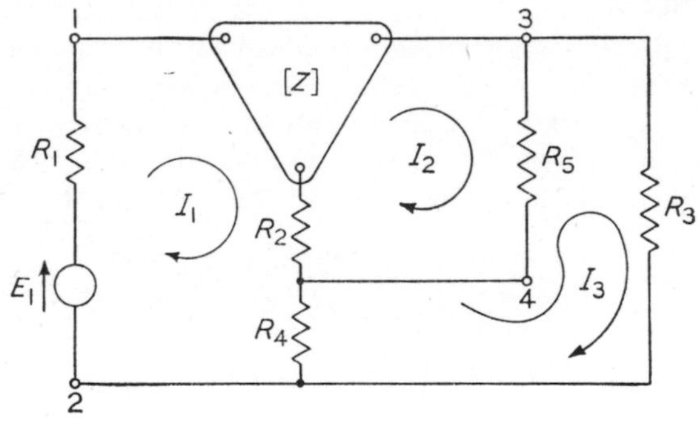

Fig. 4-30.

The mesh equations for Fig. 4-30 have the matrix form

$$\begin{bmatrix} r_{11} & r_{12} & r_{13} \\ r_{21} & r_{22} & r_{23} \\ r_{31} & r_{32} & r_{33} \end{bmatrix} \cdot \begin{bmatrix} I_1 \\ I_2 \\ I_3 \end{bmatrix} = \begin{bmatrix} E_1 \\ 0 \\ 0 \end{bmatrix} \tag{4.134}$$

where

$$\begin{aligned}
r_{11} &= R_1 + R_2 + R_4 + R_{11} = 2.12 \times 10^3 \\
r_{12} &= -(R_2 + R_{12}) = -0.12 \times 10^3 \\
r_{13} &= -R_4 = -0.5 \times 10^3 \\
r_{21} &= -(R_2 + R_{21}) = 980 \times 10^3 \\
r_{22} &= R_2 + R_5 + R_{22} = 30.1 \times 10^3 \\
r_{23} &= -R_5 = -10 \times 10^3 \\
r_{31} &= -R_4 = -0.5 \times 10^3 \\
r_{32} &= -R_5 = -10 \times 10^3 \\
r_{33} &= R_3 + R_4 + R_5 = 20.5 \times 10^3
\end{aligned}$$

Scaling the numerical values by 10^3 and substituting in eqn. (4.134) gives

$$\begin{bmatrix} 2.12 & -0.12 & -0.5 \\ 980 & 30.1 & -10 \\ -0.5 & -10 & 20.5 \end{bmatrix} \cdot \begin{bmatrix} I_1 \\ I_2 \\ I_3 \end{bmatrix} = \begin{bmatrix} E_1 \times 10^{-3} \\ 0 \\ 0 \end{bmatrix} \tag{4.135}$$

In finding the determinant of the R-matrix, it is an advantage to choose an expansion that includes cofactors that will also be needed for finding the currents. Thus,

$$\Delta = 2.12\Delta_{11} - 0.12\Delta_{12} - 0.5\Delta_{13} = 8{,}400$$

where

$$\Delta_{11} = 517, \qquad \Delta_{12} = -2.01 \times 10^4, \qquad \Delta_{13} = -9.78 \times 10^3$$

The input resistance at terminals 1–2 is

$$R_{\text{in}} = \frac{E_1}{I_1} - R_1 = \frac{\Delta \times 10^3}{\Delta_{11}} - R_1 = 15{,}300 \text{ ohms}$$

The current in the load R_5 is $I_2 - I_3$, and the potential fall in the sense of I_2, which represents the output voltage, is

$$\begin{aligned}
V_2 &= (I_2 - I_3)R_5 \\
&= \frac{E_1(\Delta_{12} - \Delta_{13})R_5}{\Delta \times 10^3} \\
&= -12.3E_1
\end{aligned}$$

These results are in good agreement with Example 2.7. In addition, the voltage-gain relative to terminals 1–2 is

$$\frac{V_2}{V_1} = \frac{V_2}{E_1} \cdot \frac{E_1}{V_1} = \frac{V_2}{E_1} \cdot \frac{R_1 + R_{\text{in}}}{R_{\text{in}}} = -13.1$$

REFERENCES

1. Brune, O.: *E. N. T.*, Vol. 9, No. 6, p. 234, 1932.
2. Guillemin, E. A.: *Communication Networks*, Vol. 2 (John Wiley and Sons, Inc., New York, 1935).
3. Austen Stigant, S.: *The Elements of Determinants, Matrices and Tensors for Engineers* (Macdonald, London, 1959).
4. Margeneau, H. and Murphy, G. M.: *The Mathematics of Physics and Chemistry* (D. Van Nostrand Company, Inc., New York, 1943).
5. Tropper, A. Mary: *Matrix Theory for Electrical Engineering Students* (George G. Harrap and Co. Ltd., London, 1962).
6. Deards, S. R.: Explicit Formulae for Ladder 2-ports, *The Matrix and Tensor Quarterly*, Vol. 11, No. 4, June, 1961.
7. Nichols, K. G.: The Use of Transfer Matrices in the Analysis of Conditions of Oscillation, *Jnl. Brit. I.R.E.*, Vol. 25, No. 1, Jan. 1963.

5

ANNOTATED PROBLEMS

The following problems, which are approximately in the order of the text, are intended to augment the principles embodied in the Illustrative Examples, rather more than as exercises in network arithmetic alone.

Problem 1. A network has 5 nodes, *a*, *b*, *c*, *d*, and *e*. The branches are numbered 1 to 10 in the order *ad*, *ab*, *bc*, *cd*, *ae*, *be*, *ce*, *de*, *ac*, and *bd*. A current-source of 1 ampere is connected between nodes *a* and *c*, and acts towards *c*. An e.m.f.-source of 1 volt is in series with branch 10, and acts towards *b*. For simplicity, the branch immittances are pure resistances of 2, 6, 1, 9, 3, 10, 8, 5, 7, and 4 ohms, in the order 1 to 10 respectively.

(a) Draw an oriented graph and select a tree.
(b) Form tie-sets and obtain the tie-set matrix.
(c) Use the tie-set matrix to formulate an ordered set of loop-current equations with numerical coefficients.

Comment

See Illustrative Example 1.1.

Answer

There are as many equivalent sets of equations as there are possible trees. For the tree of branches 2, 6, 7, and 4,

$$\begin{bmatrix} 35 & -18 & 16 & -17 & -24 & 27 \\ -18 & 19 & -10 & 8 & 18 & -18 \\ 16 & -10 & 19 & 0 & -16 & 10 \\ -17 & 8 & 0 & 22 & 8 & -17 \\ -24 & 18 & -16 & 8 & 31 & -18 \\ 27 & -18 & 10 & -17 & -18 & 31 \end{bmatrix} \cdot \begin{bmatrix} i_1 \\ i_3 \\ i_5 \\ i_8 \\ i_9 \\ i_{10} \end{bmatrix} = \begin{bmatrix} 0 \\ 0 \\ 0 \\ 0 \\ 7 \\ 1 \end{bmatrix}$$

Problem 2. The branches in the network described in Problem 1 are changed in value so that their conductances are 2, 6, 1, 9, 3, 10, 8, 5, 7, and 4 mhos, in the order 1 to 10 respectively. Assuming that the network is the same in all other respects, form cut-sets, find the cut-set matrix, and thence formulate a set of nodal-voltage equations.

Comment

See Illustrative Example 1.2.

Answer

For the particular tree of branches 2, 6, 7, and 4,

$$\begin{bmatrix} 18 & 2 & -12 & 9 \\ 2 & 20 & -6 & 11 \\ -12 & -6 & 27 & -14 \\ 9 & 11 & -14 & 27 \end{bmatrix} \cdot \begin{bmatrix} v_{n2} \\ v_{n4} \\ v_{n6} \\ v_{n7} \end{bmatrix} = \begin{bmatrix} -1 \\ 4 \\ -3 \\ 3 \end{bmatrix}$$

Problem 3. Repeat Problems 1 and 2 using equations (2.14) and (2.15).

Comment

See Illustrative Example 2.1.

Problem 4. Explain how to determine the sign of the mutual inductance between two coils connected in a network when the relative position and the directions of the windings of the coils are known.

Three mutually coupled coils 1, 2, and 3, of negligible resistance, are connected as shown in Fig. 1. The self inductances are $L_1 = 2\,\text{H}$, $L_2 = 3\,\text{H}$, $L_3 = 5\,\text{H}$, and for the directions of current flow shown in the diagram, the mutual inductances are $M_{12} = -1\,\text{H}$, $M_{13} = 2\,\text{H}$ and $M_{23} = -2\,\text{H}$.

Find the value of the equivalent inductance of the network between the terminals a and b.

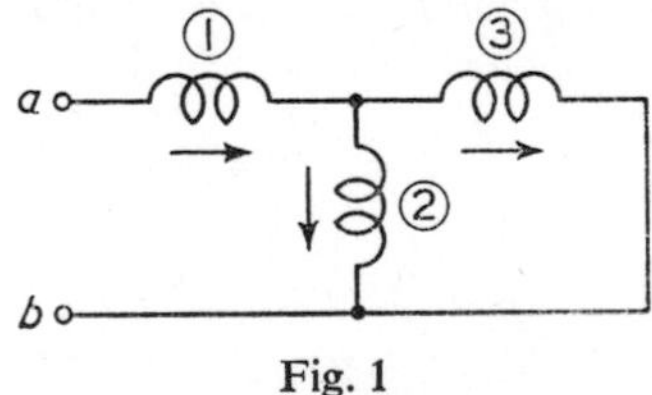

Fig. 1

(*L.U., Part 3, Electrical Theory and Measurements*)

Comment

The input impedance at terminals *a,b* is required, either in the general form $Z_{ab}(s) = E_1(s)/I_1(s)$ or in the steady-state form $Z_{ab}(j\omega) = E_1(j\omega)/I_1(j\omega)$, where $E_1(s)$ or $E_1(j\omega)$ denotes an applied e.m.f.

When mutual inductance exists between more than two coils, there is greater difficulty in the correct formulation of mesh or loop-current, or even branch-current equations, by inspection. The formal matrix procedure explained in Chapter 2 sect. 2.4 and illustrated by Illustrative Example 2.2 has merit for such problems; for although more steps are involved, the procedure is a rigorous, systematic function both of the network topology and of the sign conventions, and is thus automatically free from ambiguities or uncertainties, regardless of the complexity of the network and number of mutual inductors involved.

Answer

The branch impedance matrix is*

$$[Z_b] = [Ls] = \begin{bmatrix} 2s & -s & 2s \\ -s & 3s & -2s \\ 2s & -2s & 5s \end{bmatrix}$$

and for loop-currents I_1 and I_3 identified with the currents in branches 1 and 3,

$$\begin{bmatrix} 3s & -2s \\ -2s & 12s \end{bmatrix} \cdot \begin{bmatrix} I_1 \\ I_3 \end{bmatrix} = \begin{bmatrix} E_1(s) \\ 0 \end{bmatrix}$$

whence

$$Z_{ab}(s) = E_1(s)/I_1(s) = 8s/3$$

and

$$L_{ab} = Z_{ab}(s)/s = 8/3 \text{ H}$$

Problem 5. One phase of an interconnected power system (similar to Fig. 1-11(b)) has a basic graph with nodes *a, b, c, d* and *e* lying on a circle, and a node *f* within the circle. The e.m.f. E_1 of one generator is between nodes *a* and *b* and acts towards *b*, while the e.m.f. E_2 of another is between nodes *a* and *e* and acts towards *e*. The branches *bc, de, cd, ac, af, ad, cf,* and *df* have, respectively, admittances Y_1, $Y_2 \dots Y_8$.

Formulate a family of node-datum voltage equations, using node *a* as datum. Then transform E_1, Y_1 and E_2, Y_2 into equivalent constant-current generators and re-state the equations. Justify the equivalence of the two sets of equations.

* Note that Fig. 1 does not account for the physical arrangement of the coils and portrays only the electrical circuit.

Comment

The six-node graph requires, formally, 5 nodal-voltage equations. These include the pair, $V_b = E_1$ and $V_e = E_2$. The transformation of E_1, Y_1 and E_2, Y_2 into constant-current generators eliminates nodes b and e and reduces the equations immediately to 3.

Answer

$$(Y_1 + Y_4 + Y_7 + Y_3)V_c - Y_3 V_d - Y_7 V_f = E_1 Y_1$$
$$(Y_2 + Y_6 + Y_8 + Y_3)V_d - Y_8 V_f - Y_3 V_c = E_2 Y_2$$
$$(Y_5 + Y_7 + Y_8)V_f - Y_7 V_c - Y_8 V_d = 0$$

Problem 6. Fig. 2 shows a ladder network with its branch impedances given in ohms. Under steady-state sinusoidal conditions, the current I_2 is $(1 + j0)$ ampere.

(a) Calculate the input voltage V_1.

(b) Hence or otherwise find the current I_2 for an input voltage of $(100 + j0)$ volts.

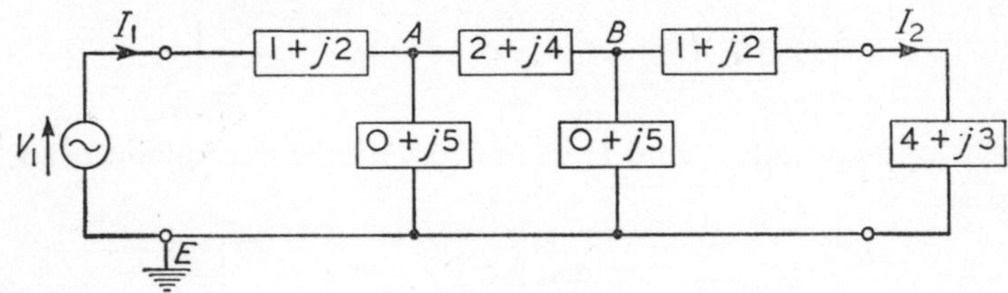

Fig. 2

(*I.E.E., Part 2, Electrical Engineering 2*)

Comment

(1) The topology suggests a nodal-voltage approach as economical, but consideration must be given to the extra work involved in converting the given impedances into admittances.

(2) While mesh analysis requires three equations, it is nevertheless economical since one of the currents is already known.

(3) Other useful approaches are (a), reduction of the graph through one easy application of Thévenin's theorem and the merging of impedances to the right of BE, noting that V_{BE} is readily available; and (b), the step-by-step calculation of I_{AB}, V_{AE}, I_1 and thence V_1.

Answer

(a) $V_1 = 24{\cdot}4 + j15{\cdot}8$ volts.

(b) Transfer impedance $V_1/I_2 = 24{\cdot}4 + j15{\cdot}8$ ohms, and $I_2 = 2{\cdot}89 - j1{\cdot}87$ amperes when $V_1 = 100 + j0$ volts.

Problem 7. Fig. 2 in Problem 6 may be represented in an alternative reduced form comprising a constant-current I in parallel with an admittance Y_1 between A and E, an admittance Y_2 between A and B, and an admittance Y_3 between B and E. Justify this representation, find all the parameters, and confirm the solution for V_1 by nodal analysis.

Answer

$$Y_1 = 0{\cdot}2 - j0{\cdot}6,\ Y_2 = 0{\cdot}1 - j0{\cdot}2,\ Y_3 = 0{\cdot}1 - j0{\cdot}3;$$
$$V_{BE} = 5 + j5,\quad I = (0{\cdot}2 - j0{\cdot}4)V_1.$$

Problem 8. A network has nodes *a*, *b*, *c*, *d*, *e*, *f* and *g*. Branches *ab* and *cb* are inductors coupled by mutual inductance M_1; *df* and *ef* are inductors coupled by mutual inductance M_2; *bg*, *bf* and *eg* are resistors R_1, R_2 and R_3 respectively; *c* is joined to *d*; and a sinusoidal e.m.f. source of angular frequency ω is connected between *a* and *g*.

Denoting the total resistance and self inductance in loop *bcdf* by R_{22} and L_{22}, show that, provided the coils are correctly orientated, the current I_3 in R_3 is zero when

$$M_1R_2 = L_{22}R_1$$
$$\text{and}\quad R_1R_{22} = \omega^2 M_1 M_2$$

Comment

It is sufficient in this case that the cofactor Δ_{13} of the determinant of the mesh-impedance matrix should be zero (see Illustrative Example 2.5).

Problem 9. What is the physical significance of *capacitance coefficients* in the case of more than two neighbouring insulated conductors with various potential differences between them?

All the capacitance values in the circuit shown in Fig. 3 are the same. Show that the net capacitance between terminals *a* and *b* is the same as the net capacitance between terminals *c* and *d*.

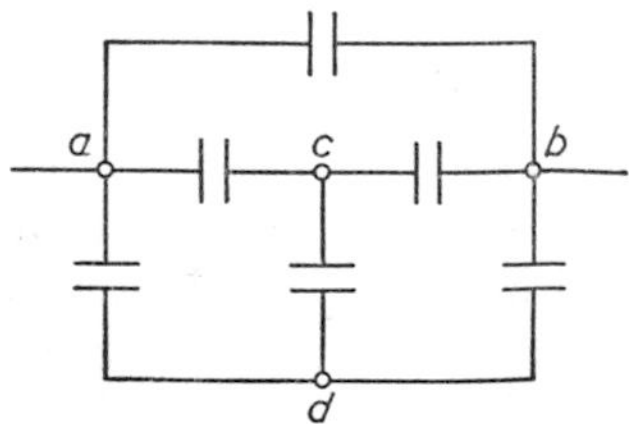

Fig. 3

If a voltage V is applied between the terminals a and b, find the charge and stored energy of each capacitor and hence, by addition, the total energy. Check the result by calculating the energy in terms of the voltage V and the net capacitance between a and b.

(*L.U., Part 3, Electrical Theory and Measurements*)

Comment

(1) The graph may be drawn in either of the forms,

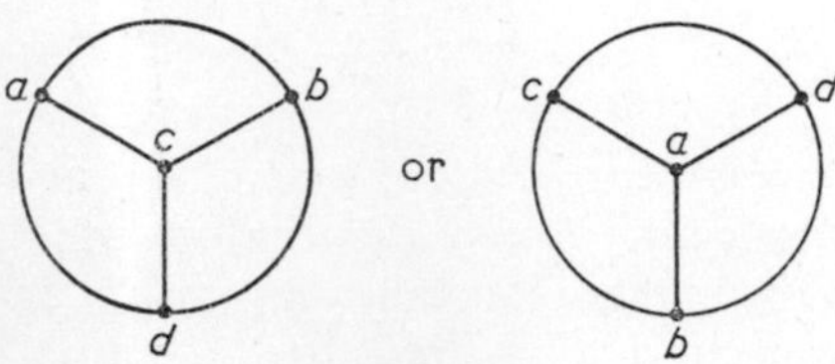

As these graphs are similar, the topology is the same whether viewed from *ab* or *cd*. Therefore, when the branches are identical, the electrical properties between nodes a and b must be identical with those between nodes c and d. In this case, the net capacitances between *ab* and *cd* must therefore be equal.

(2) As the graph is symmetrical about the branch *cd* and the branches are identical, no potential difference can exist between c and d due to a voltage applied between a and b. The capacitor between c and d is therefore redundant in respect of excitation between a and b, and can be removed from the network.

Answer

(1) Net capacitance between a and b is $2C$.
(2) The charges and energies are respectively $\frac{1}{2}CV$ and $\frac{1}{8}CV^2$ for C_{ad} C_{bd}, C_{ac} and C_{bc}; CV and $\frac{1}{2}CV^2$ for C_{ab}; and zero for C_{cd}. The energy in the net capacitance is CV^2.

Problem 10. The conductors a, b of a single-phase overhead power line are run parallel to another pair of conductors c, d, and parallel also to an earth conductor, e.

The partial capacitances, scaled for convenience to a base of 1 F, are

$$C_{ab} = 8 \qquad C_{ad} = C_{bc} = 0{\cdot}6$$
$$C_{cd} = 5 \qquad C_{ae} = C_{be} = 2$$
$$C_{ac} = C_{bd} = 1 \qquad C_{ce} = C_{de} = 0{\cdot}5$$

If the r.m.s. voltage between the power-line conductors a, b is 250 V, calculate the electrostatically induced interference voltage between the conductors c and d.

Comment

Apply the general star-mesh transformation (see Illustrative Example 3.5) and by merging capacitances reduce the graph from 10 branches to 6 (C'_{ab}, C'_{bd}, C'_{cd}, C'_{ac}, C'_{ad} and C'_{bc}). Note that C'_{ab} may be excluded since V_{ab} is specified, and that C_{cd} might be regarded as the load on a simple equivalent generator E_0, C_0, obtained with the Thévenin-Helmholtz theorem.

Answer

$$C'_{cd} = 5{\cdot}05, \quad E_0 = 0{\cdot}2 \times 250, \quad C_0 = 1,$$
$$V_{cd} = 8{\cdot}34 \text{ volts.}$$

Problem 11. A 3-phase generator, star-connected at S, has symmetrical phase voltages of sequence A, B, C. It supplies three admittances Y_a, Y_b, Y_c respectively, star-connected at N. Derive an expression for the voltage between N and S.

Such a 3-phase 416 V generator supplies three star-connected components having impedances each equal to 40 Ω in magnitude. The component connected to terminal A is purely capacitive, and the other two are purely resistive. Determine the magnitude of the voltage between the star points N and S, and draw to scale a vector diagram showing all the voltages.

(*I.E.E., Part 2, Electrical Engineering 2*)

Comment

The system may be viewed as three generators in parallel between N and S, having e.m.f.'s $E_a = E\underline{/0}$, $E_b = E\underline{/-120°}$ and $E_c = E\underline{/-240°}$. The required relation is the parallel generator theorem,

$$V_{NS} = \frac{E_a Y_a + E_b Y_b + E_c Y_c}{Y_a + Y_b + Y_c}$$

The vector diagram will show that $V_{BN} > V_{CN}$. If identical lamps are used for the resistors, the one connected to phase B will glow brighter than the other, and thus determine the phase-sequence.

Answer

$$V_{NS} = \frac{416}{\sqrt{3}} \cdot \sqrt{\frac{2}{5}}\ \underline{/-71°34'} \text{ volts}$$

Problem 12. State the Helmholtz-Thévenin theorem for a.c. networks involving a number of sources and interconnections.

A network of impedances and sources of alternating e.m.f.'s has two output terminals. The open-circuit voltage at the terminals is 260 volts. The current flowing when the terminals are short-circuited is 20 amperes, and 13 amperes when connected through a coil of 11 ohms reactance and negligible resistance.

Determine the components of the equivalent circuit feeding the terminals. What value of load impedance would give maximum power output?

(*L.U.*, *Part 2, Electrical Theory and Measurements*)

Comment

Note the theorem is not restricted to networks with sinusoidal a.c. sources, but is applicable to linear networks generally, in terms of the complex-variable s.

Answer

(a) $E = 260$ volts, $R = 12$ ohms, $X = 5$ ohms.
(b) The conjugate, $12 - j5$ ohms.

Problem 13. A lattice filter has line arms each consisting of an inductor L_1 in parallel with a capacitor C_1, and lattice or cross arms each an inductor L_2. The input terminals are connected to a constant-current source in parallel with a conductance G_1, and the output terminals are connected to a conductance G_2.

Draw the network graph and find the form of the dual network.

If the condition for a pass-band in the case of a lattice filter is that the line and lattice arm reactances should be opposite in sign, ascertain to which class of filter the original and its dual belong.

Comment

This exemplifies self-duality: the dual of a bridge-type graph is another bridge.

Answer

A lattice, of line arms each an inductor in series with a capacitor, and lattice arms each a capacitor. The source is an e.m.f. in series with a resistor, and the load is a resistor.

Both filters are high-pass types.

Problem 14. Show that in the case of two paralleled four-terminal networks, a sufficient condition for the current in their common load to be zero is that the sum of their short-circuit transfer impedances should be zero.

Use Thévenin's theorem to obtain the short-circuit transfer impedance of a T-network of series arms Z_1, Z_2 and shunt arm Z_3, in terms of an e.m.f. applied to its input terminals and the current traversing its short-circuited output terminals. Compare the expression with that for the series arm of the equivalent Π-network, for which the short-circuit transfer impedance is the value of the series arm alone. Confirm that this is consistent with the topology, when the Π-network is closed on its input side by an e.m.f. source of zero internal impedance, and on its output side by a short-circuit.

Comment

While four-terminal matrix theory answers the first point, as in Illustrative Example 4.9, an independent approach is instructive. Consider first n paralleled networks driven from an e.m.f. E and short-circuited on the output side. Then, *for this condition only*, it is valid to write $I = E(Y_{tr(1)} + Y_{tr(2)} + \dots + Y_{tr(n)})$, where I is the total current in the short-circuit, and $Y_{tr(n)} = 1/Z_{tr(n)}$. But if I is zero in the short-circuit, it must also be zero in any finite impedance that might be substituted for it. Hence the condition $\Sigma Y_{tr} = 0$ is a sufficient condition for a null, regardless of load. The condition $\Sigma Z_{tr} = 0$ is a special one limited to the case of two networks only.

With reference to the equivalent Π-network, it may be noted that both shunt arms become redundant under the conditions stated.

Answer

$$Z_{tr} = Z_1 + Z_2 + Z_1 Z_2/Z_3$$

Problem 15. One form of low-pass filter consists of a T-network in which each series arm is an inductor $\frac{1}{2} L_1$ and the shunt arm comprises a capacitor C_2 in series with an inductor L_2.

When the filter is connected between a generator and a load, the attenuation would be infinite at an angular frequency $\omega_\infty = \sqrt{(1/L_2 C_2)}$, if the resistance R_2 of L_2 were zero.

Show that when R_2 is finite, infinite attenuation, or a null in load-current, could be obtained at ω_∞ by bridging a capacitance C in series with a resistance R across the high-potential terminals of the T-network, and obtain expressions for C and R. The resistance R_1 of L_1 should be included.

Comment

Note that the shunt arm is reduced to R_2 at ω_∞.

Answer

$$C = 1/\omega_\infty^2 L_1(1 + R_1/2R_2)$$

$$R = \frac{\omega_\infty^2 L_1^2}{4R_2} - R_1\left(1 + \frac{R_1}{4R_2}\right)$$

Problem 16. A bridged T-network comprises a resistor r connected between the high potential terminals of a T-network, in which each series arm is a capacitor C and the shunt arm is a resistor R.

(a) Obtain an expression for the ratio of the open-circuit output voltage V_2 to the input voltage V_1, in terms of the general complex-frequency variable s.

(b) For $s = j\omega$, find a condition such that V_2 is in-phase with V_1 and obtain the ratio V_2/V_1 for this condition.

(c) Show that when $r \gg R$, V_2/V_1 is a low minimum when $\omega^2 C^2 Rr \simeq 1$

Comment

See Illustrative Example 4.7.

Answer

(a) $$\frac{V_2}{V_1} = \frac{(1 + s^2C^2Rr) + 2sCR}{(1 + s^2C^2Rr) + sC(2R + r)}$$

(b) $\omega^2 C^2 Rr = 1, \qquad V_2/V_1 = 2R/(2R + r)$.

(c) For $r \gg R$, numerator in (a) is approximated by $1 + s^2C^2Rr$, or $1 - \omega^2C^2Rr$ for $s = j\omega$.

Problem 17. What is the condition that a reasonably sharp null is obtained in the network shown in Fig. 4?

If $R = 10\Omega$; $C_1 = C_2 = 0{\cdot}01\mu$F and $f = 1592$ c/s at null, calculate the value of R_x.

Give a brief account of one alternative method of measuring the unknown element, and discuss fully the relative advantages of the two methods.

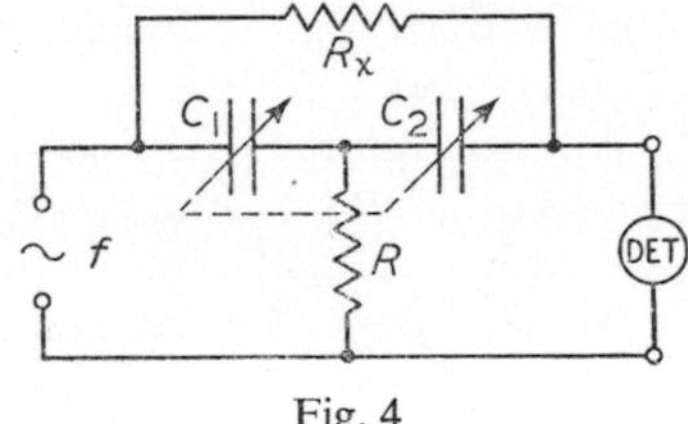

Fig. 4

(*I.E.R.E., Electronic Measurements*)

Comment

See Problem 16.

Answer

$R_x \simeq 1/\omega^2C^2R \simeq 10^7$ ohms (a very close approximation in this case).

Problem 18. A lattice network has resistors of value 10 ohms for its line arms, resistors of value 5 ohms for its lattice or cross arms, and its output terminals are closed through a resistance of 10 ohms. Determine the input resistance:

(a) by mesh analysis ($R_{in} = E_1/I_1 = \Delta/\Delta_{11}$);
(b) by reduction of the graph through the star-delta transformation;
(c) by reduction of the graph by means of Bartlett's bisection theorem.

Compare the work involved in the three methods, and consider also the extent to which this would be increased if the lattice comprised complex impedances.

Comment

The equivalent T-network, obtainable through Bartlett's bisection theorem, will be found to include a negative resistance. While this makes the T-network physically unrealisable in passive form, it does not invalidate its use for theoretical purposes.

Answer

7·14 ohms.

Problem 19. A lattice network has capacitors of value 0·5 μF for its line arms, resistors of value 600 ohms for its lattice or cross arms, and its output terminals are closed through a resistance of 400 ohms. The operating angular frequency is $\omega = 5{,}000$ rad/s.

(a) Scale the network for a terminating resistance of 1 ohm and an operating angular frequency of $\omega = 1$ rad/s.
(b) Calculate the modulus and argument of the input impedance of the scaled network, and thence find the input impedance of the actual network at $\omega = 5{,}000$ rad/s.

Comment

If this is approached through Bartlett's bisection theorem, the constitution of the T-network will be found to require a negative capacitor. While the T-network is therefore physically unrealisable as a general equivalent, for a single frequency it could be made realisable by substituting for the negative capacitor an inductor of the same reactance value.

Answer

(a) Scaled values are 1.0 F and 3/2 ohms.
(b) $1.17\,\underline{/-53^\circ}$ ohms, $468\underline{/-53^\circ}$ ohms.

Problem 20. A bridge has normalised resistances of 2, 3, 4 and 5 ohms connected, respectively, between nodes 1–3, 1–4, 2–3 and 2–4. A generator of internal resistance 2 ohms and e.m.f. 1 volt is connected between nodes 1–2, and a load of resistance 1 ohm between nodes 3–4. The e.m.f. acts towards node 1.

Find the Z and h four-terminal or two-port type matrices for the bridge, and use either of them to find the current in the 1-ohm load. Compare this procedure with conventional mesh analysis of the bridge circuit.

Comment

The problem demonstrates how the substitution of four-terminal or two-port type matrices makes the solution independent of the topology internal to the input and output terminal-pairs, and in this case reduces the necessary equations from three to two. This advantage is, however, countered by the work required to find the matrices.

Answer

$$[Z] = \begin{bmatrix} 48/14 & 2/14 \\ 2/14 & 45/14 \end{bmatrix}$$

$$[h] = \begin{bmatrix} 154/45 & 2/45 \\ -2/45 & 14/45 \end{bmatrix}$$

$I = 6{\cdot}25$ mA, from node 3 to 4.

Problem 21. In Fig. 5 (a), T is an ideal transformer of voltage ratio $1:\lambda$ in the sense indicated. Obtain the Z-matrix from first principles,

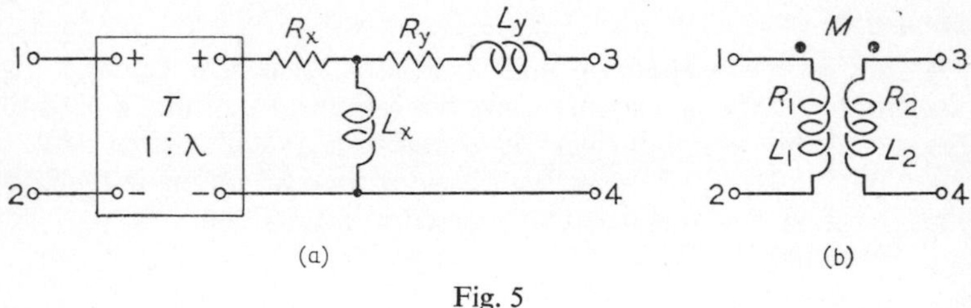

Fig. 5

and thence show that the network is exactly equivalent to Fig. 5(b) when

$$\lambda = k\sqrt{(L_2/L_1)},\ R_x = \lambda^2 R_1,\ L_x = k^2 L_2,\ R_y = R_2, \text{ and } L_y = (1-k^2)L_2$$

where k is the coefficient of coupling between L_1 and L_2.

Answer

$$[Z]_a = \begin{bmatrix} (R_x + sL_x)/\lambda^2 & sL_x/\lambda \\ sL_x/\lambda & R_y + s(L_x + L_y) \end{bmatrix}$$

$$[Z]_b = \begin{bmatrix} R_1 + sL_1 & sM \\ sM & R_2 + sL_2 \end{bmatrix}$$

These matrices become identical when the stated substitutions are made.

Problem 22. Terminals 2 and 4 of the mutual inductor shown in Fig. 5(b) are connected together, and a capacitor C is connected between terminals 1 and 3. If V_1 is an input voltage between terminals 1 and 2, while V_2 is the output voltage between terminals 3 and 4, show that when R_1 and R_2 are zero,

$$\frac{V_2}{V_1} = \frac{k\sqrt{(L_2/L_1)} + s^2 L_2\, C(1-k^2)}{1 + s^2 L_2\, C(1-k^2)}$$

and that, for $s = j\omega$, $(\omega_0/\omega_\infty)^2 = k\sqrt{(L_2/L_1)}$, where ω_0 and ω_∞ are the angular frequencies at which V_2 is zero and infinite, respectively.

Comment

The equivalence proved in Problem 21 should be considered as a basis for calculating Y_{21} and Y_{22}.

Problem 23. An asymmetrical T-network having input terminals A, B and output terminals C, D, with BD common, has, in normalised values, a 3-ohm resistor in series with a 1-farad capacitor for the series arm to A; a 4-farad capacitor for the series arm to C; and a 1-ohm resistor for the shunt arm.

A transformer has its input terminals E, F connected, respectively, to C and D, its output terminal H is connected to F, and its other output terminal G is connected through a 4-ohm resistor to A. The transformer may be regarded as ideal, and terminals E and G have like polarities.

(a) Find the voltage-ratio λ for the transformer, that will make the whole network behave externally as a symmetrical one.

(b) Show, for λ satisfying the conditions for symmetry, that

$$\frac{V_2}{V_1} = \frac{20s^2 + 8s + 1}{28s^2 + 12s + 1}$$

where V_1 is an input voltage at A, B and V_2 is the output voltage at G, H.

Comment

See Illustrative Example 4.8.

Answer

(a) $\lambda^2 = Z_{11}/Z_{22} = (4+1/s)/(1+1/4s) = 4$, or $\lambda = 2$, stepping-up from E,F to G,H.

Problem 24. A passive T-network has series arms Z_1 and Z_2, and shunt arm Z_3. Obtain the equivalent Π-network by means of the star-delta transformation, and confirm that its Y-matrix is the same as that for the T-network as obtained by inversion.

Answer

$$Y_{11} = 1/[Z_1 + Z_2Z_3/(Z_2+Z_3)]$$
$$Y_{12} = Y_{21} = -1/(Z_1+Z_2+Z_1Z_2/Z_3)$$
$$Y_{22} = 1/[Z_2+Z_1Z_3/(Z_1+Z_3)]$$

Problem 25. An admittance Y_1 is connected between the anode and control grid of a valve having an amplification factor μ, or mutual conductance g_m, and anode a.c. resistance r_a, or conductance $G_a = 1/r_a$.

Making the approximation of treating the valve as a linear four-terminal network, with grid and cathode as input terminals and anode and cathode as output terminals, draw an equivalent linear network including the admittance Y_1, and using the usual polarity conventions, find the Y-matrix.

A load Y_2 is connected between the anode and cathode output terminals. Use the Y-matrix to find expressions for the amplification V_2/V_1 and the input admittance between grid and cathode.

Comment

Either the constant-e.m.f. $(-\mu V_1, r_a)$ or constant-current $(-g_m V_1, G_a)$ representations may be used for the valve, although the latter is apposite. The matrix may be worked out either by adding that for the valve to that for the bridging admittance, or directly in terms of the whole circuit. This approach should be compared with Illustrative Example 3.4, in which V_2/V_g corresponds to V_2/V_1 in this problem.

Answer

$$[Y]_{valve} = \begin{bmatrix} 0 & 0 \\ g_m & G_a \end{bmatrix}$$

$$[Y]_{circuit} = \begin{bmatrix} Y_1 & -Y_1 \\ g_m - Y_1 & G_a + Y_1 \end{bmatrix}$$

$$\frac{V_2}{V_1} = -\frac{Y_{21}}{Y_{22} + Y_2} = -\frac{g_m - Y_1}{G_a + Y_1 + Y_2} = -A$$

$$Y_{in} = \frac{I_1}{V_1} = Y_{11} - \frac{Y_{21} Y_{12}}{Y_{22} + Y_2} = Y_1(1 + A)$$

Problem 26. The circuit of Problem 25, with load Y_2, is modified by inserting an additional admittance Y between the control grid and the high-potential input terminal (similar to Fig. 3-12(a)). Use the Y-matrix found in Problem 25 to show that

$$\frac{V_2}{V_1} = -\frac{AY}{Y + Y_1(1 + A)}$$

and that $V_2/V_1 \to -Y/Y_1$ as $A \to \infty$.

Comment

Convert V_1 in series with Y into an equivalent constant-current source, $V_1 Y$ in parallel with Y. Then, denoting the actual grid-cathode voltage as V_g,

$$(Y + Y_{11})V_g + Y_{12}V_2 = V_1 Y$$

$$Y_{21}V_g + (Y_{22} + Y_2)V_2 = 0$$

from which the required results are easily obtained.

See also Illustrative Example 3.4.

Problem 27. A four-terminal non-reciprocal network is represented in the form of a ladder structure having input terminals 1, 2 and output terminals 3–4. 2 and 4 are common. The branches, from input side to output, are respectively a series admittance Y_1, a shunt admittance Y_2, a series admittance Y_3 and a shunt admittance Y_4 in parallel with a current-source $g_m V_1$. This flows away from terminal 3 for an input voltage V_1 oriented towards terminal 1. Find the Y-matrix.

Comment

A neat approach is to apply the star-delta transformation to the branches Y_1, Y_2 and Y_3, which reduces the topology to that of a Π-network for which the Y-matrix is easily found by inspection.

Answer

$$[Y] = \begin{bmatrix} \dfrac{Y_1(Y_2+Y_3)}{\Sigma Y} & -\dfrac{Y_1 Y_3}{\Sigma Y} \\ g_m - \dfrac{Y_1 Y_3}{\Sigma Y} & Y_4 + \dfrac{Y_3(Y_1+Y_2)}{\Sigma Y} \end{bmatrix}$$

where

$$\Sigma Y = Y_1 + Y_2 + Y_3$$

Problem 28. An admittance Y_1 is connected in series with the input side of a four-terminal network specified by a Y-matrix. Find the elements of the Y-matrix for the combination of network and series admittance.

Comment

The elements can be found by manipulating the equations

$$Y_{11}(V_1 - I_1/Y_1) + Y_{12}V_2 = I_1$$

$$Y_{21}(V_1 - I_1/Y_1) + Y_{22}V_2 = I_2$$

into the forms

$$Y'_{11}V_1 + Y'_{12}V_2 = I_1$$

$$Y'_{21}V_1 + Y'_{22}V_2 = I_2$$

Answer

$$Y'_{11} = \alpha Y_{11}, \qquad Y'_{12} = \alpha Y_{12}$$

$$Y'_{21} = \alpha Y_{21}, \qquad Y'_{22} = Y_{22} - \alpha Y_{21} Y_{12}/Y_1$$

where $\alpha = Y_1/(Y_1 + Y_{11})$

Problem 29. Fig. 6 is the *hybrid*-Π representation for a transistor in the common-emitter circuit at high frequencies. Typical numerical values (for a Mullard OC44) are $R_1 = 110\Omega$, $R_2 = 2{,}500\Omega$, $R_3 = 2\text{M}\Omega$, $R_4 = 25{,}000\Omega$, $C_2 = 410\ \mu\mu\text{F}$, $C_3 = 10{\cdot}5\ \mu\mu\text{F}$, and $g_m = 39\text{mA/V}$.

Consider how the Y-matrix of complex elements might be calculated for a given high frequency, such as 10 Mc/s.

Comment

The topology resembles that in Problem 27, with $Y_1 = 1/R_1$, $Y_2 = j\omega C_2 + 1/R_2$, $Y_3 = j\omega C_3 + 1/R_3$, and $Y_4 = 1/R_4$. But the current-source $g_m V_{b'e}$ is not an explicit function of the actual input voltage V_1, and therefore the solution of Problem 27 is not applicable with rigour. However, the Y-matrix for the Π-network excluding R_1 is easily calculated. Consider then Problem 28.

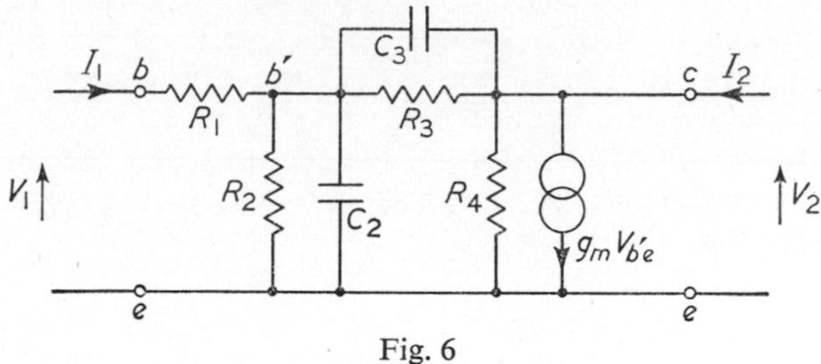

Fig. 6

Problem 30. The three-terminal network in Fig. 4-28(b), Illustrative Example 4.13, is a transistor whose Y-matrix is

$$[Y] = \begin{bmatrix} 6{\cdot}67 \times 10^{-4} & -6{\cdot}67 \times 10^{-7} \\ 3{\cdot}27 \times 10^{-2} & 1{\cdot}73 \times 10^{-5} \end{bmatrix}$$

The circuit conductances in micro-mhos are $G_1 = 1{,}000$, $G_2 = 10{,}000$, $G_3 = 100$, $G_4 = 2{,}000$ and $G_5 = 100$.

Calculate the voltage-gain V_2/V_1 by nodal-voltage analysis, where V_1 is the input voltage across G_1 and V_2 is the output voltage across G_5.

Answer

$$V_2/V_1 = -13$$

Problem 31. A ladder network has series impedances and shunt admittances in the order Z_1, Y_2, Z_3, Y_4 ... Z_{n-1}, Y_n. Show that the input impedance can be expressed as a continued fraction of the form

$$Z = Z_1 + \cfrac{1}{Y_2 + \cfrac{1}{Z_3 + \cfrac{1}{Y_4 + \cfrac{1}{Z_5 + \cdot}}}}$$

$$\cdot$$
$$\cdot$$
$$\cdot$$

Comment

The pattern is revealed by working back from Y_n. The impedance to the right of Y_{n-2} is $Z_{n-1}+1/Y_n$. Consider then the impedance to the right of Y_{n-4}, and so on.

This property of the ladder topology is very important in network synthesis. When a desired input impedance, expressed as a polynomial function of s (or $j\omega$), can be put in the form of a continued fraction having terms $\alpha_1 s$, $\alpha_2 s$, ... $\alpha_n s$, where α_1, α_2 ... α_n are all real and positive (i.e. the function must be *Hurwitz*), the elements of a ladder network realising this impedance are recognisable by comparing corresponding terms: $Z_i(s)=\alpha_i s$, $Y_j(s)=\alpha_j s$.

INDEX